10¢

THE
MIDWEST PIONEER

HIS ILLS, CURES
& DOCTORS

THE DOCTOR ON HORSEBACK

THE MIDWEST PIONEER

HIS ILLS, CURES, & DOCTORS

By
MADGE E. PICKARD
and
R. CARLYLE BULEY

HENRY SCHUMAN
New York
1946

To the Pioneer Doctor who boldly faced the wilderness; and to the Pioneer who bravely faced the Doctor.

FOREWORD

*I*n this book, first published in a limited edition in 1945, the authors have endeavored to render a brief, non-technical but substantial account of pioneer medicine in the Middle West. They have found the subject quite interesting and believe that it has importance as a chapter in the social history of the region and period. Their goal has been set somewhat short of that of the western doctor who, a century ago, launched a short-lived medical periodical with the intent "to treat of the general principles, laws, and phenomena of mind and matter: the world within us, and the world without us; commencing at the perfection of nature, or man; and travel down through all stages of animal existence. From man to brute life, from animal to plant, from plant to crystal, from crystal to clod, from intellect to feeling, from feeling to form, from form to shapeless matter; from the most inveterate disease to the mildest complaint; from the strongest remedy to soothing means, from simple to compound, from pills to powders. We shall endeavor to follow the footsteps of nature through the nice, and ever descending scale of that which surrounds us."

The older spellings have been used for Pittsburgh and Cleveland in contemporary references, and newspaper citations are to the titles which the papers carried at the time. Though documentation has been reduced to the barest essentials and the bibliography streamlined, it is hoped that enough remains to serve as a guide to the more curious or ambitious student of midwest medical history.

Special thanks are due Mr. Paul Angle of the Chicago Historical Society, who permitted Dr. Carter's monumental work to leave his guardianship on divers occasions, and to Mr. R. E. Banta of Crawfordsville who did likewise with that of Dr. Smith. The authors trust that these two doctors and some of their contemporaries would in no wise be piqued at any publicity given their rather peculiar and naive thoughts. After all, they brought it upon themselves.

Bloomington, Indiana
July, 1946.

M. E. P.
R. C. B.

CONTENTS

CHAPTER I

"The dawn will break upon us, and bright day shall go forth and shine; when we may hope to live with the dear objects of our love, until ripe and full of years, we shall be gathered to our fathers."

—Dr. Samuel Robinson, Lecture IX, Cincinnati, 1829.

*T*he pioneer wife was alone with her children. The Indians around the cabin, though bent on grabbing hot bread rather than scalps, were getting out of hand. When one started to crawl through the cabin window, she cracked him on the skull with the wooden potato masher, pulled him on in, and barred the shutter. A while later a somewhat more sober Indian was pushed out the cabin door to find his companions. The wound and contusion on his head had been bathed in cold cider vinegar and neatly bound in a poultice of squirrel brains and crushed ginseng leaves. So well did the job meet with the Indians' approval that thereafter, when they more politely asked for the hot bread which was, next to liquor, their greatest weakness, there was much thumping of skulls and grunting laughter.

A man was riding across the prairies one warm winter day, when the temperature began to fall precipitately.

Within a few hours it was well below zero. The rider was lightly clothed, and it was miles to the nearest house. Though he valued his horse, he valued his life more. When he felt himself beginning to freeze, he sacrificed the animal, gutted the carcass, crawled inside, and lived to tell the tale.

A pioneer husband was called back to his cabin from the clearing where he worked to confront the emergency of a premature delivery. The six-year old daughter was dispatched through the woods to a neighbor's, but the trail was rough, and help was slow in coming. Relying upon common sense and his experience with cows and sheep, the farmer officiated at the birth of his first son.

A doctor found his patient unable to deliver herself of child. Whatever was to be done had to be done quickly. In an unfloored and unchinked cabin, by the light of candles shielded by blankets to prevent their being blown out, with a case of ordinary pocket instruments he performed a successful Caesarian section, probably the first in the West.

A strange young man stepped into the grocery filled with Irish canal laborers assembled around the whiskey barrel. After a few minutes he announced that within three weeks one-fourth of those present would die of smallpox. Since there was no smallpox in the region, his statement was received with derision. But the smallpox came, and with it many deaths. Impressed with the accuracy of his own prediction — he did not know on exactly what grounds he had made it — the young man took up medicine and became a successful doctor.

Isolated and exceptional incidents these, but incidents which had a habit of happening on the frontier in a period which, in the minds of many unsuspecting moderns, was characterized by "the simple life." From one viewpoint pioneer life was much more simple than life in the complicated industrial order of the twentieth century, with its many interdependent relationships and delicate balances, but on the other hand, to one who might be transferred from a modern farm of central Illinois or southern Michigan to the same scene of a century and a quarter ago, the processes of getting the mere essentials of life — food, shelter, clothes, and medicines — to say nothing of conveniences, travel, and amusements, would no doubt make life seem infinitely complex. Water did not come from taps, food did not come from cans, nor did the doctor and ambulance respond to the telephone.

As the pioneer advanced into the virgin forests and far-reaching prairie lands of the Middle West he was faced with many problems. In the early days there was the Indian, ever a nuisance, sometimes a terror. For almost two centuries the Indian had been a part of the environment; the struggle with him was a conditioning factor as important as the climate, the topography, and the vast distances in determining the character of the American pioneer.

There was the task of chopping, grubbing, and hewing a home out of the wilderness, of getting enough food to carry life through the early years, of creating a domestic economy which would make that home in a large measure self-sufficing. In time came the necessity of acquiring title to land; of laying hands on enough money to pay for it. Obtaining cash required means of getting produce to markets—roads, boats, canals, railroads—the business of transportation. There was the need for governments, local and state; of men and money to run them; of schools, lest the next generation grow up savage and ignorant. In addition, seriously weighing on the minds of many, was the incubus of the devil and all his works, matters not so much of this life as of the next.

More basic than any of these problems, however, was that of health. Unless the settler survived, all other problems were relegated into insignificance; he simply never got around to them. Although nothing was more vital in the conquest of the wilderness than health, over none of the factors involved did the people seemingly have less control.

Just as first settlers at Jamestown and Plymouth suffered heavily from the diseases of a new environment, so did the whites who reached the Mississippi Valley. French explorers, fur traders, and the *habitans* around Detroit and Vincennes became familiar with the diseases of the region. The Jesuit missionaries recorded summer illnesses among the Indians around the missions: they connected them with the eating of new corn, squashes, and watermelons. Sometimes it was "a malignant fever, of the purple kind." At Fort Miami in 1749 the twenty-two French inhabitants, including the commandant, had the fever.

British and Americans had similar experiences. George Morgan, Philadelphia merchant, western trader, and ambitious empire builder, wrote from the Illinois country in 1766: "Ague & Fever has been remarkably prevalent — Insomuch that of the Garrison & Inhabitants of Fort Chartres & Kaskaskia few have escaped being more or less afflicted therewith & altho 'tis not in itself Mortal yet the frequency of it must be the Occasion of other Disorders that are so — Insomuch that not a single Person Male or Female born at the Illinois of Parents of fifty Years of Age & very few of Forty — Neither has there been any French Native of the Country known to have lived to an old Age. . . ." Again in 1768: "every officer & almost every private Man, have been most Violently attacked with a Feaver — For want of Experience — Attention & Attendance, they were brought to a Most distressed Situation. . . . They cintinued helthy until about the 20th of September, When they Were Attack'd by twentys in a day & so severely that in the Course of about a Week there was but Nineteen Men capable of Duty at Fort Chartris & every Officer was ill at the same Time. . . . The Groans & cries of the Sick Was the only Noise to be heard within the Fort. . . . The Febrifuge you so warmly recommended will do very well from this till May next, When each of Us may expect to be attack'd in Turn." And George Butricke, garrison officer, writing on October 30, 1768, said: "in 3 days time there was not one Commissioned Officer, non Commissioned or Private man But one Sergt. 1 Corpl. and about nine men but what was seized in the same manner. . . . We have now sent to the Grave three Officers, twenty five men Twelve Women and fifteen Children, since the 29th Sept. and many more in a Very dangerous way, tho' I am in hopes the could Wether will soon help us." In 1789 Major Hamtramck wrote to General J. Harmar of the Vincennes garrison: "forty nine men are this day sick with the intermitting fever. . . ." Years later Dr. B. G. Farrar, prominent early St. Louis physician, said he could distinguish the inhabitants of the American Bottom lowland on the Illinois side of the Mississippi, by their pale faces.

In the 1790's and early 1800's, as the settlers moved into Kentucky and the Ohio country, in addition to the familiar diseases of smallpox, measles, and scarlatina, they began to suffer from epidemic fevers and influenzas. For the latter they blamed the "unhealthiness" of the climate. In 1807 an epidemic of malarial fever swept the Ohio Valley.[1]

"It ought not to be concealed that . . . there are many sick people; and we believe that there are many situations, some of which have been noticed, that may properly be denominated *sickly* . . . ," wrote David Thomas, botanist and traveller, of the Wabash country in 1816. He listed the prevailing ills as bilious, intermittent, and remittent fevers, with some liver complaints.

"The principal objection I have to this country is its unhealthiness the months of August and September are generally very sickly," wrote Gershom Flagg in 1819 from Edwardsville, Illinois, after he had been ill of fever and ague for two months; and he decided, if another season did not bring improvement, to sell out and leave the country. The *Edwardsville Spectator* in 1820 announced that its hands had been so disabled by the influenza that it would issue only half a sheet. "Forerunner" and "Old Rustic" wrote long communications in which they advocated that mills be closed and the dammed-up waters be released during summer to eliminate the stagnant-water effluvia which caused the common bilious fevers. But Morris Birkbeck, prominent English settler and large-scale farmer, reasoned that this would only make things worse, as effluvia rose from the mud rather than from the water. Another dry season in 1834—no rain to speak of from April to September and temperatures from 90° to 103°—resulted in much sickness in southern Illinois. Conditions remained much the same for years.

Around the recently established town of Indianapolis toward the end of the summer and during the fall of 1821 epidemic intermittent and remittent fevers and agues assailed the people to such an extent that the few unafflicted were employed night and day ministering to the sufferers, and one-eighth of the population was swept away. Dr. Samuel G. Mitchell reported from Indianapolis in 1822 that "Out of one thousand souls in town on the donation and the farms surrounding the town, at least nine hundred sickened during the prevailing epidemic." At Vevay, Indiana, where a rapid influx of settlers resulted in two or three families occupying a single house, one in six of the inhabitants died of bilious fevers during the summer and fall of 1820. The next autumn the sluggish, green, putrid waters of the Wabash and White rivers affected towns in Indiana and Illinois. "The situation of this town is at present truly deplorable," wrote the Vincennes *Western Sun.* "Nearly one-third of the population appears to be confined on beds of sickness, while the houses of the humane farmers in the vicinity are crowded with our fugitive convalescents." Dr. Asahel Clapp of New Albany reported in 1823 that "Last season has been unprecedented in the annals of the Western States for malignant diseases." For fifty years after their first settlement the river towns along the Ohio and the Wabash suffered from malarial diseases.

In the middle 1830's the people of Elkhart County had an epidemic of typhoid and pneumonia and in 1838 almost half the population was affected with bilious disorders. The wave of erysipelas which enveloped the whole Northwest in the early 1840's struck Indiana with unusual severity. Dysentery, scarlatina, phthisis (consumption), pneumonia, bronchitis, occasionally yellow and spotted fevers, whooping cough, and diphtheria appeared in many parts of the state. The summer of 1838 was a bad one, and "the afflicting dispensations of Providence" laid many low along the Ohio, the Wabash, the Illinois and lakes Michigan and Erie. Again in 1845 came a "disastrous and melancholy sickly season" in the West; the South Bend *St. Joseph Valley Register* noted that it was the seventh year from the last bad outbreak, as if that explained it.

In Michigan as soon as the land was plowed up and "the malarial gases set free, that country became very sickly. . . . Crops went back into the ground, animals suffered for food, and if the people had not been too sick to need much to eat they, too, must have gone hungry. The pale, sallow, bloated faces of that period were the rule; there were no healthy faces except of persons just arrived," said an old pioneer in whose family ten had been laid low with fevers at one time. In Detroit in the autumns of 1819, 1823, and 1826 bilious diseases were very prevalent. Filth in the streets and the fact that drinking water was scooped up from the lake shore were partly blamed. As late as 1839 whole villages were at times laid out temporarily, but after a few days people would crawl about like yellow ghosts, fortunate if they got enough to eat, for appetites were ravenous though food digested little more easily than stones.

> "Don't go to Michigan, that land of ills;
> The word means ague, fever and chills."

In Ohio, too, generally prevailed the most distressing sickness and great mortality, particularly from bilious fevers and cholera morbus.[2] Said James Kilbourne, prominent Ohio journalist and legislator: "Respecting the healthfulness of this country, I have to repeat that it is in fact sickly in a considerable degree." He reported the presence in 1800 of bilious fever which returned with more violence the following year: "Almost all were sick, both in towns and country, so that it became difficult, in many instances, to get tenderers for the sick. In many instances whole families were down at a time and many died. . . . What seems strange to me is that the Indians who were natives of the country are as subject to the disorder as the whites. Of the few who remain in the territory some are now sick with it and they say it has always been so, and that they have often been obliged to move back from the meadows and bottoms where they always lived, into the woods and uplands during the sickly season to escape it."

The autumn of 1819 in Ohio was particularly bad along the Scioto River bottoms, "whence deleterious exhalations arise." "The angel of disease and death, ascending from his oozy bed, along the marshy margin of the bottom grounds . . . floats in his aerial chariot, and in seasons favorable to his prowess, spreads mortal desolation as he flies," mourned the Portsmouth *Scioto Telegraph* in 1820. In 1821, "even in the memory of the oldest Indian, so unhealthy a season was never known here before," reported the *Piqua Gazette*. Of the one hundred sixty-five thousand people in the seventeen counties within a radius of fifty miles of Columbus, more than one-half were sick in September, 1823. "The most extravagant imagination can hardly picture desolation greater than the reality." Actual conditions substantiated political desires when the *Steubenville Gazette* and the Zanesville *Muskingum Messenger* called for removal of the capital to Zanesville. At Cleveland in 1827 there was perhaps more fever and ague than at any time since its first settlement. Almost twenty years later (1846) a northern Indiana paper reported in October that western Virginia, Ohio, Indiana, and Illinois "have been shaking worse than we have the past season. They must have a good time of it."

On the whole, newspapers were reluctant to report sickness in their own localities; it was usually somewhere else. Land sale promotions and local pride required rather the "puffing" of that particular climate for "healthiness"; ordinarily it was claimed to be quite "salubrious." As early as 1802 James Kilbourne had reported favorably to the

Scioto Land Company regarding the "healthfulness of the country." The September 2, 1825, *Illinois Intelligencer* stated that "The clamor which exists abroad about the sickliness of Illinois is entirely unfounded. Prejudices have arose against our town [Vandalia] even by the citizens of the state, on account of its health, but we have no hesitation in saying, that it is entirely unjustifiable." The *Milwaukee Sentinel* of October 9, 1838, boasted that, notwithstanding the fact that the season had been bad in most sections, Wisconsin had no prevailing diseases. "Physicians say that our Territory is *distressingly* healthy." Both the *Sentinel* and the Green Bay *Wisconsin Democrat* attacked the *Chicago Democrat* for including Wisconsin in the sick belt. They reported that canal work had been suspended in Illinois and Indiana, that the people were much too sick to harvest crops, and that there was nothing that looked like life, even in the populous towns. The *Daily Chicago American*, May 2, 1839, declared that "the whole West was unusually sickly" the preceding fall, that Michigan, Ohio, and Indiana suffered most, but that Illinois was affected only among the Irish laborers along the canal lines.

There were those who felt that the habits of the settlers were as much to blame for prevailing illness as the environment. James Hall of Vandalia, in years to come to be the West's most famous historian and advocate, took this view. In his address at the first meeting of the Illinois Antiquarian and Historical Society in 1827 he stated that the pioneer's exposure to the weather, his food — too much meat and not enough fresh vegetables, excessive use of ardent spirits, and lack of attention to simple diseases, were more responsible than the climate.

Early in the century the *Medical Repository* had commented on the eating and drinking habits of Americans: "The inhabitants are almost constantly in a state of repletion, by stuffing and cramming, and by the use of stimulating drink. The consumption of animal food is probably much greater in the Fredonian [United] states, than in any other civilized nation; and it ought likewise to be observed, that the quantity of ardent spirits drank by our people, exceeds every thing of the kind, that the world can produce; the appetite for inebriating drink seems to be increasing and insatiable."

And years later, after long and varied observation, Dr. Daniel Drake concluded that "As a general fact, the people of the Valley [Mississippi] eat too much. . . . I cannot attempt to enumerate on the vicious modes of cooking." By the same authority, alcoholic intemperance seriously affected the stomach, liver, and lungs, caused swelling of the feet, sore eyes, epileptic convulsions, and even leprosy. Worse than all this, there was always the chance of spontaneous combustion, to which intemperance predisposed the body. "On this point facts have multiplied, until the most incredulous inquirer can scarcely retain his doubts. The bodies of corpulent inebriates, when asleep, have, in several instances, taken fire, by the accidental contact of a burning coal or candle, and all the soft parts have been reduced to ashes, or driven off in clouds of thick smoke. To conceive of the possibility of this revolting catastrophe, we need only recollect the combustible nature of fat, and the still more inflammable quality of ardent spirits, which is composed of the very same materials; and which, being swallowed, daily, in excessive quantities, with reduction of food, may be presumed to alter, to a certain degree, the chemical composition of the body. Meanwhile its vital powers become greatly reduced, and thus render it an easier prey to fire or other external agents." Considering the number of pioneers who took no specific precautions against this ailment, the number of deaths recorded as a result of the "revolting catastrophe" is exceedingly small.

Of all the ills to which the new country was heir, the ague was the most common. So nearly inescapable was it that many refused to regard it as a disease, but considered it, like hard work, a concomitant of the frontier. "He ain't sick, he's only got the ager," was the usual view. The symptoms were unmistakable: yawnings and stretching, a feeling of lassitude, blueness of the fingernails, then little cold sensations which increased until the victim's teeth chattered in his jaws and he "felt like a harp with a thousand strings." As the chills increased, the victim shivered and shook "like a miniature earthquake." After an hour or so warmth returned, then gradually merged into raging heat with racking head pains and aching back. The spell ended with copious sweating and a return to normal.

As a veteran sufferer described it:

"You felt as though you had gone through some sort of collision, thrashing-machine or jarring-machine, and came out not killed, but next thing to it. You felt weak, as though you had run too far after something, and then didn't catch it. You felt languid, stupid and sore, and was down in the mouth and heel and partially raveled out. Your back was out of fix, your head ached and your appetite crazy. Your eyes had too much white in them, your ears, especially after taking quinine, had too much roar in them, and your whole body and soul were entirely woebegone, disconsolate, sad, poor, and good for nothing. You didn't think too much of yourself and didn't believe that other people did, either; and you didn't care. You didn't quite make up your mind to commit suicide, but sometimes wished some accident would happen to knock either the malady or yourself out of existence. You imagined that even the dogs looked at you with a kind of self-complacency. You thought the sun had a kind of sickly shine about it. About this time you came to the conclusion that you would not accept the whole state of Indiana as a gift; and if you had the strength and means, you picked up Hannah and the baby, and your traps, and went back 'yander' to 'Old Virginny,' the 'Jerseys,' Maryland or 'Pennsylvany.' "

In 1836 it was said that members of one family in the Illinois country shook so severely that the workmen were frightened from their task of shingling the cabin roof. A Wisconsin pioneer frankly admitted that when he went to that place he "had a wholesome fear of two things: fever and ague and rattlesnakes." An early settler in the Michigan Territory "shook so that the dishes rattled on the shelves against the log wall." There it was even reported that an Indian dog had the malady, the cattle were said to lean against the fence and shake, and children were born with it.

There were different kinds of ague — dumb ague, shaking ague, chill fever — and variations. Some sufferers had the combined chills and fever each day, or on alternate days, or even every third day; others had the chills one day and the fever the next. Whichever brand was "favored," it was regular, but, like the moon, a bit later each day it appeared, and often came back in season for years until a sort of immunity was established. Work schedules were fixed to accommodate the fits. The justice arranged the docket to avoid the sick day of the litigant; the minister made his appointments in keeping with the shakes; the housewife hurried through her morning chores, then sat down to await her visitor; and even the sparking swain reckoned the ager schedule of self and intended. Neither a wedding in the family nor a birth or death would stop the shakes.[3] Travellers were almost unanimous in noting the sallow and jaundiced complexions of the Westerners.

The ague and malarial diseases were usually classified by the doctors as autumnal fevers. Types and names varied. Dr. Daniel Drake's classification is as good as any. Under that heading in his *Diseases of the Interior Valley of North America* he listed: intermittent fever, simple, and inflammatory; malignant intermittent fever; remittent fever; malignant remittent fever; and protracted, relapsing, and vernal intermittent fevers. Together with the geography, causes, and consequences he gave eleven chapters and one hundred eighty-two pages of this treatise to the subject.

Perhaps to make this fever matter clear we should quote Dr. William Daily of Louisville, on types and courses:

"*Continued*: very slight evening exacerbations, and morning remissions. Total absence of remissions and exacerbations very rare, if ever.

"*Remitting:* prominent and regular remissions and exacerbations.

"*Intermitting:* regular paroxyms and perfect intermissions.

"One paroxysm, with its intermission, constitutes its *revolution.* According to the *duration* of the *revolution,* fevers are divided into:

Quotidian, occupying 24 hours.
Tertian,   do.   48 do.
Quartan,   do.   72 do.

"The *form* which fevers assume in this respect is called their type. There are, therefore, three principal types: *i. e.,* the quotidian, the tertian, and the quartan types. Quotidians generally come on in the morning; tertians about noon; and quartans in the afternoon.

"Tertians divided into *simple* and *double.*

"*Double tertians:* paroxysms occur daily; but the paroxysms of the alternate days are similar in violence, time of occurrence, and duration, and differ in these respects from those which occur on the intervening days.

"Intermittents rarely are of the *double* tertian type, *from their commencement:* they generally commence as *simple tertians,* and duplicate their type afterwards; the new or accessory paroxysms generally milder than the original; double tertians generally return to the simple type, before they terminate; a change from the simple to the double type, is unfavorable.

"Other variety of compound types: *tertiana duplicata; haemitritoeus; — tertiana triplex.*

"The quartan type is also susceptible of duplication. The double quartan has two paroxysms every fourth day. Authors mention triple quartans, three paroxysms occurring on every fourth day — these are very uncommon. The difficulty of arresting the course of an intermittent, in general, is proportionate to the time occupied by each paroxysm.

"Intermittents are said to be *anticipating,* when the paroxysm comes on earlier every succeeding recurrence — and *postponing,* when it occurs later at each return. When the paroxysm is postponed to about eight o'clock in the evening, it frequently does not come on until the next morning. In like manner, the paroxysm of an anticipating ague, occurring at eight o'clock in the morning, will have its next paroxysm on the evening of the day preceding that on which it should happen. (Wilson.) Favorable, when the paroxysms are *postponed;* unfavorable when *anticipated.*

"*Attypic, or erratic fevers:* no regular type; rheumatism —catarrhal fever."[4]

The fact that he was confronted with so many interesting possibilities no doubt consoled the sufferer when he began the misery of the shakes.

Milk sickness or "*Morbo Loacteo*" was also encountered in many localities. Pioneers called it the milk sick; it was also known as sick stomach, the trembles, the slows, and puking fever. The usual symptoms were irregular respiration, cold and clammy skin, subnormal temperature, constipation, and bloated abdomen. The patient would be overcome with weakness and prostration of the voluntary muscles, then came nausea, and finally a comatose condition with periods of agonizing pain—or as the botanic Dr. H. T. N. Benedict, editor of the *Medical Investigator,* described it in 1847: "ungovernable thirst, great prostration, hiccup, stupor, etc., etc., death."

Not much was known about this disease. It had first been noticed by travellers in the West in the early 1800's. Dr. Drake was studying and writing about milk sickness in the period 1810-15. The chairman of a Kentucky Senate committee appointed to study the disease sent out in 1827 a questionnaire of twenty-four items—concerning its prevalence, who got it, causes, cures if any, and percentage of death—and editors were requested to copy and circulate. Residents of Dearborn County, Indiana, were actively seeking the solution to the mystery during the 1840's and 1850's.[5] Many articles on it appeared in the medical journals of the West during the period.

The disease affected both cattle and persons and was

endemic rather than epidemic. Chickens which ate the flesh of milk-sick animals also became affected. "Buzzards eating the diseased flesh often die and some of them lose the power of flying for some days. One of my dogs having partaken of diseased beef, run after a rabit across the field, and then fell down and died; another dog died in the same way, whilst in pursuit of a hog," wrote John Miller of Goose Creek, Tennessee.

Since the symptoms of milk sick were so similar to those of arsenic poisoning, one explanation offered was that spring water absorbed the poison from arsenical iron pyrites. Other theories explained the trouble as due to vegetable poisoning, conveyed through milk or flesh of domestic animals.[6] Dr. Drake rather inclined to blame the marsh exhalations. Indian doctors, folk curists, regular physicians, and botanics were alike helpless in the face of the milk sickness. Calomel and bleeding proved as futile as Lobelia No. 6 or the powerful dilutions of the homeopaths. At times whole communities were so seriously depleted that the remaining inhabitants contemplated moving on to safer regions.

The milk sickness baffled not only the pioneer, but continued to worry the scientist until the 1920's. When finally traced to its source, it was found that some of the pioneers had been warm on the scent when they suspected certain poisonous plants which their cattle ate. Among the chief offenders were white snakeroot and jimmyweed or rayless goldenrod; the former was present in the Ohio Valley. The poison is tremetol. Even today there are no fairly certain antidotes.[7]

When the settler moved West he did not leave behind him the afflictions of the older communities. The usual diseases, contagious and otherwise, migrated with him, appeared in varying degrees of severity, but were probably no more prevalent in the West than in the older settlements. Scarlet fever, diphtheria, measles, mumps, and smallpox were seldom long absent from any settlement; often they were epidemic. Erysipelas, sometimes called

Black Tongue, was epidemic at different times, as was influenza. Skin eruptions of a severe nature were not uncommon and spread throughout whole settlements, respecting neither age, sex, color, social position, nor creed. In Michigan one disorder was dignified with the name of "Michigan rash," but when an outsider noticed the naturalness of the motions of the afflicted and suggested brimstone and lard, some were unkind enough to call it the "seven years' itch."

Pneumonia, or "lung fever," attacked many people in winter, but many believed that it was milder in form during the days of cabins and fireplaces than later when tighter houses and stoves came into general use. Quite a few children died from the croup, or "bold hives." Rheumatism and attendant troubles were common as one would expect from the pioneers' exposure to all kinds of weather, the practice of allowing wet clothing to dry on the body, and perhaps in part to neglected teeth, tonsils, and other local infections.

Typhoid epidemics came and went and no doubt took a heavy toll of lives, but since nothing much was known concerning the cause or spread of this disease, little attention was paid to it by physicians prior to about 1845. Dr. A. A. Benezet in his *Family Physician* listed typhoid as typhus fever. Dr. John C. Gunn classified it as nervous fever, while many of the pioneers called it brain fever. Causes were generally supposed to be night air, putrid vegetable and animal matter in the air, grief, fear, unripe fruit, want of sleep, and intense thought.[8] Dr. William W. Gerhard of Philadelphia, who published his observations in the *American Journal of the Medical Sciences* in 1837, was one of the first to differentiate between typhoid and typhus fevers. Many of the cases and fatalities listed under bilious fevers, autumnal fevers, and the like, were typhoid. Living conditions with reference to disposal of offal, absence of screens, uncertain water supply, and careless handling of milk, as well as ignorance of cause and method of transfer, were conducive to the development and spread of this disease.

Dr. Nathaniel Potter, one of the editors of the *Maryland Medical and Surgical Journal,* writing of the western country, reported pleurisies, rheumatisms, and inflammations as generally prevalent during the winter months. Catarrh, too, was common and often terminated in consumption, which he called the endemic of the region, serious enough in many districts and seasons to account for one-fourth of the mortality. Quinsy in various forms, inflammation of internal parts of the body, scarlet fever, and measles came in cycles at three- or four-year intervals. Nettle rash, asthma, and cholera afflicted the children, particularly in the summer months. Apoplexy and palsy were not so much endemic as they were the frequent result of intemperance. Asthma, epilepsy, dropsy, and St. Vitus's dance were no more peculiar to the new country than elsewhere. Rickets were rare ... ; scrofula was more common. From one affliction Dr. Potter thought the West suffered less: the active habits of the people left little time for hypochondria.

It was a common belief that measles, whooping cough, diphtheria, and the like were inevitable and unavoidable, and that to try to escape would be to defy Providence. Hence, when the weather was seasonable and the blood in good condition, children were often deliberately exposed to these contagious diseases.

Knowledge of vaccination for smallpox came to the United States in 1800. A year later Dr. William Goforth of Cincinnati was using the new discovery,[9] and by 1803 Dr. Samuel Brown of Lexington had vaccinated five hundred persons. In 1809 Dr. Saugrain gave notice in the *Missouri Gazette* of the first vaccine matter brought to St. Louis and promised to vaccinate "indigent persons, paupers and Indians" gratuitously. Notices appeared in some of the western papers in 1814 that James Smith of Baltimore, recently appointed vaccination agent by the President of the United States, would furnish vaccine matter to any physician or other citizen of the country who might apply. In 1817 Dr. Heath of Madison announced in the *Indiana Republican* that he would inoculate for one dollar, or gratuitously if necessary. In 1824, when smallpox became bad in the West, the Cincinnati City Council placed a doctor in the council chamber to vaccinate all who came at a fee of fifty cents if able to pay, otherwise free. The doctor expected "to be enabled soon to supply upon the ordinary conditions country physicians and others with the genuine vaccine matter" through "an agency or connexion with the agent at Philadelphia." Later this same year it was announced that "County Physicians can be supplied with genuine Matter at all times, at moderate prices," and that for an additional charge of fifty cents each person desiring vaccination might be attended at his own dwelling. Vaccination did not become generally available to the pioneer until many years after its first use in the cities, and even when available it was often refused by the pious as contrary to the will of the Almighty. Smallpox epidemics varied in severity, but the disease was at all times feared. Even though the sufferer survived, the disfigurement sometimes made him wish he had not.

Degenerative diseases of the heart, kidneys, liver, and other organs which mostly affected persons well along in years, attracted no special attention in the West. Their incidence was not so high relatively as today, since most people did not live long enough to develop them.

In addition to its own maladies the West was subjected in 1832 to the attacks of a strange invader. Since 1816 the Asiatic cholera had been creeping westward from India, leaving its path of destruction. By 1830 it had reached Moscow and the Near East and within twelve months had spread to western Europe, England, and Ireland. Early in 1832 an emigrant ship which landed at Quebec bore this deadly passenger. The disease ascended the St. Lawrence to Montreal, thence travelled to Albany and New York. By July death reports were emanating from New York, Philadelphia, and Erie with alarming frequency.[10]

General Scott's troops on the way from Buffalo to the Black Hawk War landed at Detroit on July 4 with the disease, and death and panic followed. The upper story of the capitol building was used as a hospital. Fifty-eight cases were reported in the town, twenty-eight deaths resulted in two weeks, and the tolling of funeral bells was discontinued because of the demoralizing effect. The death cart passed day and night with the cry, "Bring out the dead." The wasted remnant of the troops was taken on to Fort Dearborn to spread the disease in Chicago and the West. The soldiers arrived there July 10 and it was reported that eighteen died within thirty hours. Soon there were thirty or more cases in Chicago, and those inhabitants who could leave did so. The Indian agent there wrote on July 16, "Every family has left Chicago, and gone in different directions to escape from this malignant disease." By July 28 the Indianapolis *Indiana Journal* listed one hundred fifty cases and fifty deaths, and yet another account told of fifty-eight deaths in one week from the two hundred cases in the Fort Dearborn hospital.

Apparently nothing could stop the progress of this plague as it spread around the lakes to the Wisconsin country, across Illinois to the Mississippi, thence up the Ohio to Cincinnati, and down the river to localize in New Orleans. By August the plague had crept around from Detroit to attack Cleveland. After October Cincinnati was almost demoralized as the deaths mounted to three hundred fifty-one in about three weeks. People fled to the country to escape, business was disrupted, newspaper carriers were gone and no one knew their routes. From Cincinnati the disease passed by stagecoach and river boat to Maysville, Lexington, Nashville, and Florence, Alabama; the tributary rivers furnished avenues of transmission both north and south but the epidemics in the Middle South were not very severe, because of the lateness of the season and unfavorable conditions. Only five cases were reported at Lexington and a few more at Louisville. Madison, Indiana, however, had forty-two cases and twenty-two deaths by November 8. It was estimated that Philadelphia and Baltimore had lost one thousand each and New York even more; the New Orleans dead, rumored to be about three hundred per day, were buried in trenches, if at all.

Henry Clay introduced a joint resolution in Congress for a day of prayer, and Governor Noah Noble of Indiana proclaimed a day "for fasting and prayer to an overruling Providence, beseeching Him to arrest the progress of the disease, with its train of calamities," and urged all who believed in the efficacy of prayer to participate.

With the coming of cold weather the ravages diminished, only to return in the summer of 1833 with greater severity and over a wider range. Cincinnati suffered even worse than the previous year; total cholera deaths there for the year ending September 18, 1833, were eight hundred thirteen, or one in every forty people, as contrasted with the rate from all causes for the four years preceding of one in thirty-four. The disease spread to Columbus and the state penitentiary; to Aurora and Salem, Indiana, where one hundred out of eight hundred inhabitants were said to have died within a week; north to Bloomington, where the Indiana College had to be closed; and to Indianapolis, where sixty-two deaths occurred in a month. Apparently the Wabash towns were not affected. Wheeling, Louisville, Lexington, and Alton were also visited. From Maysville, as news of an impending epidemic spread, nine-tenths of the inhabitants scattered before the lapse of thirty-six hours, and for over two weeks the city remained nearly deserted. The population of Lexington was reduced from more than six thousand to fewer than four thousand; people had been dying at the rate of from fifty to sixty a day during the peak of the epidemic. The Michigan Territory legislature authorized the towns to establish a quarantine against travellers, and even Governor Stevens T. Mason was arrested when he tried to go through Ypsilanti. By autumn southern Illinois papers were announcing that there were no more cholera cases. It returned, however, to visit Rushville, Pekin, Springfield, and St. Louis in 1834.

Madison, Indiana, was revisited in 1835, when thirty-two deaths were reported to June 24, fifteen having died in one day.

In 1840 Asiatic cholera again started on its march—from Calcutta to central Asia, Russia, along the trade routes to Europe, and by way of German emigrants to America. In the autumn of 1848 two ships brought the scourge to New York and New Orleans. Deaths in the latter in the winter and spring were near four thousand. Steamboats and railroads, as well as stagecoaches, spread the disease more rapidly than in 1832-33. Louisville and St. Louis received boatloads of passengers and cholera in December. Soon the whole interior valley was afflicted; the pestilence seemingly broke out spontaneously. By spring it was rampant. Evansville, Indiana, had one hundred fifty deaths, New Albany forty, and Salem thirty. The village of Napoleon lost thirty-five of its two hundred fifty inhabitants. Dearborn County was very hard hit. Cincinnati, with a population of approximately one hundred ten thousand, had 5,969 deaths in fifteen weeks. Again all was in confusion. Dayton lost one hundred twelve lives, one hundred died in the penitentiary at Columbus, and the fatalities at Lexington totalled three hundred forty-two. St. Louis deaths numbered about forty-five hundred; the population declined from seventy thousand to fifty thousand as people fled. Chicago and Detroit fared relatively well with three hundred fourteen and eighty-one deaths respectively.

It was not so much the number of cases and high fatality of the disease, but the mysteriousness and suddenness with which it struck that filled people with a dread and fear which often reached panic. Persons in excellent health were suddenly stricken with a feeling of uneasiness and shortly were consumed with inward burnings and a craving for cold drinks; then came vomiting, intestinal spasms almost as severe as in tetanus cases, and finally general debility, slow circulation, sunken eyes, cold lifeless skin, and collapse. The fate of many victims was decided within a few hours.

As Dr. Thomas D. Mitchell of the Medical College of Ohio described it:

"The pestilence stalks in the midnight gloom
And mantles the gay with the pall of the tomb
Nor beauty nor youth from its clutch can flee
It kills on the land, it blasts on the sea."

Much speculation as to causes and keen interest as to treatment were aroused. As in the yellow fever epidemics earlier, various theories were advanced. Bad air, exhalations from the bowels of the earth, insensible changes in the atmosphere, comets, and animalculae — insects too small to see — in the air, were offered as explanations. Dr. Reese, of New York, listed among the exciting causes: indigestible vegetables, ardent spirits, beer, ale, and wine; pork, lobsters, and crabs; green corn, clams, and oysters; watermelons, cucumbers, strawberries, peaches, and pears; cabbage and greens; cheese, opium in any form, jalap and other drastic cathartics, and nostrums of all kinds. Others merely said the disease was contagious and let it go at that.

Dr. Drake of Cincinnati, probably the best known medical man in the West, whose writings on cholera were copied widely in the newspapers, inclined to the animalculae hypothesis — a rather close approach to the later germ theory. He called attention to the city filth, the neglected vaults, the lack of personal cleanliness, adequate ventilation, and proper diet; he advised normal diet, continuation of one's normal habits regarding liquor, a calm and hopeful mind, and if one could afford it the wearing of thin flannel over the trunk of the body. Quarantine he considered futile, as well as embarrassing to commerce.

When it came to treatment, Dr. Drake's ideas hardly seem so sensible and modern. He thought calomel, jalap, rhubarb, opium, mercury, weak lye, and mustard might possess some efficacy, but most startling was his recommendation of the old standby of the regular doctors, bleeding:

"To bleed a patient who cannot be raised from his pillow without fainting, whose pulse is nearly imperceptible, whose skin is cold, and extremities shrunk up to half their ordinary size, would at first view, seem rash and unwarrantable. But experience, which in medicine can grant warrants for any procedure, has sanctioned the use of the lancet even when all these and other symptoms of extreme prostration, are present. . . . The quantity taken must vary with the effect. It generally flows with difficulty . . . and sometimes not at all, though large veins be opened. In every desperate case, recourse should be had to the juglars, from which blood will flow when it cannot be elicited from the arms; and flowing, must contribute more to the relief of the oppressed brain, than when drawn from the extremities."[11]

Others advised cleaning the streets, alleys and privies; recommended avoidance of excessive exertion, eating and drinking; warned against sitting in the sun or a current of air; and advocated airy, clean rooms and a daily bath. Warnings were issued by doctors against the "infallible" quack remedies. All one could do, according to one Dr. Rigdon, quoted in the *Hamilton Intelligencer*, was to keep in good health and take prompt care of bowel and stomach disorders by putting the feet in hot ashes and water, taking ten grains of calomel and one of opium, covering up in bed with hot bricks and boiled ears of corn, and using warm mint tea inside, and mustard poultices outside, the stomach.

The Botanics, of course, had slightly different ideas. A widely copied recipe called for a mixture of one gallon of fourth-proof West India rum, one gallon of molasses, one quart of number 6 [Thomson's lobelia, etc.] and two ounces of cayenne pepper — three doses daily for prevention, one-half glass every half hour for cure. In the 1849 epidemic Dr. Herrick, of Chicago, published an article in the *Northwest Medical Journal* in which he claimed sulphur was an effective specific. Soon thereafter a Dr. Bird was advocating sulphur and charcoal pills, with testimonials. This popular remedy faded with the discovery that morphine was the main ingredient of the pills.

Hardly to be classified as diseases but certainly as ubiquitous and sometimes as deleterious in effect were the pests and varmints of the woods and swamps. Although house flies were not present when the first settlers arrived, the stock flies and mosquitoes were. From the woods and lowlands they swarmed by the millions in season to bleed man and beast. Often cows could be milked only under the protection of a rotten wood smudge. Fleas and bedbugs, the latter considered almost a domestic necessity by a certain class of inhabitants, emerged from the cracks and crevices of cabin and house to irritate and consume. Despite a relatively late arrival the house fly soon made up for lost time. In the absence of screens or sprays this insect had the freedom of barn and home. It wallowed in milk crocks and blackened drying fruit; it covered the sleeping baby's face and crawled persistently over dunghill, carrion, and food. At harvest-time meals, wedding dinners, and on other occasions for company-meals boys and girls minded the table with leafy branches or paper-strip fly shooers so that people could eat. Although regarded as a minor nuisance, the fly played its part as an arbiter of health. Two generations of science and education and the crusading spirit of Dr. John N. Hurty and others were required to make the people conscious of the disease-spreading propensities of the fly.

Other dangers lurked in the form of venomous snakes, which frequently disputed the white man's occupation of the land as effectively as did the Indian. The spreading viper put up a vicious front, but was a 'possum at heart and not in the least dangerous. It was the rattlesnake and the copperhead which caused the trouble. Although the former was supposed to declare his hostile intent before striking, he had an unpleasant habit of lying on the other side of log or rock to be trod upon by the unwary. The copperhead was entirely oblivious of the rules of war. Snake drives were participated in by neighbors during off-seasons on the farm. Statistical summaries of these hunts are astonishing to a person familiar with the country a century later. Sometimes several hundred rattlesnakes, from three to ten feet in length, were killed.

In a period of active life in the open — when women as well as men chopped wood, handled horses, and worked around open fires, when men plowed without socks, and children went barefoot — cuts, bruises, sprains, and broken bones were regular occurrences. Soiled clothing, infrequent bathing, and intimate contact with germ-infected soil often resulted in serious consequences. "Blood poisoning" and "lock jaw" were all too often fatal.

Certainly not a disease, but nevertheless a hazard, at least for the women, was childbirth. Early marriages and large families were the rule, for a young man could support a family as soon as he could do a man's work on the farm. Said a Kentucky congressman in 1824:

"Why sir, you may visit the humblest cottage in our country, and you will find everything to admire. So soon as the faithful dog, by his saluting bark, announces that a stranger is coming, your astonishment would commence; you would have the singular felicity of beholding a most delightful spectacle — about twelve or thirteen fine, ruddy, well-formed, hearty-looking young *Democrats,* would run out to see the stranger; and upon entering the house, you would be met by a very plain unaffected woman, to all appearances about thirty years old, whose countenance would at once tell you to make yourself easy; you would meet with kindness, and, in casting your eyes around, you would see two more little fellows, who were too small to run out at the first alarm."

Such descriptions indicate an ideal or culture trait of the time. Politicians thought of votes, man-power, increasing wealth. Some parents thought of children as economic assets; others took seriously the injunction to be fruitful and multiply, or took pride in their large broods as evidence of virility and social standing; many gave the matter little or no thought. Exhausting physical labor in field and home was apparently no deterrent; children came in almost annual crops.

For some pioneer women, rugged and toughened by hard work, childbirth was not an event seriously to interfere with the routine of life. There were instances of outdoor deliveries, even in winter, after which the mother carried the infant some miles to shelter, neither seemingly the worse off for the experience; but these were the exceptions rather than the rule. Even after the prejudice against calling male physicians for childbirth had passed, wives were frequently far from the services of a doctor when their time came, and were dependent upon the help of neighbors, among whom there probably would be at least one who made profession to midwifery. True, some of these local "grannies," as well as pioneer doctors, were very skillful at child delivery; by common sense and practical experience they often overcame the handicap of lack of instruments and other aids. For instance, when the baby proved too reluctant to enter the world "on its own," a bit of dried snuff blown into the mother's nose by way of a goose quill would bring on sneezing paroxysms and probably the desired results. (Persons so introduced were spoken of in later life as having been quilled babies.) Then, too, puerperal infections and other dangers which have to be carefully guarded against in hospitals were comparatively rare among these isolated cases.[12] Nevertheless, when added to the other hardships of life, the burden of too frequent childbearing and inexpert attention usually exacted its penalty. All too many women lost their bloom with their teens, were tired out and run down by the twenties, and old at forty. Tombstones in the churchyards bear testimony that many a wife, having delivered numerous progeny, died young, to be followed by a second who contributed her quota and labors, and perhaps by a third who stood a good chance to outlive the husband.

Infant mortality was high. The prayers for large families[13] were usually followed in pioneer journals and reminiscences by depressing records of early deaths: "The giving up of our little son [sixth child], — who departed this life second month, 26th, so earnest and thoughtful for his age, pierced our hearts deeply." In the next paragraph: "Our little daughter, was born 29th of eleventh month, and departed this life eighth month 13th. Our little daughter came as a jewel into our family, remaining with us only eight months and fourteen days. She was as beautiful as the sunlight and as sweet as a rose. Her visit was short in this beautiful world." A year later: "Our son — was born first month, 29th — a frail delicate child." Nine children and then the mother died. "She left us and the pleasant scenes of time going into the Beyond, fourth month 12th, feeling an assurance that all would be well with her." But it soon became "an imperative duty to secure a companion for myself and a mother for my children." In due course were recorded six more children and several more deaths, mostly from preventable diseases. In later years this rugged and exemplary go-getter, who had accumulated even more acres than offspring, seemed to have had slight doubts. "As I look back over the years gone by, I conclude I would be much better satisfied if I had put up a small stable near the school house, and provided a horse and vehicle for the children to ride to and from school." As for the poorer and less responsible folk, they were troubled neither by "imperative duties" nor by post-mortem retrospection.

Babies being no rarity, they received no special attention: they were raised, not reared. The same rule of thumb, or trial and error, methods that applied to crops or cattle were good enough. The science of infant care was not yet, and instead of a vitamin, baby got a bacon rind, sometimes attached to a string so that when accidentally swallowed it might be recovered. When weaned, usually by the almanac, youngsters began to eat cornbread, biscuits, and "pot likker" like grown-ups. The fittest survived, and the rest "the Lord seen fitten to take away."

Although mental disorders do not fall within the scope

of this survey, an exception is made for the "hypo." Few pioneer women had the time or inclination to cultivate an interesting pallor or the art of attractive fainting—some could swing an axe like a logger or "chaw 'baccy" like any man—yet there were exceptions who reserved the rights and prerogatives of the weaker sex. A Michigan settler had a wife who was subject to fits of hypochondria. After stopping work a number of times, riding miles for a doctor and returning with him only to find her about her affairs as usual, he remonstrated mildly and told her he did not believe the spells were necessary. Whereupon she proclaimed: "Elmer Bacon, 'tain't no use talkin', I *can* have fits, and I *will* have 'em." But more about the hypo later.

When pioneers met it was more than mere courtesy which called forth the inquiry concerning the health of families and acquaintances. All too often the answer was that so and so was ailin' or "was poorly, right poorly." If at times there were individuals who enjoyed poor health, there were energetic souls who would not stop working; of them it could be said, "they hadn't orter be a doin'." Were no serious illness present, the answer would be "tolerable, just tolerable." Things seldom got better than that.

HOME REMEDIES AND DOMESTIC MEDICINE

CHAPTER II

*"My medicine, though made of herbs, doth wond'rous
cures perform,
And yet each one may practice it without producing
harm."*

—Dr. Richard Carter

*M*uch of the medical treatment in pioneer days was domestic and primitive. Provided a doctor were available, it required time and money to get his services and he was, generally speaking, called only for serious cases. Even then home remedies or folk cures were likely to have been used before the doctor was called. Besides being responsible for the domestic economy of the home — everything from food and clothing to spelling and courting — the mother, wife, or woman of the house was by prerogative and default the custodian of medicines, and administratrix of treatments. If home resources did not suffice, there was usually someone in each community who was handy in caring for the sick and steeped in his or her lore or system of cures — a combination of homemade science, empiricism, and superstition.

Naturally Indian influences were strong, and many early settlers relied upon the "yarb and root" doctors who worked largely with remedies obtained from forest and garden. For a century French *voyageurs* and *coureurs du bois* had preferred the Indian treatment of wounds and chronic sores with poultices and herbs to that of the whites. Native medicine men also doctored many other ills with concoctions of herbs, drinks, sweatings, and rubbings, usually accompanied with ceremonials, incantations, ghost shooting in the night, and similar aids. They even sucked out manitous, or evil spirits. In some western communities in the earlier years there were Indian doctors who were held in quite as high repute as regular white doctors.

Many pioneers who practiced their cures in the Indian tradition did so as an avocation — to stand out among their fellow men, or to be neighborly and helpful. Others made it a full-time pursuit and their advertisements in the newspapers were not uncommon. For instance, at Springfield, Illinois, in the mid-1830's, appeared the announcement of T. J. Luster, an "Indian and German Root Doctor." He offered numerous favorable testimonials regarding his success in curing "Sciatic, weak lungs, fits, inward weakness and nervous affections; liver complaints, fever and ague, pleurisy, asthma, coughs, colds, dyspepsia, rheumatism, cancers, rickets, fever sores, piles, worms and tape worms, and many other diseases that affect the human system." In Connersville, Indiana, there was a "doctor" who had "nailed up to the weather-boarding of the hotel, an enormous swamp-lily root, almost as large as a man, with head, eyes, nose, ears and mouth nicely carved, arms and legs with feet stuck on, and just above the sign on a board, marked with chalk, 'Joseph S. Burr, Root Doctor; No calomel.' Hundreds came from all parts of the country to see the doctor and the big root." They must have consulted him, too, for the regular doctors went after him, the people took sides, a law suit and trial followed, and the root doctor ran away.

One of his pupils, "Thomas T. Chinn, constable three weeks before and barely able to write his name, became

'Dr. Chinn, Root Doctor and No Calomel.' " According to one of his own accounts:

"I lost only nine fine patients last week, one of them an old lady that I wanted to cure very bad, but she died in spite of all I could do. I tried every root I could find but she still grew worse, and there being nobody here to detect my practice, like the other regular doctors I concluded to try calamus, and dug up a root about nine inches long and made a tea of it. She drank it with some difficulty, turned over in the bed and died. Still I don't think it was the calamus that killed her, as all the calamus doctors are giving it in heavier doses than I did."[1]

Doctors of this type dispensed with the hocus-pocus of the Indian shamen and adapted the cures to their own uses, but the basis of their treatments was essentially the same as that of the natives. The recipes and cures in the "yarb and root" category were legion. Not all were of Indian origin; as did the folk charm-cures, they derived from ancient Egypt, China, India and elsewhere, as well as from the New World, where they had developed independently.[2]

The first English book devoted exclusively to herbs was Banckes's *Herbal*, 1525, which was apparently compiled from various earlier sources. The fact that this small work went through about twenty editions established its position as the most popular English herbal. The quaint and blunt recipes, though fascinating, did not include American plants. These became generally known in England half a century later, when, 1577-80, John Frampton "Englished" the works of Doctor Nicholas Monardus (1493-1558), physician of Seville. Monardus was one of the first Europeans to collect medicinal lore from the New World and make it available to physicians of his time; his museum, established in 1554, was a collecting center for products of the West Indies. He had, 1545-69, written on the "Bezaar" stone, the herb Escuerconera, and added a sketch of plants of the West Indies. In 1571 he made a contribution on "the thinges that are brought from the Occidentall Indias,

which Serve for the use of Medicine," and on "the Snow
and its vertues." These two works were combined in 1574
and Frampton published incomplete translations in 1577
and 1580. The first complete edition was the third, published in London, 1596, under the title *Joyfull Newes Out
of the New found World. Wherein are declared, the rare*

The Saſſafras.

*"From the Lande of our Occidentall Indies . . . thei bryng a
woodd of a tree of greate vertues . . . and beyng sicke of any
maner of evill . . . sharpe or large, hot or colde, greevous or
otherwise, they doe cure all . . . without makyng any difference . . . and so they have it for a universall remedy, for all
maner of deseases."*

*and singular vertues of divers Herbs, Trees, Plantes, Oyles
& Stones, with their applications, as well to the use of
Phisicke, as of Chirurgery, etc.*

Of the herbs of the New World Monardus gave special attention to "the Tobaco and of his great vertues," and to the sassafras. The tobacco had important curative powers for "paynes in the head," "wormes," toothache, "Chilblaynes," "venomus carbuncles," cankered wounds, hunger, thirst, and "any griefe of the body."

The sassafras roots and water "healeth opilations," "comforteth the liver and the Stomock," "give appetite to eate," cast out stones, "provoketh urine," and, used hot, "maketh a man goe to the Stoole." Further, "Where there is windinesse, it consumeth and dissolveth it, and also any maner of colde of the belly, and it dissolveth the swelling of it, curing any manner of disease which proceedeth of the Mother." Hence, since it was the "greate colde that is ingendered within the Mother, which doth hinder the cause of generation," it was recommended "to make Women with childe." Warning was issued, however, to those who "have much heate, or bee of a hot complexion." Such persons were to take sassafras in very moderate doses.

Monardus got his herb recipes from Spanish and French explorers and soldiers, who in turn had learned of their use from the natives. No other work of the sixteenth century so widely disseminated the medical knowledge of the New World in Europe; some of this, in turn, came back to America from Europe. Medicines imported by Spain from the New World found their way to England, where Frampton's work helped popularize them. In a way, the Frampton-Monardus writing might be considered the forbear of the many books of this type which followed in England and English America.

The first known American medical book, the Badianus Manuscript of *An Aztec Herbal* of 1552, was not published until 1940.[3] This work with its scores of plant color plates, is a mine of information for the botanist as well as the medical historian. Obviously it could have had no influence on the Spanish and English herbals, but Aztec medicine did reach Spain and England, as well as Indians north of the Rio Grande, both by word of mouth and through the writings of Spanish explorers and historians.[4]

Herb recipes in the Middle West were not confined to the herbals and formal medical works; they were passed along from person to person, copied down in odd places, recorded in household remedy books, and published in almanacs and newspapers. Many of them were later taken over by the various botanic medical schools. Some sixty of the drugs used by the American Indian may be found today in the modern materia medica and among the formulae manufactured by standard pharmaceutical houses. Of thousands of recipes used originally a few will suffice for samples. Some were administered for specific ills; others were taken just on general principles.

For fevers were recommended sweating and snake root, with a purge of white-walnut bark peeled upward;[5] also sassafras, dogwood, willow, or a glass of pearl ash and water. The breaking out in eruptive fevers, such as measles, was hastened by the use of sheep-dung tea, popularly known as nanny tea. For pleurisy (if no bleeders were at hand): catnip or pennyroyal, or butterfly weed tea, and applications of brimstone, sulphur and eggs, or boiled hot nettles. For indigestion: rhubarb bitters or cayenne pepper in spirits applied to the stomach outside, and water and good old spiritous liquor within. For "summer complaint" or dysentery would be prescribed a poultice of peppermint and tansy leaves, syrup of rhubarb with niter, or slippery elm. If a child so afflicted wished to indulge in ripe blackberries, old cheese, or fresh ham and eggs it should be allowed to do so. Bloodroot was also good for dysentery, or a strong decoction of mullen mixed and simmered in new milk would promote immediate improvement.

Did baby have a fit, it was due to worms, and "pink and senna" were quickly administered; or else a dose of twenty to forty grains of scrapings from pewter spoons. Green copperas, or sugar and turpentine had their advocates. A tapeworm was not treated so roughly, for pumpkin-seed tea was the proper remedy. For colds and sore throat: a piece of fat meat with pepper tied around the neck; grease from the Christmas goose; mustard and onion poultices; bloodroot or cherry bark; and rock candy and whiskey. For croup and asthma, alum, Indian turnip root in molasses, or onion and garlic juice sometimes proved helpful. Garlic rubbed on the spine was a good whooping cough cure. A cold might properly be treated with a mixture of flaxseed, licorice, raisins, sugar candy, and white vinegar.

Rheumatism was treated externally with rattlesnake-, goose-, or bear-oil, and internally with a mixture of calomel, tartarized antimony, cayenne pepper, and gum camphor, or with a tincture of butterfly weed roots or ripe pokeberries in French brandy. If fever was present one might add bleeding. Too, rheumatism might be cured by oil of the cajipul tree, which was also good for sciatica, lumbago, epilepsy, stings, burns, and snake bite. Strong tea of pokeberry leaves or rattleweed was recommended for smallpox victims. Saffron tea would bring out the measles; a bag of pounded slippery elm bark over the eyes of the measles sufferer would draw out the fever; a poultice of scraped raw potato was supposed to cure headache. A wash of diluted essence of sassafras would cure "the most inveterate case" of sore eyes in a few days.[6] The itch cure was hot water and soft soap applied with a corncob, followed by a lotion of sulphur and lard, or gunpowder and lard. Erysipelas called for a mixture of bitter root, yellow root, and slippery elm to be taken internally.

Consumption, having various causes, deserved various remedies. Among them according to the Hamilton, Ohio, *Miami Herald* of January 29, 1818, were: drink only water and eat only water gruel; eat only buttermilk and white bread; take spring water, new milk, and two ounces of sugar candy; drink one glass before each meal of a handful of sorrel boiled in a pint of whey; eat twenty ivy leaves and three sprigs of hyssop boiled in one pint of skim milk and one-half pint of small beer ("has cured a desperate case"); take a cow heel, two quarts of milk, nine ounces of hartshorn shavings, two ounces of ising-glass, one-fourth pound of sugar candy and a race of ginger, set in a pot in the oven, let cool, and let the patient live on this; cut a hole in the turf, lie down and breathe in it a quarter hour each morning ("deep cases been cured so"); inhale burning frankincense; inhale steam of white rosin and beeswax; etc., etc. For last stages suck a healthy woman, and (or) eat apples and milk, water gruel with fine flour, cider whey, barley water, or apple water sharpened with lemon juice.

Snake bite offered a wide choice of remedies, from white plantain boiled in milk, ash bark tea, alum water, or whiskey internally applied, to incision and application of salt and gunpowder, black ash leaves, crushed garlic juice, or salt and tobacco. To cuts and burns were applied crushed horse-radish leaves in vinegar; a salve of pokeberry leaves boiled in flour, honey, eggs, and sweet oil; or poultices of slippery elm or flaxseed. Jimson-leaf salve was recommended for infection, Indian turnip or bog onion for carbuncles; and of course the camphor bottle was usually available. Smoke of burning honeycomb was supposed to be efficacious in drawing out the poison from a rusty nail wound; a compound of tar, feathers, and brimstone on hickory coals was considered wonderful for mortifying flesh. Dropsy could be cured by steeping two handfuls of inner bark of white elder in two quarts of Lisbon wine for twenty-four hours, and taking a gill each morning on an empty stomach. One cancer cure called for the application to the affected part of a teaspoonful of scrapings from a brass kettle mixed with mutton suet, same not to be removed until the patient got well. Boiled or bruised root of the narrow-leaf dock applied over the sore, with tea of the same plant taken internally, was also recommended. Fluor volatile alkali was known to have cured apoplexy, and a mixture of ivory comb scrapings and honey was considered effective for yellow jaundice, typhus, and "putrid diseases."

Home remedies and botanical medicines were esteemed in proportion to their potency or bitterness. The old reliable for general purposes was the bottle of bitters, concocted according to various favorite recipes from dewberry, crane-bill, wild cherry, yellow poplar, or sarsaparilla — stewed, crushed, distilled, and combined with witch hazel leaves, cider, whiskey or brandy, and sumac or bitter roots. Another possibility was a brew of sassafras, burdock, red beets, and spirits; or the buds of the sweet apple tree, steeped in rum or cider. Some, of course, swore by sulphur and treacle, which was not properly an herb. A favorite of the Botanics was bruised lobelia and red pepper pods covered with good whiskey. Such bitters were good for cholera infantum, "yaller janders," phthisic, croup, whooping cough, colds, coughs, and catarrh. Each spring the mixture was taken as a tonic to drive the humors out of the system and purify the blood. (After a winter of corn bread and pork the blood and "jint water" had to be thinned for the more active existence anticipated with the coming of spring. Teas or bitters taken in the autumn might have disastrous results; if the blood was too thin in winter one ran a chance of freezing to death.) Those whose faith in the vegetable remedies was weak might obviate the necessity of spring purification by wearing a bag of camphor on the chest over winter, or if this had not been done, by drinking the waters from the last snow in March, or eating a few hailstones from the first good storm in spring. Then there was always goose-grease, inside and out, good for almost anything which the forthcoming season might bring.

All told there were between two and three hundred of these simples which constituted the materia medica of the pioneers.[7] One of the first important publications in this field was Dr. Jacob Bigelow's *American Medical Botany, being a Collection of the Native Medicinal Plants of the United States, Containing their Botanical History and Chemical Analysis, and Properties and Uses in Medicine, Diet and the Arts.* The three volumes, which were published at Boston, 1817-20, were adorned with sixty full-page colored engravings designed and executed by the author. Almost simultaneously Dr. William Paul Barton published his two-volume *Vegetable Materia Medica of the United States or Medical Botany* at Philadelphia. This compendious treatise of botanical descriptions and medicinal properties of plants indigenous to the United States was also illustrated with colored plates. Barton did not vouch for the efficacy of the medicinal properties of the fifty plants included in his study. His comments rarely extended beyond citations of their uses as domestic cures, such as: "Umbellata as a topical stimulant for domestic medicine; is used in Delaware for scrofula and rheumatism; useful for horses"; "Alum-root widely used in the west for dysentery"; "Dog fennel widely used for hysteria, epilepsy, dropsy, scrofula, asthma, rheumatism"; "Common blackberry much used by domestics."

Another was the two-volume *Medical Flora; or Manual of the United States of North America*, published at Philadelphia in 1828-30, by Constantine Samuel Rafinesque-Schmaltz, the eccentric Transylvania naturalist. This work contained descriptions of medical plants with their "names, qualities, properties, history, &c. and notes or remarks on nearly 500 equivalent substitutes," and was illustrated with over one hundred drawings. Although Rafinesque also instituted his own system of cure-all, in this work his intent was merely to compile a medical botany which would be used by physicians and pharmacists of the period. He stated that "There are many modes of effecting cures by equivalent remedies, but vegetable substances afford the mildest, most efficient, and most congenial to the human frame."

Among "105 of the most active and efficient medical types" he listed: "Black Snake-Root, Botrophis Serpentaria (squaw root) — astringent, diuretic, sudorific, anodyne, repellent, emenagogue, subtonic &c — to be used for rheumatism, acute and chronic, to facilitate parturition, for sore-throat, dropsy, hysterics, Psora, ague and fever, yellow fever, snake-bite, diseases of horses and cattle"; "Aralias — vulnerary, pectoral, sudorific, stimulant, diaphoretic, cordial, depurative, &c — use roots bruised or chewed or in poultices for all kinds of wounds and ulcers. Fomentations and catoplasms for cutaneous affections, erysipelas, and ring-worms. Infusion or decoction, for all diseases of the blood, syphilitic complaints, chronical rheumatism, local pains, cardiology, bellyache, &c. Syrups, cordials, decoctions, &c. have been found useful in coughs, catarrh, cochexia, languor, pains in the breast, &c. Cordial recommended for gout, and juice for ear-ache and deafness"; "Common strawberry — diluent, refrigerant, subastringent, analeptic, diaphoretic, diuretic, pectoral, eccopratic &c. — useful in fevers, gravel, gout, scurvy, and phthisis. Cooling, promotes perspiration, gives relief in diseases of the bladder and kidneys . . . possesses also property of curing chilblains. Fine wine can be made from them."

Since remedies of this sort were so widely used, the art of simpling or root and herb collecting in the forests and cultivating in the gardens was a routine activity for many pioneers, and a part-time vocation for some.

One of the most interesting of the Indian-medicine books, and the first medical book published in the West, was Peter Smith's *The Indian Doctor's Dispensatory*, published at Cincinnati in 1813. Its full title was *The Indian Doctor's Dispensatory Being Father Smith's Advice Respecting Diseases and Their Cures; Consisting of Prescriptions for Many Complaints: And a Description of Medicines, Simple and Compound, Showing their Virtues and How to Apply Them. Designed for the Benefit of His Children, His Friends and the Public, but more especially for the Citizens of the Western Parts of the United States of America.* "Having an insatiable taste and constant desire for relieving the afflicted and diseased," the author offered this little book to the public for one dollar, reasoning "that 75 cents would be enough for a common book of this size" and charging only "25 cents for 50 years of labor and observation." He would no doubt be surprised at the price which his book commands today, a hundred thirty years after its publication.

The treatise was designed particularly for the citizens of the West. "The natives of our own country are in possession of cures, simples, etc., that surpass what is used by our best practitioners." To simplify matters Smith reduced all diseases to two types: (1) those of plethora and irritation; (2) those of debility, weakness, and languor. The human body discharged as perspiration "half or more of all that we eat and drink daily. It would surprise you to see this floating all over you, in a state of health, like water over a piece of watered meadow, and a steam flying from you in every direction, like your breath on a frosty morning. . . . If the air be cool and clear it will always have elasticity, as it is called; it will swell and fly back again easily, when we receive it into our lungs." Whenever anything upset this salubrious state of affairs, Dr. Smith was prepared with ninety prescriptions to restore it. These ranged from the Home Ipecacuanha or Indian Physic to the famous *Leotrill*, which he claimed to have got from Flanders. There were the usual purges, tonics, and poultices, an interesting concoction for cure of derangement or mania, and the late discovery, or snail cure, for cancer.

Two prescriptions were rather unusual.[8] "Preserving the teeth, and curing an odious taste in the mouth, may always, I presume, be affected by this little simple process: Only wash and rinse your mouth every morning in your own urine. . . . Relief from the ill taste I have proved, and I do not think the remedy worse than the disease. Those who know this in their youth, and will not try it, who can pity them when they have the tooth-ache!" The other, "for a diarrhaea, or looseness of the belly," was particularly efficacious and had been given with success to both man and beast: "Take the yard or pizzle of a buck (get it saved and dried by a deer hunter), reduce it to powder, put a spoonful of the powder in a bottle with a pint of spirits; take this solution in small quantities, every hour, till relief is obtained."

Father Smith held the regular doctor in little esteem. "Now if we can do better without calomel than with it, both in debility and plethora; why should we not throw by the use of it? . . . We should always remember, when we are about to take medicine, *if the Lord will*, we shall do this or that with success; *if the Lord will*, I shall get well by this means or some other." Fantastic though his prescriptions were, his thoughts on hygiene and the importance of light and air were ahead of his time.

Better known than Peter Smith's book was that of Dr. Richard Carter of Kentucky. The single-volume first edition was published in Frankfort in 1815 under the title of *Valuable Vegetable Medical Prescriptions for the cure of All Nervous and Putrid Disorders;* the rare two-part edition, published at Versailles in 1825, bears the title *A Short Sketch of the Author's Life, and Adventures from his Youth until 1818, in the First Part. In Part the Second, A Valuable, Vegetable, Medical Prescription, with a table of Detergent and Corroborant Medicines to Suit the Treatment of the Different Certificates.* This work is a classic, unequalled for variety, originality, and completeness. Dr. Carter was a system unto himself — a composite of Indian medicine, regular practice, poetry, mysticism, advice to the lovelorn, and Carter.

Part I of this opus, possibly in way of preparation for the Carter cures, starts with a discourse on Death and Resurrection. It then continues with the disconnected life-story of the author: He was born on the south branch of the Potomac in Virginia in 1786. His father was an Englishman who, according to his tale, was regularly "bred to the practice of physic" in London. The senior Carter's first wife having died, he came to the United States, where an injury forced him to become a cobbler. He then married a woman whose mother was half Indian and something of a doctoress, and in due course of time two children, Richard and Melinda, arrived.

Young Richard was an unfortunate and disobedient child. As an infant, while his mother worked in the field, he was occasionally left in a fence corner, where sometimes his clothes froze to the earth. When he began to get around in the world, so vile was his disposition that if the parents would not gratify his whims, he was wont to "fly into a pet

SHORT SKETCH OF THE

AUTHOR'S LIFE,

AND ADVENTURES FROM HIS YOUTH

UNTIL 1818, IN THE FIRST PART.

IN PART THE SECOND,

A VALUABLE, VEGETABLE,

MEDICAL PRESCRIPTION, WITH A TABLE OF

DETERGENT AND CORROBORANT

MEDICINES TO SUIT THE TREATMENT OF THE

DIFFERENT CERTIFICATES:

BY DR. RICHARD CARTER,

VERSAILLES, KY.

Printed by JOHN H. WILKINS, Commonwealth Office.

::::::::
1825.

"I flatter myself that I have been as successful as any physician whatever, who has not had a better opportunity. . . . Courteous reader, before I close this little book I purpose inserting a few certificates stating the benefit derived from my medicine . . . not that I feel disposed to sound my own trumpet . . . but had I have obtained certificates from all those whom I have healed, three such books as this, would not have contained them."

and gallop around the house on all fores like a tarripin, as hard as I could for several times before I would stop." Although his parents went on for some years together "rejoicing in harmony and peace," the boy was "as prone to evil as sparks are to fly upwards." He grew up with few inhibitions. In one of his tantrums, while galloping around the house with a cat in his hands, he became inspired to plunge the poor animal into a boiling pot of cabbage and bacon. When he became old enough to observe and reflect, he was taken to church and to a funeral. Shortly thereafter, when caught preaching to the cats, he was so chagrined that he took one out and buried it alive.

Since by this time he had a knowledge of right and wrong, he realized that he was a very bad boy. He repented and resolved to do better, but soon was wallowing in the mire again. Evil companions made matters worse. Once when the boys were playing, a cousin threw a pet owl onto a horse, which in its fright kicked an orphan boy "and broke the rim of his belly," so that the boy died. At another time young Carter got flogged by an old woman for stealing his mother's cream and felt that it did as much good "as a dose of medicine would a sick person." The cure was not permanent, however, for soon thereafter he stuck a knife in a horse's leg, and when the horse kicked him in the head, blood ran from his nose, mouth, and ears. Whereupon he decided that "Wit is best if not bought too dear," and later proceeded to write a poem about the event.

At the age of twelve "Devil Dick" accompanied his father to Baltimore, where he saw a gang of convicts at work. He was so deeply impressed by the sight that he reflected that if hell were as bad as the penitentiary, he would pray to Almighty God that He keep everyone out of it and that "we be directed into an honest path and like good Republicans provide well for our families . . . ."

In moving to a better farm the Carter family almost starved for a spell, but greater plenty came with time. Richard went to school to a good teacher but had an inclination to quarrel and fight. The teacher used the rod to no effect, then made the wicked pupil stand on a block for an hour at a time, pointing his finger at a certain hole in the wall, "but this done no good." He regretted that he did not get more severely lined out, for early discipline saved many a man from a bad end. "The reader will discover by this that when a child is whipped and receives not enough to humble it, the rod does more harm than good."

By this time his mother was "kissing black betty" rather frequently; so was vile Dick. Once when she came home "three sheets in the wind" her husband shut the door on her. When she broke it down with an axe, the husband got out the shotgun. The boy grabbed at the gun, whereupon it went off and blew a hole in the door, but stopped neither mother nor son from drinking. "What a hard spectacle is the drunkard?" Liquor "inflames the blood; causes the eyes to be sore; it causes dropsies, gouts, scolding wives, empty dishes, naked children, weedy cornfields, bad fences, hollow-horned cows, broken shins, bruised heads, black eyes, bloody noses, empty purses and bad reputations." The only blessing was, if one did not hug the bottle it could never prove a Delila.

But like the old lady "who was in the habit of kissing black betty very frequently, until she began to pat her foot, and at last she would cry out reach me the bottle John, for the more I drink the better I feel," Devil Dick was a willing repeater. When about fifteen he got drunk, went to sleep in a chestnut tree, and never knew how he got down. Scared, he swore off, but somewhat later went to a frolic, was tempted and succumbed, so went to an old house to sleep under the straw. Shortly a couple came and sat on him; "They talked and sported for some time." After the man left, the woman became greatly frightened when the undercover visitor was forced to crawl out.

At the time of writing his life Carter stated that he had never been beastly drunk but three times. "The last time I lay limber for the space of three hours without a hope being entertained by the spectators of my recovery. But I recovered, and then I vowed never to drink any more spir-

ituous licquors, unless I was by myself or in company; and
not then unless I chose, and I have found it just as good
a promise as I could make."

Carter eased up on drinking, but was still a refractory
sinner. Caught smothering and hanging "rabits" he was
sent by his father to witness the hanging of a man. When
two old women came to see his sick father he routed them
over a log by a yellowjackets' nest. The log broke, the
yellowjackets attacked with fury, and altogether it was
a delightful affair. But God got even, for soon thereafter
Carter fell from a high chimney on which he was working,
and practically killed himself. As a result he began to think
of his Soul's eternal welfare; he visited grave yards and
saw "that there was as many graves shorter as there was
longer than myself." He contemplated death.

The father lingered on until fall, and then expired.

> *"I then to reading did betake,*
> *And all my idle ways forsake;*
> *And many a book perused by night,*
> *Served to instruct and to delight.—*
> *Thus I gained the art to heal,*
> *Which this book to you'll reveal.*
> *Thousands have I eased of pain,*
> *My labours hard and small my gain."*

But serious effort soon proved dull, so the youth began
"rambling through the world, by which I learned a different view of things." He met, fell in love with, and became
engaged to a young woman, half Indian. He went home
to arrange some business, then returned "to execute my
contract with the girl whom I loved to the highest degree
of superiorigation." (He submitted a poem of eleven stanzas as additional evidence.) But Providence intervened, for
Carter became ill and the six-months' absence had been too
much; she had married another. "When we met, we both
cried heartily, and parted."

Followed more wandering. At Lynchburg he first saw the smallpox and was impressed. After almost drowning on the way home, he again entered school and applied himself for two six-months' terms. He then went to live with an uncle on the "headwaters of Marietta." Here for several months he studied botany—the power and use of herbs. Several more months he spent with an "Indian Doctoress" and an Indian doctor who possessed "great skill in pulsation." Under these preceptors the student worked hard; also at night in books left by his father, "applying myself so intensively . . . that I was very near producing a caterack in my eyes." He had a good memory and retained much of what he was taught.

On returning from a trip to Carolina, Carter, as a result of wading many streams, lost his health. Soreness in the breast and swelling in the stomach alternated with dysentery and prolonged constipation. Some thought he was poisoned. Neither an Indian doctor nor a local practitioner could help. The sufferer's pulse was about gone and so was he, when another doctor applied a "glister . . . of green bitter gord guts," whereupon he shortly passed a "gallon of blood and corruption," and, though the doctor predicted he would die about midnight, proceeded to live. Months of torture followed. A water doctor told him his liver was destroyed and that he was bound to die. "It is an awful thing to reflect on seeing our friends lingering around our bed, waiting to take their final farewell—to feel your tongue cleave to the rough of your mouth, and the blood settling under your nales—your cheeks pale, your lips blue, and your hands clinched, and your breathing perceptibly growing shorter."

With nerves weakened, pains and running sores in the chest, sores on the hips, inward fevers, dysentery, tremblings in the lungs, and a palpitating heart, the patient was in a fairly bad way. Mercury given by a physician he threw away, but a friend skilled in herbs prescribed a brew of dewberry briar roots, burdock roots, wild cherry bark, inside bark of sassafras, and white ash tops. This he used for a regular drink, with essence of peppermint on going to bed. The blood was enlivened and nerves twitched and jerked. The hip sores were treated with powder of burnt mussel shells and sweet oil. Poultices of "beat mustard seed" were applied to wrists, "ancles," and feet, and an Indian sweat treatment taken by way of steam from "a point of whiskey and a point of strong vinegar," mixed and poured over hot stones in a pit. This stopped the nerve-jerking and relieved some of the pains. Remaining stiffness in the joints was removed by an ointment of camomile flowers, goldenrod, flowers of pinks, pine beans, and double tanzy boiled down and mixed with sweet oil. For the still present dizziness, aching, and such, a drink made of the bark of dogwood roots, rue, pine tops, black snake root, rusty iron, and apple cider was used, the patient meanwhile abstaining from cider, bacon, sweet milk, and cabbage. The bloating, night sweats, bad appetite, and dysentery now disappeared, yet there remained a soreness in the breast for three years.

Then began a stomach ache, "dispepsy," flatulency, and dry tickling cough. This condition was met with a dosage of tar and saltpeter in good rye whiskey, with glauber salts, oyster shell lime, and a bit of stone-coal dust in water, on the side.

Again in tolerably good health, Carter sold his land and moved to Botetourt County, where he set up shop "and got a pretty good run of custom." When after a few months his health again became impaired, he moved to Lincoln County, Kentucky. He had resolved to withhold his medical skill from the public, but having cured a neighbor's Negro woman, he was started again. In time so extensive did his practice become that two to four active students could hardly administer the preparation of medicines and write the prescriptions. Experience taught him one important principle:

> *"Since man, to man, is so unjust*
> *'Tis hard to know, whom I may trust;*
> *I've trusted many, to my sorrow,*
> *So pay today, I'll trust tomorrow."*

Operating on this plan he managed to "squeeze through the world pretty well; generally having money enough to pay my debts, and wherewithall to support my family."

No doubt part of Carter's interest in medicine came from his own ailments and injuries; off and on he seemed to enjoy rather general poor health. At one time or another he was nearly frozen, drowned, and "crushed into atoms by a rolling log"; he was shot while duck hunting; suffered a cut artery, and nearly fell into the river when he fainted from the effects; had the "main leader and small leg bone cut"; had "three several attacks of bilious fever"; had "disentary"; was "three times severely afflicted with the flux"; and suffered from the ennui or hypo — "in fact died away three times." As he summarized it at the age of thirty-nine: "My life, indeed, is an eventful one of afflictions, accidents and misfortunes."

> *"When first in nature's form I came,*
> *My mental powers confin'd;*
> *By all mankind, I was the least,*
> *But could not be resin'd.*
>
> *"E'en from an early stage of life,*
> *My trials have been great;*
> *Surrounded I have been with strife,*
> *Which still indeed's my fate.*
>
> *"My parents they were very poor,*
> *When I their child was born;*
> *They had not much for to bestow,*
> *On me their only son.*

"They laboured hard their son to raise,
  In credit and renown;
  But never I deserved much praise,
  But their most bitter frown.

"I turn'd myself about to see;
  What danger I was in;
  I cried Oh Lord! mine's cruel fate,
  I've lived so long in sin.

"I then beheld the scene I'd past,
  Of life's short narrow space;
  And that I soon must occupy,
  My own appointed place.

"To ascertain the state of man,
  My thoughts began to soar;
  I thought my life was but a span,
  And I should be no more.

"And then it was I did converse,
  With nature and with art;
  You are my friends while here on earth,
  But soon we'll have to part.

"Then lend to me your friendly aid,
  Give sight unto my eyes;
  That I may gain the chiefest life
  Which never fades and dies.

"There's nothing here that's worth our care,
  Compared to that above;
  Then let us view the things more near,
  And live in perfect love.

"For few and evil are the days,
  Of man while here on earth;

Yet eagerly each one displays,
His talents from his birth.

"But could we turn our thoughts from nice
To that which is more dear;
How soon would virtue us entice,
And evil banish far.

"I do desire to live in peace,
Which God doth justify;
And may my usefulness increase
Until the day I die.

"I know it is my hearts delight,
To do what good I can;
As far as God has gave me sight
I'll heal the sons of man."

Dr. Carter in part I, following the sketch of his life, dealt with such subjects as: "Directions for Gardening," "Of Signs from the Pulse," "Of the Bad Effects of Mercurials," "The Morbid Effects of Poisons in the Air," "Of Signs from the Urine and Other Excretions," "Of the Crisis," "Remedy for Weak Nerves, Rheumatisms, &c," "Internal Dropsy of the Brain," "I Here Insert a Few Recipes," "For the Yellow Jaundice," "For the Fever and Ague," "For Convulsive Fits, Palsys, Appoplexy's, &c," "For the Hysterics," "On the Hypocondriacs," "For Old Running Sore Legs," "For the Consumption," "For the Stomach Ach, &c, &c," "A Caution to those who drink Mineral Water," "Of the Urine" (which included poetry to the tune of Yankee Doodle), "Indian Lexicon," "The Best of Wives" (Poem), and "Gutta Serena." The illustrations of certain nefarious characters from the canine world which he added, gave further opportunity for moralizing.

SNAP.

This dog is very outrageous. And I think from
name, ways and actions, is a relation of Sly's. He is
not so old in name or nature; but does much mischief
in our land; he barks at every thing. We hear his whin-
ing and barking, and growling against laws, against
rights, against widows, orphans, men and their wives;
setting every thing in an uproar. We hear the sound in
the pulpit, with different persuasions. We hear the
sound at the bar; he barks loudest when there is no danger near; he is like a wolf or a bear, he can change his
voice according to season. When you are with him, he
seems as innocent as a dove, but when you are out of
sight, he compasses you round. If he bites you there is
a poison under his tongue that's sweeter than honey, and
as strong as a lion. When you are in your bed at night
reposing on your pillow of rest, he is baying of you.
    Even those in their graves do not escape him.

The rich he will flatter,
The poor he'll dispise;

*"There has many young women been destroyed the remainder
part of their lives by the sound of his voice. . . . Sometimes he
moves a man and wife, to strive, and take each others life.
Sometimes friends he brakes asunder, alarms poor females with
bold thunder. A great deal more I have been told, he done to
folks in times of old."*

*The versatile Dr. Carter probably executed his own woodcuts
as well as the poetry.*

Carter's compendium of cures—omitting the poetry—
was contained in his sixty-three "receipts," several of which
were usually prescribed for the same ill. The doctor or
patient might try a number of them on the theory, perhaps, that one might hit the jackpot. Most of the preparations required a bit of doing. Some were apparently
intended for practitioners, others for home dispensing.
Since they are so representative of remedies of this type,
three are herewith reproduced in full:

"RECEIPT THE 22nd: Fill a twenty gallon kettle with
sliced elecampane roots, and boil them well in water, pour
off the sirop and fill the kettle with water again, and boil the
same roots the second time, pour off the sirop as before, then
clean your kettle and strain all your sirop through a flannel
cloth, into it, and boil it down to about eight gallons and a
half, then strain it into your barrel. Then get green com-
phry slice fine and fill a ten gallon pot with it, and boil it
down in the same way, until you have about six gallons of
sirop, then strain it and add it to the same barrel. Then boil
half a bushel of angelica roots well to a gallon of sirop,
strain it and add it to the barrel. Then fill a twenty gallon
pot full of life-everlasting, boil it well in the same way,
down to two gallons, and add that to the barrel after you
strain it well. Then boil thirty gallons of spikenard roots in
the same way, down to six gallons of sirop, strain it and add
it to the barrel. Then boil ten gallons of the roots and tops
of ground ivy well, strain the sirop in a tub. Then boil five
gallons of white plaintain leaves well, and strain the sirop
in the tub with the other. Then boil the same quantity of
heart leaves—in the same way, and strain the sirop in the
same tub. Then put the whole of the contents of the tub
in a vessel and boil it down to two gallons and add it to
the barrel. Then fill a ten gallon pot full of the bark of
the roots of yellow poplar, and boil it down and strain it,
and then reduce it to two gallons, and strain it in the barrel.
Then fill a five gallon pot with mullen roots and boil and
strain it as the rest were done and then strain it in the
barrel, when it is reduced to half a gallon. This makes in

all twenty-eight gallons, to which you must add five gallons and a half of good clean honey, a quart of good Madeira wine, a pound of pulverised columbo, a pint of the elixer of vitroil, and ten gallons of good apple cider (after boiling it down to five.) Then let it work well and settle, and if it is too sharp or strong for the patient, you may add more honey. There will be agreeable to this arrangement about forty gallons, about thirty of which, is pure medicine. The dose may be varied as necessity requires, from half a table spoonful to a table spoonful, and in most cases should be given morning, noon and night, and in pulminary complaints, coughs, &c. a tea spoonful of linseed oil, sweet oil, or dog's oil should be added to each dose; but if the patient's stomach will not bear it, fresh butter warmed, and neither washed nor salted will make a very good substitute. This medicine is wonderfully efficacious in all cases of consumptions, phthisics, hooping cough, measles, a cough proceeding from the last stages of a fever, and a cough proceeding from the dropsey. The patient should not make use of any salted hog meat, sweet milk, cider nor spirits, but may be permitted to use fresh shoat, beef, chickens, squirrels, mutton, panado, rice, buttermilk, and a little water and wine.

"RECEIPT THE 23rd: Get thirty gallons of good strong apple cider, and put three table spoonfuls of ground black mustard seed, and a handful of beat horse radish roots to every quart, and three pound of salt petre to the thirty gallons. Fill a ten gallon pot full of dried elecampane roots, and boil them well in water, strain the sirop, and boil the same roots the second time in the same way, strain the two sirops together, and boil it down to four gallons, add it to the cider, then add a gallon of parsley roots, and let it stand about ten days and it is fit for use, and may be given in doses from the contents of half a table spoonful to a table spoonful, which may be given three times per day, and in severe chronic complaints, may be increased to two table spoonfuls three times per day. The diet of the patient should be light and cooling, and consequently he or she should abstain from the use of sweet milk, strong coffee, and rusty bacon, and keep out of wet, damp or night air, but breathe freely in the open morning air. This medicine and regimen is good in cases of sciatic gouts, rheumatisms, palsies, ague, apoplexies, convulsive fits, gravel, dropsies."

"RECEIPT THE 41st: Fill a twenty-five gallon still with elecampane roots and water, distill it and preserve the proceeds, then fill the still with spikenard roots and water, and still it in the same way, and in like manner preserve this, then fill the still with horehound, and treat it likewise, then run off two still fulls of ground ivy in the same way, after which clean the still, and put back all the liquid that has been extracted from all those herbs and roots above mentioned, and add five gallons of good whiskey, run it off as you would in making whiskey and save it as long as there appears to be any strength in it. Then put it in a cag, and to every gallon add half a gallon of honey, a table spoonful of refined nitre, a table spoonful of dried pulverised Indian turnip, and a pint of middling strong lie made of the ashes of dry cow dung.

"Then get a peck of pollepody, a peck of cinquefril, and a peck of white plantain; put these into a pot and boil them well in water, strain it, add three gallons of cider to it, boil it down to three gallons, and to every gallon of this add a quart of the above sirop. This medicine may either be taken in a little wine and water, or new milk. We give from half a tablespoonful, to a wine glass full, three times per day, during which time the patient must not eat any thing high seasoned, strong nor sweet, and he should be very careful that he does not take cold or even heat his blood. It is best to commence with small doses at first, and increase the dose as the patient's strength increases. This medicine is not at all dangerous unless you give too much for the patient's strength. If this medicine causes the patient to sweat, produces a soreness in the breast, or increases the cough, you may know that it is too strong, and consequently it must be weakened with honey until those symptoms abate. This is good to break any fever, and is excellent in the last stages of the consumption, phthisic, and the cold plague. If the cough is very hard add to every dose a tea spoonful of sweet or linseed oil.

"The herbs and roots that you are herein directed to distill, will not produce as well in the heat of summer, as they will in the spring or fall, so by these directions, you may know how to regulate it so as to get all the strength and should not run it too far."

In keeping with the Carter practice of breaking the heavy scientific content with a bit of variety we here insert "a small peace solely intended to divert and refresh the mind."

THE BEST OF WIVES

"*A man once had a vicious wife,*
The most uncommon thing in life,
Whose days and nights were spent in strife,
Unceasing.

"*Her tongue went glibly all the day long,*
Sweet contradiction still her song,
And all the poor man said was wrong,
And ill done.

"*From a truce without doors or within,*
From speeches long as statesmen spin,
To rest from her eternal din,
He found not.

"*He every soothing art display'd,*
Tri'd of what stuff her back was made,
Failing in all to Heav'n he pray'd,
To take her.

"*Once walking by a river side,*
In mournful terms my dear he cri'd,
Let no more feuds our peace divide,
I'll end them.

"So *tie my hands as fast behind*,
As *art and nature both combin'd*,
Then *to my fate I'll be resign'd*,
While *drowning*.

"With *eager haste the dame complies*,
While *joy stands glistening in her eyes*,
While *in her thoughts her husband dies*,
Before *her*.

"But *when I view the rolling tide*,
Nature *revolts, he said beside*,
I *would not be a suicide*,
And *die thus*.

"While *here I stand upon the brink*,
If *I was in soon I should sink*,
So *push me in, nay never shrink*,
But *do it*.

"Her *ill designs now to perfect*,
Some *twenty yards she ran direct*,
To *give the blow the more effect*,
And *drown him*.

"But *he being far more wise than brave*,
Did *slip aside himself to save*,
So *swce she dashes in the wave*,
Of *water*.

"Dear *husband help! I sink she cri'd*,
Thou *best of wives the man replie'd*,
I *would but you my hands have ti'd*,
God *help you*."

For fever and ague the Carter cure called for a mixture of calomel (unusual for the vegetable doctor), salt peter, Jesuit bark, pulverized columbo, elixir of vitriol, spirits of niter, and a pill of steel dust. At the same time blister plasters should be applied to the patient's wrists and ankles and an opened young pullet to the soles of the feet.

Rheumatism, Dr. Carter believed, "proceeds from the congress and mutual effervency of salts, which are of a different origin and nature, viz. of the fi salt arising from the blood, and of the acid salt coming from the nervous liquor, the subjects of both of which salts are superfluous dregs, deposed from the aforesaid humours, forced into certain teogescencies, and discharge sometimes on one part, and then on another of the system; wherefore, that the disease may be cured, let both the turgescercies of the humours be appeased, and their superfluous dregs be purged forth, and let the salts degenerated both ways, be reduced to a state of valatility."

For a disease with so simple a cause the cure would be a poultice of slippery elm, poke root, Jamestown weed leaves, woodbine root, and rye meal; after a few days this should be followed by an ointment brewed from tanzy leaves, red pepper, tobacco, pine roots, elder roots, rum, neats foot oil, salt peter, laudanum, and a pint of red fishing worms. An accompanying drink was made of dogwood and "sasapharilla" roots combined with whiskey.

A gentle massage of dog oil was even more highly recommended. This brew, "For the gout rheumatisms, cramps, infirmities of the sinews, joints, &c" was simple to make and use. One had only to:

"Take a young fat dog and kill him, scald and clean him as you would a pig, then extract his guts through a hole previously made in his side, and substitute in the place thereof, two handfuls of nettles, two ounces of brimstone, one dozen hen eggs, four ounces of turpentine, a handful of tanzy, a pint of red fishing worms, and about three-fourths of a pound of tobacco, cut up fine; mix all those ingredients well together before deposited in the dogs belly, and then sew up the whole, then roast him well before a hot fire, save the oil, annoint the joints, and weak parts before the fire as hot as you can bear it, being careful not to get wet or expose yourself to damp or night air, or even heating yourself, or in fact you should not expose yourself in any way."

At dropsy Dr. Carter was a whiz. There was the case of Mrs. Ruth Wray, who was "taken with the dropsey, (or rather in the winter) I first was taken with a pain in my wright side, which still increased more and more as also did the swelling. I was in such a condition that I thought I never should recover. . . ." Though "Dr. Rush advised sea bathing, travelling, sudden surprise, or scareing the patient," Carter tackled the disease with an ointment of camomile flowers and fresh butter and dosage of horse-radish roots, parsley roots, mustard seed, refined niter and a "small handfull of alicumpane" put down in hard cider. Lest the treatment be not effective and swelling return, the doctor recommended a flock of other mixtures including burnt egg shells strained through a silk handkerchief and mixed with jalap and cream of tartar. "And with this regimen, medicine and treatment, she soon became sound and well."

> *"Behold a female in distress*
> *Afflicted with the ascites,*
> *Her system swell'd and rack'd with pain,*
> *While she upon her bed is lain;*
> *The Doctors they have had their will,*
> *While Doctresses have tried their skill,*
> *And yet the patient's growing worse,*
> *So what to do they're at a loss;*
> *Observe the last alternative,*
> *They all agree she cannot live;*
> *So then to me she is conveyed,*
> *To see if I could give her aid;*
> *With all my might to work I went,*
> *And used my skill to the extent;*
> *And through God's mercy did direct,*
> *The means which did a cure perfect;*
> *So notwithstanding I'm abused*

And by some folks my means refused,
Yet as God calls me I remain
Rebuking both disease and pain."

Then there was the case of Mrs. Sarah Lasure, whose testimonial was attested by seven citizens good and true:

"I DO CERTIFY, That in the year of our Lord 1810 that I was taken with the dropsy, and became very low. I sent for a Doctor, and mended a little, but never left me, but still grew worse for two years . . . and my feet and legs swelled to that degree that they bursted and run a great deal . . . . When I commenced taking medicine of Doctor Carter I was about fifty years of age, and since that I have had a fine daughter. . . . I do certify that I also had a daughter who had a white swelling in her leg, which was hollow from the knee to the ancle, and out of which came sixteen pieces of bone, and this same Doctor Carter attended on her and she has got nearly well, so that it don't hinder at all from walking."

"This woman, aged fifty years,
The dropsy had, as it appears;
Who was laid low and almost gone,
Until her legs did burst and run.

"While at the point of death she lay,
Without the hope of the next day;
Then by God's blessing and my skill,
She was restored, sound and well.

"Observe the means which I did give,
Has almost made the dying live;
And from affliction now has free'd,
And made this aged woman breed."

Fits caused by worms in children should be cured by Carolina pinkroot stewed in water and sweetened with honey. Dr. Carter suggested, however, that it was "best to add to each dose about one-eighth of an ounce of manna; the importance of which addition, will appear when it is remarked, that the pink root is poisonous, and if given in too large quantities, kills the child to whom it is given." Alloes, Jesuit bark, bear's foot, table salt, wormwood, garlic, and wormseed made an effective bitters. Calomel either by itself or combined with jalap to the tune of five to thirty grains for the child, gun powder on an empty stomach, red onions "beat fine" and bound to the navel, iron rust in hard cider, or steel filings in honey, all had at different times proved their merits — even once to the extent of destroying a long-standing ten and one-half foot tapeworm of an old sea captain.

Ordinary fits, such as those with which Sarah Silvey would die away "about every full and change of the moon" were nicely handled by a simple routine treatment. First jalap and chicken soup while abstaining from cold water, milk, and hog meat; then tonic of columbo roots, orange peelings, "jentian" roots, camomile flowers, and "beaver castor" stewed in Madeira wine. After ten days of this, foot- and leg-baths in a strong ooze of iron weed roots, tanzy, "hoarhound," and spicewood were given on alternate days. As the spasms became more infrequent, calomel and alloes were administered, followed by castor oil, powdered birch bark, fennel seed, and pechoon roots in hard cider; meanwhile the patient's abdomen was rubbed with camomile flowers melted in unsalted butter. The fits disappeared but the ensuing colic had to be treated with pills made from asafoetida, alloes, rhubarb, and spirits. Thereupon Sarah Silvey was restored to perfect health and her doctor hoped she would become an affectionate bride, "not only for company sake, but to promote health." Anticipating the event, he felt induced to insert a few lines:

ON A WEDDING NIGHT

"O call the bridegroom to the bride
All decked in her beauteous pride;

May all the pleasures and the sweets,
Which does attend the genial sheets;
And Hymen's chains and loving bands,
Be now resigned into their hands.
And may soft joys now them re-wed,
And be the curtains of their bed;
And may fair honour and delight,
Now crown their day, and grace their night
While thus their oft repeated kisses,
Unite in both their happy wishes;
And may the mild embrace of love,
Be soft and sweet as Venus' dove.
But oh! the raptures of that night,
What sweet concussions of delight;
Now in each other's arms involved,
They lay confounded and dissolved;
Body's mingled, sexes blending,
Which shall be the most contending;
Darting fierce and flaming kisses,
Thus plunged into boundless blesses."

Dr. Carter was at his best on the ennui or hypo. This dread disease manifested itself by feelings of dullness, fear, indefinite pains, and lack of desire to attend to any business. When one had it, he "felt disposed to be retired," to tell his troubles, and to feel that he was afflicted with any disease which anyone else had. Carter did not diagnose this affliction as a real disorder unconnected with any other, for it made its appearance only when the "system was released from any cause; such as hard drink, colds, fevers, dropsies, gouts, night air, loss of sleep, incessant studying, loss of friends, and scolding companions." He reasoned that the body and mind were so inseparably connected that one could not suffer without the other's participating. The idea that the complaint was entirely of the mind was erroneous. "My opinion of the hypo is, that it is very hard to exterminate, when it has once taken good hold, it becomes ingratiated, and is in a measure second nature."

Like the hypo, but operating only on the female sex, was the hysterics (hi-sterics to Dr. Carter and his pioneer patients).

When affected with hypo or hysterics some persons insisted they were teapots; others thought that they were town clocks, that their legs and feet were made of glass, that they were actually dying or else already dead. One man insisted that he had died at twelve o'clock the night before and was brought to only after his neighbors came in and reflected that no doubt he had gone to hell, " 'for if he is not gone there I see not what use there is for such a place.' " An old gentleman who went to bed in a room with a small boy tried the next morning to get into the boy's pantaloons instead of his own. When he failed, he fell to the floor, awakened the household with a terrible roar, and went into the agonies of death. When help arrived and he was asked what the trouble was, he yelled, " 'What's the matter? Why can't you see what's the matter? I'm swelled as big as an ox. I can not get my big toe into my pantaloons.' " Then there was the old woman who tried in vain to keep her head warm, though "she wore a cap, three handkerchiefs, and a boulster of feathers on it." This same old woman proclaimed that she was able to "travel a small path the darkest night that ever came" by the aid of nine lighted candles which came out of thin air and stuck to the back of her head.

A patient whose system and nerves were somewhat weakened by the fevers got the idea that his belly was full of young ducks, which he said he could hear and feel plainly. When his doctor was unable to dissuade him from this notion another was called in for consultation. The latter conceded that the patient had a case and stated that he could cure him with a purge. Having procured some young ducks, he placed them in the proper receptacle so that the patient was satisfied that he had delivered himself of them. The sick man was then curious to know how the ducks could have accumulated in his belly. The doctor explained that no doubt the patient "had eat a great many eggs in his time, which had collected and hatched; which explanation entirely satisfied the patient, and in a short time he was as well as ever he was in his life; but never could be prevailed on to eat another egg." Dr. Carter once heard of a man "who became so desperately in love with a young woman, that on her denying him, (although he had ever been considered a prudent man, and managed his estate well,) yet he became so extravagant, as to patiently sit for three months on a goose egg. If this was not the hypo, it was very much like it, if not worse."

One of the worst cases of hypo recorded was that of an old urine doctor who, feeling bad, set aside a specimen to be examined after it had settled. While he was out of the office a woman "who imagined from circumstances that she was in a state of pregnancy" decided this would be a good time to find out. "She therefore discharged the phial of its contents, and filled it up with her own water.— When the Doctor returned (not suspecting any thing of what had transpired,) his consternation was inexpressible to find from the appearance of the urine, that he was in a state of pregnancy, and found [from] the organization and structure of his system he saw no chance of delivery. He became almost frantic at the discovery, and nothing saved him absolute dispair, but the discovery of the real facts, as they transpired."

In a somewhat similar mistake the embarrassing situation was solved by a bit of mental hygiene. "The gentleman concluded that it was a fact, that he was in a state of pregnancy, and would soon go to shut-eye town. But it happened that this gentleman, for a particular purpose, stepped out and placed himself against an old stump, and just at the critical moment, out jumped a rabbit from the stump, which he owned for his child, but it being rather fleet for the old man, it escaped, and he returned to the house with great joy, &c."

A complete cure of the hysterics, or hypo, Dr. Carter thought, was very seldom obtained, particularly after it became deeply rooted in the system. Blood-letting was in certain cases recommended, also foot-baths, injections, and dosages of calomel and alloes. Some radical cases called for stomach blisters, "frictions nearly all over the skin; give a strong camomile tea to drink, wine, bark and steel; riding on horse back; cheerful company and interesting engagements." Pills made of asafoetida, "rusian caster," and opium were likewise helpful. Sometimes instant relief was obtained by "the vitriolic ether given from thirty to fifty drops in a cup of some kind of drink." "Gold filings given in doses (night and morning in honey) about as much as would lay on the point of a penknife" had been known "to cure a person who had been too weak to work for three years. Or take bear's gall and put in rum and drink as a bitter, is excellent for this disorder; and when the choaking is bad, a tea spoonful of wheat flour mixed in water and drank, will stop it; or chew orange peels and swallow your spittle &c."

(It would be interesting to know what books the elder Carter had in his library; whether, for instance, there might have been a copy of E. Jorden, *A Brief Discourse of a Disease Called the Suffocation of the Mother,* London, 1603. If so, his son would have learned "that diuers strange actions and passions of the body of man, which in the common opinion, are imputed to the Diuell, haue their true naturall causes, and do accompanie this disease"; that is, were due to "fits of the mother," or in modern language, hysteria.)

Not quite so serious as hypo but still worth attention were the diseases of scolding and drinking. Carter's calendar of health warned against "letting of blood or taking of physick" in February; March was the month for that. "In the month of May, labourers of all kinds, almost, should begin to think about work . . . rising early in the morning, let every garden, field and hedge, produce food and medicine. Sage tea, and butter, makes a very good breakfast, clarified whey, with sage and scurvy grass therein, is also very fine, as well as wormwood beer." Herbs were to be gathered and dried in the full of the moon in June and

July. July also was the time to strew rue, wormwood and gall upon floors to keep away fleas. In October "it would be very well to counsel your Doctor . . . as well as your tailor."

Scattered among the "receipts," poems, and testimonials were scraps of suggestions for a happy married life; even illustrative love letters were included in his volume: "Through earth, air, fire or water, I would dig, dive, swim, or fly to possess her"; "I have shewed your letter to my mother, and I assure you, that such letters as you write, are generally pleasing to old people, and particularly so to her." "Would you most beloved of girls, condescend to honor me with a line, informing me whether your mind has fluctuated or no? and whether my presence would be agreeable at your fathers." Riddles also were incorporated, as were observations on life, and essays on God, Man, and the Devil. The woman whose hysterics were caused by jealousy was advised to "make as good a trade of a bad bargain as you can, and give your husband good words. See how honey will gather flies and vinegar drive them away." People were warned that "The calls of Nature should never be postponed. Delicacy is a virtue, but that which induces persons to risk their health or hazard their lives cannot be deemed a genuine virtue."

Above all, one should ever keep in mind that "The cure of diseases is never to be attempted . . . by violent methods, but rather by degrees and gentle means," waiting for a suitable opportunity. "If any application is likely to do more hurt than good, it should be abandoned." Perhaps, if abandoned soon enough, Dr. Carter's system would truly conform to his own previously quoted description of it:

> *"My medicine, though made of herbs, doth wond'rous cures perform,*
> *And yet each one may practice it without producing harm."*

Something of an anticlimax after Carter's book was that

of his son-in-law, Dr. S. H. Selman, which was published at Columbus, Indiana, in 1836. In 1825 Carter had mentioned by name his "last student," to whom he meant to reveal his whole secret of practice. Whether he did so or not, it is apparent that he later gave young Selman the revelation. Selman settled in Columbus but toured the state and advertised widely. His book, *The Indian Guide to Health or a Valuable Vegetable Medical Prescription for the Cure of All Disorders Incident to this Climate*, was designed as a guide to families and young practitioners.

Selman derived many of his remedies from Dr. Carter, to whom he gave full credit, and whom he praised, somewhat ambiguously, as a man "on whom all powers of ratiocination in possession of the faculty [the regular doctors] were expended without effect." Like Carter, he ran the gamut of frontier ailments from ager to snake bite, but was particularly good on "the Incubus or Night-Mare." This misery (as well as the hypo) could be caused by anxiety, despondency, or intense thought, possibly also by diet. The remedy was blood purification by way of the following procedure: "Into a copper kettle and five quarts of water put a handful each of bark of the yellow poplar, dogwood (from the north side), wild cherry, yellow sarsaparilla root, and the roots of the running briar. Boil slowly to two quarts, add a pint of whiskey, and take a tablespoonful two or three times a day. Let the diet be confined to chicken, squirrels, beef, mutton, and broths not too highly seasoned." This recipe has been characterized by a recent writer as sounding like "something invented by a bartender with the female trade in mind."[9] His remedy for the hypo was the same as Carter's, but he added among his cases that of a man who thought, because of a "great vacancy in his breast which he had never felt before," that his liver had all been regurgitated.

At Canton, Ohio, in 1838 was published *The North American Indian Doctor, or Nature's Method of Curing and Preventing Disease According to the Indians*. The author, Robert L. Foster, also included a "catechism" of anatomy and physiology, a treatise on midwifery with treatment necessary during pregnancy, and a materia medica of Indian remedies or vegetable compounds. From its relative scarcity today, this book is assumed not to have had a wide circulation.

Although Dr. William Daily, M.D., called his book, published at Louisville in 1848, *The Indian Doctor's Practice of Medicine or Daily's Family Physician,* it included elements of the Thomsonian vegetable-heat treatments. Two remedies, one for dysentery and a Pain Extractor, he valued too highly to include with the price of his book. These could be purchased separately for a dollar.

A good sample of the Indian-medicine household handy-book was James Cooper's *The Indian Doctor's Receipt Book* published at Uniontown, Stark County, Ohio, in 1855. For a dollar one got not only several dozen assorted cures for blind piles, palpitation of the heart — digitalis, by the way — cholera, and worms, but also the latest and best information on freckle lotion, how to make the hair curl, make ink, kill rats, keep potatoes from rotting, make soft soap and shoe blacking, catch fish by Hindoo art, distill gin, drive away ants, and make home "pleasing to an erring husband." In Part Seven was a valuable formula "to make yourself loving and be loved in return":

"In the first place it will be necessary for you to find an object upon which to fix your affections, at the same time being careful to select such an one as you could live with agreeably. When you have succeeded in this, you must devote one hour of every day, evening or night, to thinking of that object, alone. Try, if possible, to so arrange it that you can retire alone, always at the same hour of each day, and if you cannot keep your mind fixed, spell the name of your object, letter by letter until you have succeeded, which will require but a few sittings; before which time you should avoid his or her company as much as possible, but afterwards you may go into company as much as you choose, but by all means, refrain from paying marked attention to any one, not even excepting the one you wish to please, for hundreds have ruined their chances for mating themselves by being too precipitate. It will do, however, for you to feign to be confused when spoken to by the object of your desires; but never make remarks about the weather, probability of short crops, low water, market prices, &c.,—such things should never be subjects for conversation between males and females who are candidates for matrimony. Let your conversation be of an interesting and intellectual character, but do not venture upon a subject you are not posted up on, or you may make the matter worse than if you had not spoken at all. Continue in this way for a few weeks, when you may venture, if a male, to call upon your lady once a week (not oftener) and proceed as in a common courtship. *But do not neglect the private sittings,* much more depends upon them than is commonly believed; but the day has gone by when "Mental Alchemy," "Mesmerism," "Psychology," "Spiritualism," &c., were hooted at as humbugs, and reasonable and unprejudiced persons, all agree that one mind in the body can establish communication, mutually with almost any other mind, and at any distance, so that when you retire, as above directed, to think of a particular person, your image will rise up before the mind's eye of that person so vividly as almost to make them believe you stand before them, and oftentimes your very thoughts will be telegraphed to the mind of the person you think of."

"Dr. Cooper," who called his system "Eclectic," was one of the few to include the horse in the family; "certain cures" were provided for founder, heaves, farsey, windgall, bots, and the sweany. One can imagine Dobbin's delight, especially in summer, after he got his treatment for the bots—"Drench the horse with sweet milk and molasses."

*   *   *

Besides the Indian medicine men, botanists, and whatnot the pioneer doctor had to compete with superstitions and the arts of the amateur healer. Said a country physician: "Among the most disagreeable things attending the practice of medicine, are the prejudices the physician must constantly meet with, either in the mind of the patient, or in those of his friends. It is easier to cure the bodily complaint of a hundred persons than to eradicate the prejudices from the mind of one."[10] Sickness and death, surrounded as they were with an air of the supernatural, easily called forth the folklore of primitive medicine. Powwowing, charm-cures, and magnetic healers all had their devotees. Those who possessed "the power" guarded it carefully and passed it along with discretion, always to one of the opposite sex. A man might tell a woman a charm, or a woman tell a man, but if man told man or woman told woman, the charm was lost. Some formulae were community property, but others were jealously guarded, perhaps recorded on sheets in the family bible along with births, deaths, and the proper time to plant beans. A fortunate few — a seven months' baby or the seventh son of a seventh son — were born with special curative abilities. Some were gifted with the knack of "blowing out the fire" and were called upon to treat burns. Others by magic words and a red thread could cure erysipelas.

Many persons had implicit faith in charm-cures, and failures were charged to some deficiency or dereliction on the part of the patient rather than regarded as a fault of the cure. Besides, there was frequently an "out" in the formula itself, such as "Corn beef and cabbage is good for a blacksmith with cramps, but ain't worth a d——n for cramps in a minister." If one remedy failed another was tried. All honor was granted the cure last used before the body mechanism, in spite of the remedies, restored its natural condition. Madstones, loadstones, various woods, and minerals were widely used, and the astrological signs heeded. July and August were the "dog days," when Sirius cast a baneful effect on the blood and air. Wounds would then become infected, disease was readily caught, and even the old swimming hole was viewed askance for its paludal influence.[11]

From prenatal days to the grave and even after, the life of an individual was hedged around by these practices and beliefs. Woe betide the pioneer baby, who in his anxiety to get into the rapidly developing West, decided to enter society a month early. Only seven-months' premature babies were supposed to live. And should the powers that be defy the laws of nature by deciding that he shouldn't enter the world at all, 'twas said that drinking of water in which nine eggs had been boiled would do the trick. Delayed entry could, of course, be expedited by quilling, but this was hardly a superstition. The rattle of a rattlesnake sewed in a black silk cloth and put in the hands of the parturient woman, provided she neither knew what the bundle contained nor opened it, was said to hasten delivery. Once the baby's arrival was satisfactorily explained to the other children — that he had been discovered in the spring, the creek, the cabbage-patch, or the midwife's apron — he began to run the gantlet of superstition and home cure.

Any birthmarks could be obliterated by rubbing them with the hand of a corpse or the head of a live eel for three successive mornings and then burying the three eel heads, tied together, beneath a stone under the eaves. If baby's face was washed in his baptismal water, he would be beautiful. If Mamma cut his hair before he was a year old, she thereby cut short his life; if she pared his nails before nine weeks, he was doomed to the life of a thief and would be forced to scratch for a living. Crawling through an open window or between the legs of tables or chairs — unless he crawled back the same way — would immediately stop his growth. If a child were "afflicted with short growth," the string which measured his length and showed it less than seven times his foot-length was looped, the child was passed through the loop three times while words were repeated, and then the string was twined around the grindstone. When the string wore out the child would be of proper length.

Should he look into a mirror before he was nine months old his life would be full of trouble. Were the empty cradle carelessly rocked, measures had to be taken immediately, else colic would result. Scrapings from the table cover or a spoonful of baptismal water would be indicated. If croup threatened, the right front foot of a mole tied around baby's neck with a blue thread would prove effective. Relief could also be afforded by the sufferer's standing on the warm spleen of a freshly slaughtered beef until the spleen grew cold. Better still, a hair of the child's head, taken from the crown, hidden in a hole bored in an ash or oak tree would prevent the ailment. (This preventive ceased to operate when the child grew to the height of the hole.) If convulsions occurred, pouring baptismal water over the peony bush or covering the infant with his father's wedding coat would effect a cure. Since most of baby's fits were caused by worms, treatment with either specifics or charms might be used. For the more violent type (of fits) a little bag containing the leg of a toad worn around the neck was known to be good. Almost as effective as this or "punkin" seed-tea was conjuring in the name of God. Were bedwetting baby's weakness, fried-mouse pie, burned-hog's-bladder powder, or spanking with a bake-oven mop was reputed to help.

Whooping cough could be conquered by a bag of little live ground-bugs hung around the neck, white ant tea, or passing the sufferer through a horse collar three times. If this were not convenient, he could eat the cast-off skin of a snake or eggs obtained from a person whose name had not been changed by marriage, drink mare's milk or tea made of blue clover blossoms, or wear a piece of stolen blue ribbon. His parents might place him in the hopper of a mill until the grist was ground; or they might seek to transfer the affliction to nine worms placed in a bottle and hidden, or to a live fish, which, after being returned to the water, gave the ailment to his fishy friends, as was evident from the fact that thereafter they came to the surface of the water to cough. Kissing a Negro before the age of one year would prevent whooping cough entirely. The ravages of diphtheria could be warded off by a poultice of cow dung held in place by means of a stocking turned wrong side out.

Baby should never be left alone with the house cat, for

the latter was likely to steal his breath. If, however, baby suffered from marasmus and was puny and short of energy, he could eat out of the cat's dish; the cat would die, but baby's vigor would be restored. About the only thing the child did not have to worry about was snake bite, for that just naturally could not happen to him until he was seven years old. Then, when bitten, if he did not approve of good liquor or gunpowder, he could tie on a toad to draw out the poison. If the toad died, another was tied on. When the toad lived, all the poison was out. Carrying an onion in the pocket provided insurance against snake bite, but if one were bitten, it was necessary for him to eat the heart of the offending reptile if he would gain further immunity. Spitting into the mouth of the snake would kill it and prevent serious harm, or the curse of Adam ("God created everything and it was good; save thou alone, snake, are cursed; cursed shalt thou be and thy poison") might be put upon it, and then it would sneak away and die of shame.

Once the child was past infancy the repertory of possibilities in both diseases and remedies widened. The best charm for earache was the insertion of the kinkiest hair to be had from a Negro's head, or oil from the ears of a weasel of the same sex as the sufferer. If immunity from toothache had not been acquired by rubbing the child's gums during the first six months with the brain of a rabbit or the rattle of a rattlesnake, or if Dr. Smith's recipe had not been followed, the pain could be eased by picking the offending tooth with a splinter from a tree struck by lightning, a coffin nail, the needle used in making a shroud, the nail of the middle toe of an owl, or a woodcock's tongue. Further recurrence could be prevented by paring the nails only on Friday or Sunday and burying the parings on the north side of the house; or by putting on the left stocking and right coat sleeve first when dressing. Biting into an apple immediately after coming home from first communion guaranteed exemption from toothache pains, too, as did wearing around the neck a string which had been used to hang three mice, or one on which was suspended a rabbit's tooth.

The activities of childhood exposed the pioneer child to a galaxy of cares and cures. From contagious diseases there was little or no escape, though a generous sprinkling of sliced onions about the sleeping room would go far toward warding them off. Epidemics of erysipelas struck often and few preventives were known. Effective treatment could sometimes be rendered by a woman with twin boys if she would "strike fire" with flint and steel on the head of the afflicted one, or by a shovelful of hot coals thrown over the affected parts. A skein of red woolen yarn first carefully used to measure the chest, head, and limbs of the sufferer, then smoked in a barrel, was a good remedy; when the thread was properly cured, the patient would be, also. A never-failing remedy was the hanging of nine catkins of a birch branch, collected on a Friday morning without speaking to anybody, upon the swollen and inflamed parts. Mumps could be eradicated by rubbing the swelling against the pig trough, or even with chips from it. An onion carried in the pocket would prevent smallpox; scars could be warded off by an application of three or four small live toads boiled in olive oil.

Sties and warts were not uncommon in the life of the pioneer child. He soon learned that an efficacious means of removing a sty was to have it touched by the proper person with nine gooseberry thorns. A healer might also remove a ringworm by touching it nine different ways with a thimble. Cures for warts were about as numerous as the warts themselves: rubbing with green walnuts, slit beans, corn, dishcloths—either belonging to the family or stolen—bacon rinds, chicken feet, silk threads, horsehairs, or raw potatoes. The removing agent was usually buried under the eaves, though if beef had been used, it was interred in the garden. Some thought warts could best be removed at midnight; others held daybreak to be the proper time. Some warts could be given away to two persons riding on a grey horse; others had to be sold for a cent, which could either be thrown away or put in the church collection. One might also place as many grains of barley as undesirable warts possessed, in a parcel along the public road. "Finders keepers"; whoever opened the package got the warts. A dead apple twig rubbed over the disfigurations, then thrown into a furrow about to be plowed, or a pebble cast into an open grave was a certain remover. Shingles could be taken care of by the application of the blood from the amputated tail of a black cat.

Boils and carbuncles occurred if the vile humors of the system had not been removed by spring purging and bitters. A poultice of bread baked on Good Friday or one prepared by mashing an onion which had been hollowed out, filled with soap, and roasted in hot ashes would compensate for this neglect. Poison ivy would cause no trouble throughout the entire year if one in early spring would but eat a small portion of its leaves or roots,[12] and immunity from ground itch could be obtained by tying around the ankle a white woolen cord.

Freckles though not a definite ill could be present in such number as to constitute an embarrassing nuisance to the adolescent. Removal could be effected by a generous dousing with May Day dew collected from stumps. Water gathered in a graveyard was helpful, too; however, like Euridice and Lot's wife, the gatherer was warned not to look back. To expedite the growth of a mustache the sap of a grapevine was almost infallible, or the young man might anoint his lip with sweet cream which a black cat should lick off on a dark night.

Bumblebees and wasps could be charmed away from an intended victim by his repeating a magic rhyme. Mad dogs, however, usually failed to succumb to such sorcery, though sane dogs would not linger in the presence of an evil spirit. Once bitten, a person could eat a bread and butter sandwich containing a hair of the offending dog, or use a madstone. One teaspoonful per day of a mixture of one ounce of burned, pulverized jaw bone of a dog, dried pulverized false tongue of a newborn colt, and one scruple of "verdigree" mixed with calomel was also effective.

To fend off the inevitable wounds and injuries it behooved every person to have the right eye of a wolf fastened inside his right sleeve. If this precaution had not been taken, there still remained a number of recourses. One was to have on hand a goodly supply of wound-wood, prepared from ash severed in three strokes by the woodsman before sunrise on Good Friday morning and gathered after the sun had shone upon it. If excessive bleeding were present the blood flow might be controlled by changing the pocket knife to another pocket, or by repeating charms, such as "Christ's wounds were never bound. In the name of the Father and of the Son and of the Holy Ghost. Amen." To mend foot-injury a piece of turf the shape of the foot could be cut out and replaced upside down. Speeding up slow-healing sores on hands or feet was brought about by tying onto the sore member a toad's foot. This was to be secured by binding a live toad with a double linen thread and, without handling his body, cutting off the corresponding member. When the foot of the toad dropped off, recovery had begun. Nosebleed could be stopped by chewing paper, tying an eelskin around the arm, recalling who sat in the next pew at the last church service attended, or three times letting three drops of blood fall on a heated shovel and then removing them.

Colds and coughs were never entirely absent, though a wool stocking tied around the neck went far toward warding off this complaint and, of course, the bag of asafoetida or camphor was good for whatever ailed one. Once contracted, a cold could be treated by crawling through a double-rooted briar toward the east. Comfort from this affliction could also be found in eating from a blue dish, wearing a blue ribbon, drinking tonic from a blue bottle, drinking stolen milk, thrusting a live fish into the throat then returning it to the water, or sewing up in a thimble, nut, or bag a spider or woodlouse and wearing it around the neck until the insect died.

The coughs and colds of childhood gave way to more serious respiratory complaints of the adult — asthma, bronchitis, tuberculosis, pleurisy, quinsy. Walking around the house at midnight alone at the full of the moon would take care of asthma, but bronchitis could be cured by the more passive means of a stocking turned wrong side out and worn around the neck over night. For pleurisy, or "liver growth," the treatment was somewhat more complicated; the sufferer should creep around a table leg three times, stopping exactly at the place of beginning. Some insisted that one must crawl backwards. A child might obtain the same result by crawling through a warm horse collar or a double-rooted blackberry briar. Consumption could be prevented by eating the fried heart of a rattlesnake which had not bitten itself. A yellow toad secured from an obliging neighbor's cellar would, when bound to the throat, absorb the poisons of quinsy.

Disappointment in love affairs often led to epilepsy. Restoration to normal faculties might be accomplished by swallowing the heart of a rattlesnake, sleeping over the cow stable, or being passed three times through the crotch of a forked hickory tree which had been wedged open. If the tree healed and grew the patient would recover. The afflicted one might prefer to remove his shirt wrong side out, then place it in a coffin under the head of a corpse, or to hang onto his right arm and left foot one slice of peony root for each year of his age; recovery would begin when the pieces dropped off. As a last resort, he might dig the roots of the white peony at the rising of the sun when the sign was in Leo and the moon new on Sunday, taking care not to handle the root with the bare hands. The root was then to be dried, enclosed with gold, and worn at the neck.

The hypo was, of course, another serious mental condition. In addition to the various specifics and herb cures, a powwow charm was often used: "Put that joint of the thumb which sits in the palm of the hand on the bare skin covering the small bone which stands out above the pit of the heart, and say: 'Matrix, patrix, lay thyself right and safe. Or thou and I shall on the third day fill the grave.'"

So many different brands of fever and ague prevailed that a general remedy was unknown. Some of the pioneers believed that three hard-boiled eggs eaten on Good Friday, or the first three hail-stones of the year, or rye heads consumed in the name of the Trinity would make a person immune. Once a fever was contracted, a polite and holy exhortation might cause it to leave: "Good morning, dear Thursday! Take away from [name] the 77-fold fevers. Oh! Thou dear Lord Jesus Christ, take them away from him!" A black cat might eat some of the soup fed to the patient, or a black dog could feast on a pound of beef boiled in the sufferer's urine. A small grasshopper, placed in a rag and provided with a lunch of a crumb of rye bread and a little salt, could be hung on the patient's skin without his knowledge of the contents of the sack. On the ninth day the charm was to be removed and cast upon the waters; relief would return after not too many days. Wine to which had been added a living crawfish, after letting stand all night, was efficacious when taken early in the morning on an empty stomach. Or one might set on a piece of paper:

A B R A C A D A B R A
A B R A C A D A B
A B R A C A D
A B R A C
A B R
A

This paper, wrapped in common plantain leaves, was to be laid on the stomach of the patient when attacks of fever occurred. If they came with unusual severity, additional papers could be placed behind the ears and in the crotch. After six hours the fever would be so thoroughly bewitched that it would not return.

For the debilitating afflictions of adulthood and old age a multitude of cures were known. If the pioneer wished to be freed for thirty years from rheumatism and joint stiffness, he had but to drink, beginning on a Friday morning in spring and continuing on Saturday and Sunday, a hot tonic of three sprays of elderberry blossoms boiled in a quart of sweet milk in a new earthen pot. Other preventives included carrying in the pocket a coffin nail, potato, horse-chestnut, or the triangular bone of a ham. A rattle-snake rattle might be worn on a string around the neck, or glass knobs could be placed under the bed posts. Water used for washing the feet could be kept overnight. If, in spite of these precautions, he still suffered, a salted mackerel tied onto the feet or the application of the blood of a perfectly black hen would furnish relief.

Dropsy yielded to a treatment of sliced horseradish tied to the feet or an internal and external dosing with a powder made of toads. Some believed this latter remedy was good for smallpox also. Tuberculosis of the bone could be treated by dog bones or an old hat burned to a powder. An uneven number of pieces of wild marjoram roots made into a necklace which was to be buried under the eaves after it had been worn for nine days took care of scrofula. Ulcers could be cured by the fresh blood of a black chicken, and heartburn would not recur if one swallowed a fishworm alive. Constipation could be effectively treated by eating soup made of chicken — feathers and all.

To rub a corn with a small piece of cotton cloth and then unobservedly hide the cloth in a coffin with a body about to be buried would cause the disappearance of the growth. Goiter succumbed to the healing touch of the hand of a corpse. A wen would dry up if a snake's head and tail were nine times drawn across it, accompanied each time by an "Amen." Other cures for wens suggested "washing twice daily in the patient's own urine and anointing once daily with grease broiled out of a wooden potlid, or the marrow of an old bakened hog's jaw, or a hubbed toad may be just knocked in the head and laid upon it." Saying three times in church while the benediction was being pronounced: "What I look at is sin. What I stroke may it vanish," would rid one of a tumor. Probably the best of the myriad cancer cures was the application of the slime prepared by dissolving common snails in salt, placing them in a pewter plate, and setting it over coals. Bedsores would vanish by placing under the bed a hitherto unused crock, an axe, or sod turned upside down.

One might prevent backache by turning a sommersault at the call of the first whippoorwill of spring. Sprains could be treated by wrapping an eelskin around the arm. Walking in the rain during dogdays caused headaches and baldness, though chronic headaches also caused baldness and gray hair. These headaches might be bound up with a halter with which someone had been hanged; the rope used in a suicide had special merits.

A good eyewash could be made of March snow; cataracts charmed away by wearing around the neck a bag of unwashed cloth containing bread, salt, and wheat; and inflammation of the eyes relieved by a few drops of the juice of a rotten apple. Congenitally weak eyes would be benefitted by frequent applications of pure water.

Forgetfulness might be caused by old age, by drying up of the brain, or by combing the hair with a fine-toothed comb after dark; regardless of its cause, it could be overcome by carrying cinquefoil on the fingers. The memory of a barn swallow could be acquired by boiling the heart of one in milk and wearing it around the neck. When finally, all remedies and cures have failed, and mortification of the brain set in, there was one last resort: sulphur, alum, gunpowder, and vinegar.

From folk cures to mechanical magic was just a step. The "wonderful century," a century of invention, was ushered in by one of the most famous medical hoaxes of all times. Dr. Elisha Perkins (1741-99) of Connecticut had observed that during operations, when metallic instruments were brought in contact with muscles, the latter contracted; also he witnessed the cessation of pain when such instruments were used to separate teeth from the gum prior to extraction. Mulling over these facts, he conceived his gift to sufferers. This contraption consisted of two rods, each about three inches long — supposedly of a mixture of copper, zinc, a little gold, silver, and platinum but probably of brass and iron — rounded at one end, pointed

on the other, half round on one side and flat on the other.
On the flat side was printed "Perkins Patent Tractors,"
commonly called Perkinese Tractors. The tractors, manufactured in a small furnace which was concealed in the
wall of Perkins's house, sold at a handsome price (five
guineas in England, for instance).

With these implements the disease was to be extracted
from the body according to directions which varied with
the malady. Sometimes the instruments were to be drawn
from the pained part to the extremities; at other times
friction was to be applied to the affected part until there
was redness from the inflammation. One principle applied
generally: the drawing was always to be downward, for to
draw upward might intensify the disease. Even Perkins did
not guarantee the infallibility of his life-saver — "The
headache that arises from drinking to excess, it does not
always cure." Its use was heartily recommended for "Rheumatism, Pleurisy, Some Gouty Affections, etc." One clergyman found it "also useful in picking walnuts." An
Indiana user cured a lame crow.

Belief in the tractors was not confined entirely to the
simple folk. Congress was in session at the time of patent-
ing, and the new invention aroused considerable interest.[13]
According to report a Virginia gentleman sold his planta-
tion and took the price in tractors. George Washington
was said to have bought a set and Chief Justice Ellsworth,
"though not altogether convinced," gave Perkins a letter
of introduction to incoming Justice Marshall. Professors
of three American universities said they believed in trac-
toration.

Benjamin Douglas Perkins, son of the discoverer, carried
the light abroad with an almost fabulous success which
made possible his leaving England some $10,000 richer. In
1804 the Perkinean Institution, which treated five thousand cases during its existence, was founded in London.
In France the workmen could not make the implements
fast enough; as omnipresent as the modern lipstick, tractors
accompanied the females, "who delighted in their use."

In Denmark notable effects resulted from their more prosaic use on horses. So implicit was the belief in their curative properties that many people were immediately cured
of whatever ailed them, even when unknowingly they used
tractors of wood, lead, nails, piece of bone, slate-pencils,
and tobacco pipes which a couple of regular doctors had
made in imitation of the authentic tractors in order to
prove that Perkins was a charlatan of the first rank.

Fellow physicians did not entirely approve the new cure-
all and Elisha was expelled from the Connecticut Medical
Society. He finally succumbed to yellow fever after having
tried to cure himself with a vinegar and salt remedy of his
own concoction; we do not know whether he availed himself of his tractor or not. Benjamin Perkins died in New
York in 1810. By 1811 people were speaking of "tractor-
ation" as one of the follies of the past, although tractors or
gadgets based on the same principle were peddled and used
in the West for years.

Another device employed by early quacks was the "Tetotum Eclecticum." This instrument had pasted on its sides
the initials of various remedies, leaving out calomel, opium,
and the lancet. The patient was permitted to elect the particular system by which he wished to be treated; the practitioner twirled the tetotum on the table at the bedside and
when it came to a state of rest, the letters which came out
on top indicated the medicine to be given.

The pioneer might also avail himself of:

"Dr. Christie's Galvanic belt, bracelets, necklace and
magnetic fluid for removal and permanent cure of all
nervous Diseases and of those complaints which are caused
by an impaired, weakened or unhealthy condition of the
nervous system. General debility, strengthening the weakened body, giving tone to the various organs, and invigor-
ating the system. Also in fits, cramps, paralysis and palsy,
dyspepsia or indigestion, rheumatism, acute and chronic,
gout, epilepsy, lumbago, deafness, nervous tremors, palpitation of the heart, apoplexy, neuralgia, pains in the side
and chest, liver complaint, spinal complaint and curvature

of the spine, hip complaint, diseases of the kidneys, deficiency of nervous and physical energy and all nervous diseases. 60,000 persons in the last three years have been entirely and permanently cured."[14]

In Cincinnati in 1829 Dr. L. M. Johnson advertised "A powerful Electro-Galvanic Resuscitating Battery which will be free for the Humane Society and the faculty for restoring suspended animation." Dr. T. J. Gazley of Lebanon, Illinois, invented an "Electerizing Machine," purchasable for $7, which was supposed to be of use in reviving persons apparently dead from drowning. Galvanic belts and such appliances did not, of course, go out with the pioneer period, nor was their use confined to the West, as a perusal of the pages of some of the slick-paper periodicals of the early 1900's would confirm.

A Dr. Williams of Cincinnati had a rather unfortunate experience. His specialty was the treatment of the eyes. He kept one bottle of "eye-water" with which he created new eyes for man, and another for a similar purpose for horses. Accidentally he got the bottles changed. "He found it prudent to quit forthwith."[15] A Negro practitioner of the Queen City catered to some of the wealthiest people. He diagnosed diseases by analyzing a tumbler of water into which the patient had dipped one finger. A young lady was told that a male had also dipped his finger in the water. When she denied this the quack told her she was pregnant with male child. She confessed to being pregnant and later had a male baby. A man was told that a dead person's finger had been placed in the water; on his way to consult his regular doctor he died. Perhaps the regular doctors knew more than they cared to tell concerning the considerable haste with which this quack left the city.[16]

Cancer doctors enjoyed a thriving business. Nor were they the least bit modest in their claims: "Dr. Floyd vouches to remove and extirpate the most obstinate and difficult case of cancer in the short space of from three to forty-eight hours." Dr. Balthasar Beckar guaranteed "Cancers cured by inspection."[17]

And then there was the great King, who advertised:

"Humble ones, my mission calls me among you. The Great Book, on being opened, announces my coming. Your pains, sufferings, and sorrows shall cease. . . . Wherever he has been, the blind have been restored to sight, the lame walked, the heart-broken made happy. More than a million of people afflicted with every ill that flesh is heir to, have applied to him for relief during the past ten years, and in every instance has a permanent cure been effected. Come, behold, see for yourselves, and watch the hand of Fate, as it points you out the course to follow. Dr. King can not attend to any calls after sundown, as he is then engaged until morning dawn in consulting the stars and the planets as to the proper treatment of his patients on the following day."[18]

One Indiana claimant to healing powers based his practice on certain apothegms: "Every joint produces a different fever. There are different colors to the different fevers from the different joints. Every man has a hundred and ten joints, and every woman has a hundred and ninety-nine joints. The fever will go out of the joints into the stomach by taking cold. Then separate the fevers, destroying whatever is to be destroyed. For headache give whisky and vinegar. For pain all over, wash all over with whisky and vinegar, then grease with castor oil. If much pain, take a tablespoonful of saltpeter and four ounces of castor oil."[19] Another Indiana quack and his wife advertised to cure all incurable diseases by their combined manipulations and charms. Attendance of the patient in person was not necessary; whoever could not go to them could be cured by sending a lock of hair.[20]

* * *

In quite a different category from the Indian-medicine and the powwow books were the household-remedy or domestic-medicine books. It is often difficult to distinguish them from the numerous offerings of the Botanics or Eclectics; about the only criterion is their use of calomel and lancet. One of the early works of this type was that of Dr. William Buchan, *Domestic Medicine; or the Family Physician: Being an Attempt to Render the Medical Art More Generally Useful with Respect to the Prevention and Cure of Diseases,* first published at Edinburgh in 1769. It went through many editions both in the British Isles and in the United States;[21] it has been said that the influence of this book was "greater than any other similar work ever published."[22] Dr. Buchan did not intend it "to supercede the use of a Physician, but to supply his place, in situations where medical assistance could not easily be obtained." This use "would not only tend to improve the art and to banish quackery, but likewise to render Medicine more universally useful by extending its benefits to society." His suggested cures, such as the one for inflamed eyes — the application of leeches to the temples or under the eyes, or a seton placed in the neck or between the shoulders ("I have known patients, who had been blind for a considerable time, recover sight by means of a seton") — did not differ greatly from those recommended by any of the other doctors. His information on preventive medicine, however, is extraordinarily modern.

Dr. Anthony A. Benezet, a graduate of the University of Pennsylvania and an honorary member of the Medical Society of Philadelphia, attempted to improve upon Buchan's book and adapt it to the western country, but he added little. *The Family Physician; Comprising Rules for the Prevention and Cure of Diseases; Calculated Particularly for the Inhabitants of the Western Country, and for Those Who Navigate Its Waters,* was published at Cincinnati in 1826. After a chapter on the western climate, its influence on health, and advice to emigrants, Benezet took up the human body, the passions, the preservation of health, and nursing. The usual diseases and casualties were described and treatments set forth. A "Dispensatory" and additional remarks on consumption concluded the work. As in other books of this sort, both the cures of the regulars — calomel, castor oil, Peruvian bark, epsom salts, opium, bleeding — and those of the vegetable kind were listed and recommended. Benezet's book may have had other editions, for it was well known in the West in its day.

The number of domestic-medicine books of this type published in the West is not definitely known. Many were of limited circulation, confined largely to the localities in which they were published. They varied in size from the six-page *Physician at Hand or a Collection of Receipts and Cures to Heal Diseases and Wounds of Various Kinds,* by Dr. W. Smith (Wooster, Ohio, 1829), with its even dozen recipes — including treatment of mortification and the leprosy — to the thousand-page Gunn.

Often these books were so similar that it is apparent that they were copied from their predecessors. Occasionally one would have distinguishing merits. For instance, A. Weyer published at St. Clairsville, Ohio, in 1831, *The Family Physician or Poor Man's Friend, and Married Lady's Companion: Containing a great variety of Valuable Medical Recipes, designed to assist heads of Families, Travellers, and Sea-faring People in curing Disease.* This work was largely botanic — though it also recommended opium, calomel, and bleeding — but certainly was not intended for use in the prohibition era. For the dyspepsia: "Take one quart of good whiskey to which add . . . ."; to purify the blood: "Take three pints of good rye whiskey . . . ."; to make a balsam: "Take a quart of rye whiskey . . . ." The printer and publisher, Horton J. Howard, was stimulated by the Botanic Samuel Thomson's visit to Ohio in 1829, but apparently did not give Thomson monopoly rights to his press. As a result he and Thomson became bitter enemies and proceeded to air their differences in print.

A *Travellers Pocket Medical Guide* was published anonymously at Louisville in 1833. The printer, Wilcox, made it of convenient pocket size by confining its one hundred fifty-two pages to a size of two by three inches.

At Connersville, Indiana, in 1834 Dr. Buell Eastman published a *Practical Treatise on Diseases Peculiar to Women and Girls,* to which was added an "eclectic system of midwifery" and a section on diseases of children. Eastman's announced purpose was to "guide the people in a plain and prompt manner in the discharge of their duty, to instruct the untaught, learn the ignorant, direct the enquiring, and guide the inexperienced in the practical path of safety . . . to collect from all other systems that which will be useful in a *practical* point of view — to place in your hands, a rule, a guide, and a touch-stone, that you may know where there is danger — be wise where there is ignorance — kind where there is suffering — that you may relieve where there is distress — that you may help where there is need — and be useful where there is opportunity."

An interesting little book is the pocket-size one hundred-page *Symptoms and Treatment of All Diseases,* "written" and printed by H. D. Mason at Cedarville, Ohio, in 1843. Mason drew largely upon Dr. Mackintosh. He was strictly up to date on fevers, listing as causes marshmiasma, contagion, epidemic influence, cold, fear, despondence, and fatigue. His treatment for remittent fever included bleeding, "10 and 10" of jalap and calomel, "Dovers poweders," pearlash and vinegar, and blisters. Brandy, bitters and quinine were to be given during recovery. For asthma he prescribed coffee, lobelia, skunk's cabbage, licorice squills, poultice of hops and flaxseed, and galvanism. For Asiatic cholera, shave the head and apply cold water; for delirium tremens use emetics, opium, cupping, and a strong tea of wormwood. Mason mixed his mercurials and botanic remedies freely.

Like Dr. Buchan, another doctor whose ideas on preventive medicine were somewhat in advance of his time was Dr. William Matthews of Putnam County, Indiana, whose *A Treatise on Domestic Medicine and Kindred Subjects Embracing Anatomical and Physiological Sketches of the Human Body* was published at Indianapolis in 1848. Dr. Matthews held in rather general contempt the medicine of the period as practiced alike by the regulars, irregulars, and quacks. There were fourflushers within the "Regular Faculty," dangerous men to be pitied, but to be eliminated, nevertheless. The other quacks "are either inexcusably ignorant, or they are designing villains" — frequently both. Aside from some of his ideas on diet — more caution should be exercised in the use of carrots and the like than in the eating of sweet potatoes, beans, and peas, and meat should be preferred over vegetables — there is little to suggest the period in which Matthews wrote.

One of the most popular of the many domestic-medicine books was that of Dr. John C. Gunn, *Domestic Medicine or Poor Man's Friend, in the House of Affliction, Pain and Sickness*. This work, originally published at Knoxville, Tennessee, in 1830, went through so many "editions" that it is impossible to enumerate them. Besides various Tennessee printings, editions appeared at Springfield and Xenia, Ohio. By the ninth edition, 1839, the book claimed sales of over one hundred thousand copies. It was topping the field in sales in the 1850's and after the Civil War; with active agents all over the West it reached its two hundred thirteenth "edition" in 1885. There were also various German printings.

As Dr. Gunn said on his title-page, "This Book Points Out, in Plain Language, Free from Doctor's Terms, The Diseases of Men, Women and Children, and the Latest and Most Approved Means Used in Their Cure, and is Expressly Written For The Benefit of Families In The Western and Southern States. It also contains descriptions of the medicinal roots and herbs of the southern and western country, and how they are to be used in the cure of diseases. Arranged on a new and simple plan, by which the practice of medicine is reduced to principles of common sense." The truth of the last sentence might be doubted somewhat by the reader but the importance of the work can not be questioned.

In the introduction of the 1835 edition the author described the fine state of health, both mental and physical, in which man lived in the "early days of nature." After his sinning "his days are shortened and encumbered with disease . . . the earth brings forth thorns and briars." Civilization was the prime mortal cause of these ills. "Professional pride and native cupidity, contrary to the true spirit of justice and christianity, have, in all ages and countries, from sentiments of self-interest and want of liberality, delighted in concealing the divine art of healing diseases, under complicated names, and difficult or unmeaning technical phrases. Why make a mystery of things which relieve the distresses and sufferings of our fellow-beings?"

He treated the usual medical topics: ague and fever, rheumatism, consumption, dysentery or flux, laxness or constant looseness of the bowels, catarrh or cold, pleurisy, gravel and stone, St. Anthony's fire (erysipelas), toothache, epileptic fits, palsy, piles, cowpox or vaccination, smallpox, poisons, scalds and burns, pregnancy, and so on. A section on diseases of children covered measles, the snuffles, fits, and the like, while another described herbs and roots and their use. Fractures, epidemic cholera, and accidents were also discussed. A dosage table was attached. Sometimes one feels that Gunn expected quite a lot from the home doctor. For instance, in "wounds of the belly . . . should any part of the bowels come out at the wound, if clean and uninjured, return it as quickly as possible; if covered with dirt, clots of blood, etc. wash it carefully in warm water before returning it."

About one-eighth of the work treated "Of the Passions" —fear, anger, hope, joy, jealousy, grief, religion, intemperance, and love—a combination of mental hygiene, morality lessons, and advice to the lovelorn. "When the passions run counter to reason and religion, *nationally* and *individually,* they produce the most frightful catastrophes." Joy and hope were beneficent passions, though the latter might have dangerous consequences. Fear was a base passion, and aggravated disease, while cowardice "disorders and impedes the circulation of the blood; hinders breathing with freedom; puts the stomach out of order, as well as the bowels; affects the kidneys and skin, and produces bad effects on the whole body. . . ." Jealousy usually had to do with love but might be merely a "disease of talking."

Love was one of the master passions and embraced all the complicated and powerful faculties of man. Its effects were determined largely by training and education. "No woman possessed of a judicious education . . . ever became the victim of a *broken heart.*" Religion concerned not only the moral condition of mankind, but health and diseases of the physical system. Medical drugs were inadequate to restrain those joys or remove those sorrows which spring from the mind itself. Resort must be had to the restraining powers and the consolations of religion and morality, for the pleasures and pains of the imagination commence where those of the memory and the understanding terminate. By the 1850's advances in the publishing arts made possible in the editions of this book beautiful colored plates illustrating Love, Jealousy, Intemperance, Infidelity, and the like, which ranged from the beatific to the ridiculous.

People of means and education, particularly in or near the young cities of the West, were dependent neither upon charm-cures nor upon home remedies. But they were, likely as not, confronted with hazards which did not bother the folk who were closer to the field and forest. Then as now fads swept the country:

"Again, young ladies at school, and sometimes with their parents, will resolve to become extremely pale, from a notion that it looks interesting. For this purpose, they will substitute for their natural food, pickles of all kinds, powdered chalk, vinegar, burnt coffee, pepper and other spices, especially cinamon and cloves; others will add to these paper, of which many sheets are sometimes eaten in a day; and this is persisted in till the natural appetite for wholesome food is superceded by a depraved and morbid desire for everything but that which is nutritious; cordials and bitters are then sometimes resorted to, in a vain attempt to restore the healthy tone of the stomach, till at last the cheek, originally pale—for fresh and blooming color is very rare in the complexions even of the healthiest and youngest in America—become deathlike in their hue, the whole frame withers, and a premature grave receives the unhappy victim. So indifferent, however, are parents to the welfare of their children, or so unable or unwilling are they to exercise parental authority to check this evil in the bud, that they look on, if not without disapprobation, at least without any vigorous effort to avert the evil. . . . Such practices as these, added to the other causes, . . . sufficiently account for the decayed and decaying state of health among the female population of the United States." Were such conditions to continue another fifty years, the writer of this observation in 1840 predicted it would require a new race of settlers in the West to supply the worn-out constitutions of the old ones, just as new lands were required to replace the worn-out fields of the seaboard states.

Yet indifference and ignorance were slowly giving way before more enlightened views. The *Journal of Health*, begun at Philadelphia in 1830, gave practically its entire attention to temperance in the use of liquor and tobacco, to fresh air, exercise and cleanliness. It attacked feather beds (except for the aged), corsets, and quackery. It advocated the same bodily exercises for boys and girls and recommended walking, gardening, tennis, and open-air games to all. Dancing under proper limitation was a "highly salutary species of exercise," and pursuit of a game called golf, formerly played in Scotland, was said by some to prolong life ten years. The following editorial on health, copied in the Madison (Indiana) *Republican and Banner* from Sears's *New Family Recipe Book*, may have expressed ideas far ahead of the times, but such advice was becoming the rule rather than the exception:

"Rise early. Eat simple food. Take plenty of exercise. Eat what best agrees with your system and resolutely abstain from what hurts you, however well you may like it. Have nothing at all to do with quacks and do not tamper with quack medicines. Let those who love to be invalids drink strong green tea, eat pickles, preserves and hot biscuits. Have your bed chamber well aired and have fresh linen every week. It is not healthy to sleep in heated rooms."

Others, too, were worrying about the degeneration of what was generally termed the gentler sex and pondering over the good old days when women were useful as well as ornamental. Mrs. Sarah Josepha Hale, the influential editor of *Godey's Ladies' Book*, was beginning her life-long crusade in favor of exercise and health for women. Although doctors recommended sweeping, polishing furniture, rope-jumping, battledore, and modified calisthenics for sedentary females, Mrs. Hale recommended the spinning-wheel. "From the universal, yet gentle exercise it affords the limbs, the chest, and the whole frame, it is altogether the best mode of domestic calisthenics that has hitherto been devised."

Milking as an exercise was advocated by some. They pointed out that thirty years earlier it had been as hard to find a man milking as a woman mowing. But times had changed. Girls now hardly knew (or at least pretended not to know) whether milk came from the udder or the horns. This was bad from many angles. Women were cleaner, more patient, and gentler. Men had to milk too early and too late. "The morning air would be bracing to their muscles, (if the modern girl has any muscles, for there begins to be a reasonable doubt in this matter); and the odor of the cow has been long known to be, and is often recommended by physicians as medicinal."

DOCTORS: BLEED, BLISTER, AND PURGE

CHAPTER III

"Your chief ambition will be to deserve the confidence of society: your greatest happiness to extend and strengthen that confidence . . . you will make science the ground work of your reputation; and acts of intelligence, honor and benevolence the material of the superstructure. You will thus become shining lights of the profession: you will sit down with the great ones of the earth: the learned will thirst after your conversation; the rich will contribute their homage, the poor will call you blessed, and your names will live and be held in honour."

—Dr. Daniel Drake, address to the class of 1821 of theMedical College of Ohio.

To the notion of many people who made a living by manual labor, lawyers, bankers, and to a certain extent doctors, were a parasitic class — useless and extravagant luxuries at the best. As frontier society became more complex, each of the vocations established its usefulness. First to do so were the doctors. In 1831 Dr. Enoch Hale wrote in the *North American Review*: "We believe that there never was a time, when they were held in so high respect and confidence as at the present day; and probably in no part of the world is this confidence more generally felt by all classes of people, than among us." The passing of the years made this true in the West as well as in the East.

Much has been written of the country doctor. He was an important figure in pioneer life. An individualist in an age of individualism, he conformed to no set type, but in general has fared well at the hands of history. Like the preacher, he often was a jack of several trades — he might farm, hunt, or do some smithing in odd hours. In the early days wolves and wildcats kept him company on the solitary night journeys through almost trackless woods, but his nerves were steady, and he knew that weird cries were not so dangerous as overhanging branches, hidden holes, and swollen streams. Like the judge and minister, he sometimes rode circuit over his territory. Tireless, fearless, often gruff, yet sympathetic, the doctor maintained a personal relationship with his people more intimate and vital than that of minister or lawyer. Though frequently short of learning, intolerant of rivals, and given to petty quarrels, he was abundantly possessed of those qualities which made his humanity triumph over both nature and human selfishness, and himself usually a figure at the same time feared, loved, and venerated.

The equipment of the country doctor was simple: mortar and pestle, a set of balances, some home-made splints and bandages, a few drugs, possibly a small assortment of instruments, perhaps a pewter bedpan, a few simple syringes, and pewter or crockery hot-water bottles. Occasionally a doctor had a pulsometer, a glass, dumb-bell-shaped container about six inches long filled with colored liquid; when the patient held one end in his closed hand, air bubbles would rise to the other end. This result was, of course, a simple physical rather than physiological action, and bore no actual relation to the pulse, but served to convince the patient that he had had a more thorough and accurate diagnosis. By the late 1830's most of the better equipped doctors also carried a stethoscope[1], a set of tooth forceps, and a few obstetrical instruments. Naturally the doctor had a horse and saddle bags. In the absence of complicated equipment for diagnosis he relied upon his fingers, eyes, ears, and nose. Temperature and pulse he could feel; color of skin, lips, eyes, and fingernails meant much, as did the sound of voice, cough, and breathing of the patient. He could smell out a case of typhoid, measles, or milk sickness.

A contemporary description by a member of the profession covers the essentials:

"The doctor had to be his own pharmacist. He made his own pills and tinctures, compounded all his medicines, and generally carried all he required, as, with saddle-bags across his horse, he wended his way from house to house, administering to the sick and ailing, always welcome and often regarded as an angel of mercy, although his homely garb and rough appearance looked anything but angelic. His life was one of peril, toil and privation. The country was new and thinly settled, and his rides were long and solitary; his patients were scattered over a wide expanse of territory; his travel was mostly performed on horseback, and its extent and duration was measured by the endurance of himself and his horse. He struggled through almost unfathomable mud and swamps and swollen streams. He was often compelled to make long detours to cross or avoid the treacherous slough. His rest was often taken in the saddle, sometimes in the cabin of the lonely settler. From necessity he was self-reliant and courageous. Every emergency, however grave, he was generally compelled to meet alone and unaided, as it was seldom assistance could be procured without too great an expenditure of time and money. His fees were small and his services were often paid for in promises, seldom in money, of which there was but little. The products of the country, called by the people 'truck', was the general and most reliable circulating medium, and with this the doctor was usually paid. But there is a bright side to this picture. The kindly life of a new country, and the dependence of its inhabitants upon each other, gave the doctor a strong hold upon the affection and gratitude of those among whom he lived and labored. They loved him when living, and mourned for him when dead."[2]

As indicated above, the pay of the country doctor was uncertain, and when received, was often in the form of produce. At the end of a year's service, including care in two smallpox epidemics, an early Wisconsin doctor had received $68 in cash.[3] Even as late as 1861, when the population of Chicago was more than one hundred thirty-five thousand, the city physician received an annual salary of only $600 and was required to furnish all medicines.[4] Another doctor, at the forks of the Kalamazoo, apparently for somewhat less than a year's work reaped much gratitude and "For service, advice and medicine — 12½c," and an old German physician in Illinois in 1842 received a stove for sixteen office visits ("at 37½c"), solutions, and powders.[5] Perhaps the patients were acting on the belief that to pay the doctor in full would cause another illness in the family. In a day of scarcity of specie and small change, and prevalence of makeshifts, a Doctor Murdock of Brookville, Indiana, in 1825 issued script bills "good for one dose of medicine." These were known as "Puke Bills." Creditor-patients rarely came back for the second dose.[6]

Charges for medical services varied. Village and country doctors were not organized and fees were not standardized. Dr. Drake said that the ordinary charge was 25 cents a mile, "one half being deducted and the other paid in provender for his horse, or produce for his family." In the earlier years the average country doctor would probably settle for 25 to 50 cents for a local visit, or a dollar if he sat up all night. The Indiana law of 1816 fixed fees at 12½ cents per mile of travel by day, double by night, but these fees were not strictly adhered to. In the towns informal agreements were sometimes made. Springfield, Illinois, physicians, for instance, agreed in 1840 to the following scale: daytime visit in town, $1; up to four miles, $2; each additional mile, 50 cents; prices double for night visits; verbal advice, $1; each dose of medicine, 50 cents; vaccination, $1; natural parturition, $5 to $10; fractures, $5 to $10; amputation of leg or arm, $25 to $100; lithotomy, $100 to $200.[7] The Bill of Rates adopted by the Belmont County (Ohio) Medical Society in 1847 included generally lower fees: visit in town, 50 cents; first mile in the country, $1; venesection and tooth extraction, 25 cents; vaccination, 50 cents; doses of medicine, 25 and 50 cents; parturition, $4 to $10; fractures, $5 to $20; amputations, $50 to $100.[8] Prices adopted by the Cincinnati Medical Association in 1821 had been similar.[9]

Doctors in larger towns and young cities of the West had more pretentious establishments than the country doctor. Their equipment was more extensive — instruments, libraries, and stables. Drug stores or apothecary shops were at hand; apprentice students or junior partners did a lot of the routine work. A few, of course, catered only to the "silver doorbell" clientele, dressed the part, and charged what were, for the period, fancy prices. The offices of small-town doctors, frequently in their homes, were usually run informally. For instance, in 1828, Dr. William Tichenor of Indianapolis advertised that: "His shop is two doors below Mr. Hawkin's tavern, where he generally will be found, except when attending to professional business."

As noted earlier, the frontiersman, self-reliant, proud, and generally poor, was usually reluctant to call the doctor, considering it a waste of both time and money. When the doctor was called, he often had to compete with all present and thereabouts to justify his system Some people thought that diseases were part of the penalty man paid for his sins, hence only God could effect a cure; others blamed the devil and were willing to stick by remedies which he understood. But for a fatality it was the doctor who was held responsible, since he had had the last chance at the patient. As one old doctor said, "The principal position of the doctor was dealing in second hand goods, and a bad quality at that."[10] Hence, perhaps, the bold treatment in these, the heroic days of medicine in which it was said of the doctor: "He came every day, he purged, he bled, he blistered, he puked, he salivated his patient, he never cured him."[11]

Since the medical theory of the regulars as well as that of the irregular sects, rested upon an empiric rather than a scientific basis, one man's opinion was about as good as another's. From the days of Hippocrates, doctors without number had based their practice on the idea of the four elements in man — earth, water, air, and fire. Corresponding to these were the four natural humors — melancholy or black bile, cold and dry (earth); phlegm, cold and moist (water); blood, hot and moist (air); and choler, or yellow bile (fire). The general theory was that man's normal constitution, or "complexion," represented a balance among these natural humors, but that an excess of any one would lead to trouble. More serious still were the effects of the unnatural humors, of which there were a number.

Although medieval medicine was aware of certain specific diseases, such as smallpox and leprosy, and Thomas Sydenham (1624-89), "the father of bleeding," described measles, dysentery, syphilis, and gout, most doctors in the mid-seventeenth century still thought in terms of humors and one disease. Further progress was made during the next century in differentiating diseases and causes. William Cullen (1710-90) of Edinburgh listed hundreds of diseases; his pupil, John Brown, classified all into two types: those due to tension and those due to extreme relaxation. Dr. Benjamin Rush (1745-1813), the most famous and influential American doctor of his day, went a step further. He stated to his students that "there is but one disease in the world." This being assumed to be true, the depletion treatment — blood-letting and purging — was universally applicable.

Dr. John Esten Cooke of Transylvania and Louisville, who published an eleven hundred-page, two-volume treatise on *Pathology and Therapeutics* in 1828, carried the Rush purge and calomel theory to the extreme. He believed that all diseases, particularly fevers, arose from cold or malaria, which weakened the heart and thus produced an accumulation of blood in the *vena cavae* and in the adjoining large veins of the liver. Consequently, calomel and other cathartics which acted on that organ were the cure. "If calomel did not salivate and opium did not constipate, there is no telling what we could do in the practice of physic," represented the main idea of Cooke, who has been called "the most elaborate of all American Systematizers."[12]

Not all doctors reduced the nature of diseases to such a simple scheme as Rush and Cooke. In general, disregarding individual systems, during the eighteenth century and to about the middle of the nineteenth, the regulars — later called "allopaths" by those not concurring with their practices — operated either on the theory that diseases could be cured by remedies which produced opposite symptoms, or on the assumption that a disease could be transferred to a less important organ or overcome by a new and stronger derangement. Under the first principle heat would be opposed to cold, narcotics to wakefulness, stimulants to enfeebling diseases, and blood letting, purgatives, and sudorifics to inflammatory affections. Under the second, a nervous disorder might be relieved by exciting violent action in the intestines, a pain in the hip by application of the hot iron, or inflammation in the lungs by use of the moxa on the skin.

If theory was in doubt, practice was even less certain. Some medical scholars admitted that there appeared to be even more false facts than erroneous theories. "There is no department of our art so overrun with the fruits of false experience as the materia medica."

"Of these virtues [of medical substances] we know nothing definitely: all we know is, that some are capable of altering the mode of actions, others stimulating, many counter-stimulating; some even irritating, and others quieting, so as to produce either a healthy disposition, and action in a diseased part, or to change the disease to that action which accords with the medicine, or to quiet where there is too much action, and our reasoning goes no farther than to make a proper application with these virtues. The difficulty is to ascertain the connection of substance and virtue, and to apply this in restraining or altering any diseased action; and as that cannot be demonstrated a priori, it reduces the practice of medicine to experiment, and this not built upon well determined data, but upon experience, resulting from probable data."[13]

Mercurials, calomel, opium, niter, Glauber's salts, Dover's powders, jalap, Peruvian bark — and by the 1840's, quinine — constituted the bulk of the materia medica of the regulars. These medicines were given in varying quantities and combinations for different ailments. A favorite purgative was "10 and 10," a mixture of calomel and jalap in equal parts, given every six hours until a slight ptyalism, or salivation, occurred. Not all doses were so conservative, nor was the salivation always "slight." One Louisiana doctor, whose practices probably did not differ much from those of the Middle West, confided to Dr. Drake that he had prescribed enough calomel to load, and withdrawn enough blood to float, the steamboat *General Jackson*. Pills were often as large as cherries and twenty to one hundred grains of calomel were given at a dose. Not many, however, went so far as Dr. John Esten Cooke of Lexington, who gave a pound of calomel in one day to a cholera patient without fatal result,[14] but softening of gums, loss of teeth, and disfigurement did occur. Dr. John Moorhead, "Old Hydrarg," learned but somewhat dry lecturer at Cincinnati's Ohio Medical College in the 1830's, talking of salivation, said: "Some of your patients, hereafter, upon a morning visit, will" (and here he carried his forefinger and thumb to his upper right canine, and motioned, as if extracting it), "will reproachfully say, 'See here, Doctor!'" And another doctor said he had seen calomel "Cause the teeth, those valuable instruments of our most substantial enjoyments, to rot, perhaps fall out; and the upper and lower jaw bones to come out, in the form of horse shoes!"

So prevalent was the hydrargyric propensity, especially in the treatment of fevers, that a doctor who failed to conform was in the popular mind almost deemed guilty of malpractice. Whether the ballad on "Calomel" was written as propaganda by some member of the botanic faith or by a suffering patient is not known, but it records what in time became a general reaction. One version, later set to music, had eleven stanzas and ended:

> *"The man in Death begins to groane*
> *The fatal job for him is done*
> *His soule is wing'd for heaven or hell*
> *A sacrifice to Calomel.*
> *Physicians of my former choice*
> *Receive my counsel and advice*
> *Be not offended though I tell*
> *The dier effects of Calomel.*
> *And when I must Resign my breath*
> *Pray let me die a natural death*
> *And bid you all a long farewell*
> *Without one dose of Calomel."*

Cinchona (Peruvian bark or Jesuit bark) seems to have been used for the treatment of fevers since 1600, when it was employed in Luxa by the Indians of Malacota. Long told, but recently disproved, was the story that the Spanish *corregidor* of this town sent to the wife of the Count Cinchon, viceroy of Peru, a packet of the bark which immediately effected her recovery from an intermittent fever; after her return to Spain she was said to have contributed to the popularization of this remedy. Jesuits used it in Europe and for some time held a monopoly of the importation of the bark.

In 1820 the extract quinine was isolated from the bark by Pelletier and Caventou of Paris. Three years later a Philadelphia chemist set up the first quinine factory in America. C. and J. Bates of Cincinnati in 1824 were advertising "Genuine Sulphate Quinine. A few ounces just received and for sale." In 1826 Dr. Henry Perrine, botanist and doctor who had practiced at Ripley, Illinois, 1819-24, published an article in the *Philadelphia Journal of the*

Medical and Physical Sciences, in which he advocated the use of quinine during the febrile stages of malaria. This was perhaps the first article on the subject to be published in America. Nevertheless, the prejudice against such use of quinine continued to prevail among the "faculty."

One notable exception was Dr. John Sappington of Arrow Rock, Saline County, Missouri, who as a medical student at the University of Pennsylvania in 1814-15 did not agree with the depletive treatment of fevers favored by his teachers. Even earlier he had stated that he was opposed to the exhaustive practices then in vogue, and that "further contact with them only served to confirm me of their errors." Records fail to show at exactly what time Dr. Sappington began to use quinine in his private practice, but it seems that he adopted it almost immediately upon its introduction into this country. When the regulars violently opposed his use of the drug, Dr. Sappington concocted "Anti-Fever Pills," containing quinine well disguised in licorice, myrrh, and oil of sassafras, and in 1832 began advertising them to the public as blantantly as "Drs." Swaim, Dyott, Lamott, and scores of other "patent" medicine venders shouted their wares. These pills, "to-wit — an agreeable, and gentle yet efficient cathartic pill; an admirable diaphoretive pill, and a most powerful yet safe and pleasant tonic pill," sold at $1.50 per box of "40 of 3 kinds of pills." A staff of from fifteen to twenty-five salesmen was put on the road; the bells of frontier towns were said to have been rung every evening at dusk to remind the residents to take Dr. Sappington's pills. In the next ten years over a million sales were reported in the western and southern states and the Republic of Texas. In 1844 Sappington published at Philadelphia his *Theory and Treatment of Fevers* in which he revealed his secret in an effort to induce an even more widespread use of quinine.

Despite the efforts of this pioneer, not until the 1840's was the drug widely used. In 1841 the $100 reward offered by the State Medical Society of Tennessee for the best essay on the treatment of fevers was given to Dr. Lunsford P.

Yandell of Louisville, who had recommended, even as Dr. Sappington had previously done, the early administering of quinine. His suggestion was soon adopted by the younger members of the profession; others gradually fell into line.[15]

In these earlier years the cost of quinine made its use practically impossible. "The first I used cost at the rate of $30.00 per ounce," said an old Indiana practitioner.[16] Another doctor as late as 1846 drove fat cattle from Hancock County in Indiana to Indianapolis and sold them at $7.50 per head to buy quinine at $6 to $8 per ounce. The price in Detroit in 1828 was the same.

To the pioneer patient the lancet, the stand-by of the regulars in treatment of fevers, was a familiar implement. One of the common types was much like a pocket knife with a small cleaver on the end of the blade; others were merely long, tapering blades.[17] Improvements brought the spring lancet which could be set to penetrate to a definite depth. The old jackknife, well sharpened on the doctor's bootleg, would suffice in an emergency. Bleeding and calomel treatments were most ably propagated by the philosophical Dr. Rush of the College of Philadelphia and the University of Pennsylvania.

Bleeding, according to Benezet, was considered proper at the beginning of all inflammatory fevers, inflammation of the lungs, intestines, bladder, stomach, kidneys, throat and eyes, and good for coughs, headaches, rheumatism, apoplexy, and epilepsy. A perusal of the medical books, however, would find it recommended by some one or other for all ills, from abcesses and angina pectoris, through putrid sore throat, to wounds of the chest. But some doctors cautioned that if the blood was extracted from the right arm when the pain was on the left side, death would result from drawing the pain across the heart. "Bleed to syncope" was advice to practitioners almost as inevitable as "pour into a well-greased pan and bake until brown" is to the modern cook. The arms of the patients were often so scarred from repeated bleeding that locating a vein for another bleeding became a difficult task. "The lancet and calomel are the two sheet-anchors in this disease [fever], and irresolution or timidity in the employment of them at the beginning of it, may cost the sufferer his life." But timidity and irresolution were not outstanding weaknesses of the pioneer doctor. "To bleed a patient who cannot be raised from his pillow without fainting, whose pulse is nearly imperceptible . . . at first view rash and unwarrantable . . . flows with difficulty . . . recourse should be had to the jugglars . . . !" So sanguinary was one Indianapolis physician reported to have been that he had a trough constructed to carry the blood of his patients from his office.[18]

Although some physicians were a little more liberal in their blood-taking than others, most textbooks of the period recommended the withdrawing of ten to twelve ounces at a time. Dr. Samuel Gross fixed the usual amount at sixteen to twenty-four ounces and said that the patient felt cheated if less were removed. The *Cyclopaedia of Practical Medicine* published at Philadelphia in 1845 recommended adjusting the amount to the action of the heart and pulse; for apoplexy it suggested forty to fifty ounces. Directions concerning the frequency of blood-letting were not so definite. Some patients, no doubt, reached the proper stage of debility earlier than others. In 1811 the *Medical Repository* reported the case of Captain Niblett, from whom was taken in fifty bleedings six hundred ounces of blood in a period of two months. This was in addition to blood taken by cups and leeches. It is hard to believe that the victim lasted for two months, much less recovered, but he did.

Besides the lancet, leeches and cups were used to bleed. Cups were of various types. Some were bell-shaped and made of glass; others were of glass and brass with stopcocks or valves. The air might be sucked out by mouth or hot sealing wax applied within the cup to expel the air. In use, too, was the lancet-cup, a brass box about two inches square with one end slotted to contain the concealed knives. These were expelled by means of a spring which, when released by a trigger, swept them upward and forward at the same time. Ordinarily twelve knives were used, six moving counter to the other six. As described by a patient, the doctor put the ". . . brass box to my left side, pressed hard down on it, pulled a trigger, and twelve sharp knives slashed into my flesh. Then he burned a piece of alcohol-saturated cotton in a small glass, or cup. This drove the air out. While still aflame but expiring, this was applied over the twelve little incisions which had been made in my side. As the air was exhausted in the cup and no more could get in, the cup 'sucked' blood."[19]

Leeches, after being dried, were encouraged to take hold by covering the skin of the patient with cream, sugar, or blood. If still indifferent to the job, they might be activated by throwing them into a saucer of beer, "until they become quite lively. It will be seen with astonishment how quickly they bite."[20]

The more the patient was bled the weaker he got and the more he needed to be bled. For fever and delirium he was bled until faint and relaxed; an emetic of ipecac was administered, then a cathartic (calomel), and possibly opium to allay irritation of the internal organs. Meanwhile the sufferer was probably confined in a closed room, sandwiched between feather beds, and forbidden cooling drinks. Few doctors paid as much attention to rebuilding the patient's strength as in depleting it. Those who did, used tonics such as mercury, iron, copper, arsenic, lime, and nitric acid. J. Murray in his *Elements of Materia Medica and Pharmacy* (Philadelphia, 1808) also named gentian, oranges, and lemons.

The following description, written in the light of later knowledge, indicates that the patient was not always satisfied with this sort of treatment:

"Then he would say, 'Yes, I see, all run down, very weak, bilious, debilitated. We must draw off all the bad blood and give you a chance to make new and get strong again, give me a bowl and a bandage.' They were brought and the poor victims gave up poor thin blood that was merely keeping the heart beating . . . . The doctor forgot his lance one day and so took his jack knife and sharpened it on his boot leg and bled all of the family of Mr. Reagan. When he came to little Susan the hurt and fright were so great that she died in his arms. He came to our house but mother would not let him touch one of her children. Father was growing worse and tried the doctor's remedy, in fifteen minutes he was dead. Another doctor came who said that was no way to do, he never bled his patients, he wound them in a wet sheet. A promising young man . . . was wrapped in cold, wet sheets and died. Yet another doctor came and he sent a man and team down to Grand Ledge to get a load of hemlock bark which he would steep strong and give them hemlock sweats when they were so weak that they died from heat and exhaustion. You may ask did these doctors get rich. Oh, no, they got the shakes, took some of their own medicine and soon died."[21]

To cure the dumb ague some thought it was necessary to bring on the shakes. "Carry then your patient into the passage between the two cabins — strip off all his clothes that he may lie naked in the cold air and upon a bare sacking — and then and there pour over and upon him successive buckets of cold spring water, and continue until he has a decided and pretty powerful smart chance of a shake." If the shakes became too violent the treatment of Dr. John Sellman of Cincinnati might be called upon: "As often as the fitts come on put her into warm water nearly to the armpits and as soon as taken out give twelve or fifteen drops of paragoric, but remember the paragoric will not be repeated oftener than once in four or five hours, tho' the frequency of warm bathing will be regulated by the urgency of the fitts."[22] Wet sheets wrapped around the sufferer were also used to drive out the fever. If pneumonia resulted, the cure was bleeding, tartar emetic, and calomel.

Another "heroic" in general use was the blister. This was an external application of mustard or the Spanish fly, ground and powdered, used to cause further irritation and redness of skin and blistering. One Dr. Shelton announced in the Cincinnati *Western Spy* of September 19, 1800, that he had discovered "a species of bug which abound in potato patches, having all the virtues of the Spanish, which cost twenty dollars per pound, while more of these American cantharides may be obtained, than will be wanted for domestic use, with no expense and little trouble." One skeptic later had "no doubt that these bugs were all humbugs."[23] Sometimes the skin was rubbed with a strong vinegar to hasten the formation of a vesicle, then the epidermis removed and drugs, such as quinine, placed on the denuded surface. The flow of water from a pricked blister was considered almost as good as bleeding.

Then there were the moxa and the seton. These were used to produce counter irritation or to provide means of escape for "peccant humors." The seton was a thread or horsehair introduced through a cut in a fold of the skin and kept there to irritate and inflame or "maintain an issue." Often a pea or small lump of lint would be kept in an incision in the thigh or leg. The moxa was a coil of carded cotton treated so as to burn slowly, so that when burned on the skin it would irritate steadily. By judicious use of the bellows "we should blow so that the moxa may burn as slowly as possible without allowing it to be extinguished." In cauterizing infections and wounds it was the iron heated to gray heat which was most irritating and torturous, hence the most effective.

No indirect attacks, these, but frontal assaults. As one of the stalwart doctors of the days of vigorous medication said: "We went into it with our sleeves rolled up, and generally came out satisfied with the result of our work."[24] And another: "We used no manner of temporizing treatment, but aimed our agents directly at the extermination of diseases. Opium, ipecac, tartarized antimony, nitrate of potassa, spirits of mindereri and spirits of niter, with other means too tedious to mention, were all frequently brought into requisition. Under the above manner of treating a case of remittent fever it was no uncommon thing on our second visit to find our patient sitting up feeling 'pretty well, except a little weak,' and within a few days able to return to his ordinary avocations."[25] In case of death there probably was no second visit. It was said that the rigorous system of the pioneer doctor "killed quick but cured slow." The doctor himself was sometimes referred to as "Death on the Pale Horse." "When we hear of a man's getting well, after being given over by the doctors, we can't help thinking how lucky he was to be given over by the doctors." That the doctors were sincere in the practice of such treatment is evidenced by the fact that many tried their own medicine with fatal results. That any patients survived both disease and cure speaks wonders for their constitutions and powers of resistance.

Though it was sometimes hard to distinguish the practice of the regulars from the home remedies of the pioneers, the regular practitioner in the West did not noticeably lag behind the general advance of medical science. As Dr. William H. Welch, first dean of The Johns Hopkins Medical School, later said: "The best of these men were, withal, abreast in knowledge, training and skill with their contemporaries of the Atlantic coast; they were men of striking originality, substantial contributors to the sum of medical knowledge and art, powerful influences in the material, as well as the medical development of what was then the far west."[26] Many of the discoveries and inventions of the period were adopted at quite an early date by frontier physicians. Vaccination was practiced in the West the next year after its introduction on the Atlantic coast. The stethoscope, invented by Rene T. H. Laennec in 1817 had made its way to the interior by the 1820's. By the end of the pioneer period microscopes were also being used by middle western doctors.

An editorial in the *Western Lancet*, 1847, within a year after Morton's public demonstration of painless surgery in the Massachusetts General Hospital, stated that anaesthesia "is employed at this time not only in every city and village in the United States, but it has likewise been introduced into the principal cities of Europe." Unquestionably the rapidity of its popular adoption was increased by the "laughing gas" sessions which had been held as early as 1821. In that year the August 10 issue of the Warren, Ohio, *Western Reserve Chronicle* advertised:

"Dr. Brooks proposes to administer 10 to 15 doses of the protoxide of azote, or the exhilarating gas, in the Warren Hotel on Tuesday next at 3:00 o'clock p. m. The sensations produced by this gas are highly pleasurable and resemble those in some degree attendant on the pleasant period of intoxication. Great exhilaration, an irresistible propensity to laugh, dance and sing, a rapid flow of vivid ideas, an unusual fitness for muscular exertion, are the ordinary feelings it produces. These pleasant sensations are not succeeded by any debilitating effects upon the system. A more full account of this gas will be given on the evening of the exhibition. Tickets of admission may be had at the printing office."

Three years later Cincinnati citizens were informed in the February 17 *National Republican and Ohio Political Register* that "On Thursday evening the Exhilarating Gas will be administered." Evidently they enjoyed the performance, for the next month a similar notice appeared.

Dr. R. D. Mussey, Professor of Surgery in the Ohio Medical College, reported in the *Ohio Medical and Surgical Journal,* September, 1848, that he had used both ether and chloroform. In his experience ether had not proved so satisfactory as chloroform, which in thirty-eight cases had caused "not an unpleasant sequel." Dr. Yandell, of the Louisville Medical Institute, stated in the January, 1849, *Western Journal* that up to the first of April, 1848, sixteen operations had been performed on patients who had inhaled ether or chloroform without a single fatality. Dr. Zana Pitcher of Michigan recorded the use of anaesthetics in 1849 in ligation of the common carotid. Dr. E. C. Bidwell of Keene, Ohio, in 1850 reported the use of chloroform in labor. Dr. M. B. Wright, professor at the Ohio Medical College, believed that if mothers suffered no pain they would have no strong affection for their children, since he felt that "In sorrow shalt thou bring forth children." By July, 1852, Dr. Mussey wrote in the *Ohio Medical and Surgical Journal* of the use of chloroform and ether without injury in more than six hundred operations.[27]

Surgery had made some progress since the time of the American Revolution, when operations were often mere butcheries, fractures were clumsily and painfully treated, and antiseptic surgery and anaesthesia unknown. No small part of that progress might be traced to frontier regions, where conditions incident to life made quick and bold decisions on the part of attending physicians a necessity. Important contributions were made by western doctors who possessed little in the way of instruments or facilities, but much of daring and courage.

In 1809 Dr. Ephraim McDowell, of Danville, Kentucky, who had more than a local reputation as a surgeon, was called to attend a pioneer wife who seemed pregnant but had passed her time with no sign of delivery. McDowell decided it was a tumor which must be removed immediately, but so dangerous and unprecedented was the proposed operation that he would not attempt it except in his own office. The woman mounted a horse, rested the protuberance on the pommel of the saddle, and rode sixty miles to Danville in midwinter. It was said that a committee of local doctors and prominent citizens endeavored to prevent the operation. Doctor and patient, however, had made their decision. "The day having arrived, and the patient being on the table, I marked with a pen the course of the incision to be made, desiring him [his nephew, Joseph Nash McDowell] to make the external opening, which, in part, he did; I then took the knife, and completed the operation . . ." while the patient gritted her teeth and recited psalms. Five days later the patient made her own bed, and on the twenty-fifth day drove home, to live thirty-one years longer.[28] Again in 1813 and 1816 Dr. McDowell performed similar operations, but when he published his article "Three Cases of Extirpation of Diseased Ovaries" in the Philadelphia *Eclectic Repertory and Analytical Review* in October, 1816, he was not believed until he demonstrated two other operations.

In Newton, Ohio, in 1827, Dr. John Richmond performed the first recorded Caesarean section west of the Alleghenies. Some idea of the magnitude of his task might be obtained from his own report:

"I had no recourse to cordials, for these could not be obtained. I was seven miles from home, and had but few medicines with me. . . . I requested advice, which, however, could not be obtained, on account of high water in the Little Miami and the darkness of the night. . . . After doing all in my power for her preservation, and feeling myself entirely in the dark as to her situation, and finding that whatever was done, must be done soon, and feeling a deep and solemn sense of my responsibility, with only a case of common pocket instruments, about one o'clock at night, I commenced the Caesarean Section. Here I must take the liberty to digress from my subject, and relate the condition of the house, which was made of logs that were green, and put together not more than a week before. The crevices were not chinked, there was no chimney, nor chamber floor. The night was stormy and windy, insomuch, that the assistants had to hold blankets to keep the candles from being blown out. Under these circumstances it is hard to conceive of the state of my feelings, when I was convinced that the patient must die, or the operation be performed. . . . The patient never complained of pain during the whole course of the cure. She commenced work in twenty-four days from the operation, and in the fifth week walked a mile and back the same day."[29]

Laryngotomy was successfully performed by an Ohio surgeon in this same year. Dr. Erastus B. Wolcott of Milwaukee in 1862 is credited with making a nephrectomy (removal of the kidney), eight years before the first one was reported from Berlin, and in 1870 Dr. Solon Marks, also of Milwaukee, performed his most famous operation, the removal of a bullet from the region of the heart, where the patient had carried it since 1864, "probably the first operation ever reported for suture of a heart wound." Dr. John S. Bobbs of Indianapolis in 1867 pioneered in cholecystotomy (opening gall bladder for removal of stone).[30]

The *Lexington Intelligencer*, December 9, 1836, considered Dr. Benjamin Winslow Dudley, of the Transylvania Medical College, the first surgeon in the West to remove a cataract from the eye. During his long surgical career he was said to have made over two hundred lithotomies (cutting for stone in the bladder) with only four per cent mortality; more than one hundred of these were done before a single death was recorded. The *Kentucky Gazette* for April 11, 1827, reported three lithotomies performed by him in one day. Dr. Dudley also successfully ligated the subclavian artery for axillary aneurysm (soft tumor, containing blood, arising from diseased arterial coats) in 1825, and the common carotid for an intracranial aneurysm in 1841. In 1828 he published a report of five successful cases in which he had trephined the skull for the relief of epilepsy due to pressure on the brain. He was probably the first surgeon in the United States to perform this operation. Dr. Dudley was among the first doctors of the Middle West to discard the lancet; the stress which he laid upon the use of boiled or boiling water in surgery at that early time is worthy of comment. He emphasized preparatory treatment, to which he was more inclined to attribute his success than to his superior skill.[31]

In the twenty-year period following 1835 records of one county of Indiana showed fourteen operations for strangulated hernia, four lithotomies, one ovariotomy (sixty-one pounds), one ligature of the common carotid, and diagnosis of four vesico-vaginal fistulas. Between October 28, 1847, and February 2, 1848, Dr. Daniel Brainard, of the Rush Medical College of Chicago, performed forty-nine operations. A Dr. H. A. Russell, who settled on the Kankakee River in 1832, made the first capital surgical operation in that locality when he operated on a two and one-half year old boy for an inguinal hernia; the child was given "a suitable dose of opium and a quantity of whisky, and tied to the table." Dr. James Mills Bush, of the Kentucky School of Medicine, was an expert with the lithotrite (instrument for breaking or crushing bladder stones), and was said to have performed two hundred ten litholapaxies (rapid bladder stone crushing or breaking) with but four deaths. One of the early Indiana surgeons boasted that he had enough bone buttons, bored from the skulls of his patients in trephining for fractures, to furnish a full set for a double-breasted coat.[32]

Physiology as well as surgery had its midwestern pioneer. Perhaps the most famous volley of buckshot ever fired in the Middle West was the one poured close-range into the abdomen of the half-breed *voyageur*, Alexis St. Martin, in 1822 at the trading post at Mackinac. From this accident grew the noted experimentation of Dr. William Beaumont, young army post surgeon. Though the doctor announced when he first dressed the wound, "The man cannot live 36 hours; I will come and see him by and by," after some months of treatment the patient recovered, except for a fistulous opening to his stomach. When the county and town authorities refused to continue maintenance of St. Martin, Dr. Beaumont took him into his own home. Little knowing the use which he was to make of this "Man with the window in his stomach," the doctor tried in vain to close the fistula; not until early in 1825 did the idea of conducting experiments on the gastric digestion occur to him. Years of work, difficulties, delays, and disappointments finally culminated in the publication eight years later, in 1833, of his *Experiments and Observations on the Gastric Juice and the Physiology of Digestion,* a work "so complete and accurate . . . that little material additional knowledge has been made to the subject in the one hundred years that have elapsed since. Even the X-ray has added practically nothing to his direct observations."[33]

* * *

Opportunities for education of doctors were limited.

Medical schools were not generally available in the West until late in the 1830's, but their absence did not too seriously retard the increase in the number of doctors, for entry into the profession was almost as easy as into the law. A young man lived at the home of some local doctor, "read medicine" with him, rolled his pills, mixed his powders, cut splints, and took care of the horse. After a time he was allowed to accompany the doctor on visits to his cases. At first he maintained a discreet silence; then, as he grew in Hippocratean stature, he was permitted to assist in diagnosis and treatment. The long hours of travel were often utilized by the doctor to hear the lessons of his student. A period varying from two to three years usually sufficed in the mind of the preceptor to warrant launching the young doctor on his own.

Then, even as now, the quality of his training was dependent in large degree upon the ability of his trainer. Not every preceptor, naturally, lived up to these requisites which Dr. Drake considered essential: 1. "It is not necessary that the preceptor should be a man of genius; but it is indispensable that he should possess a sound and discriminating judgment, otherwise he will be a blind guide." 2. Learned, at least in his profession. 3. Devoted to his profession, jealous of its character, and ambitious of its honors. 4. Conscientious in the performance of his duties. 5. A man of business — punctual, accurate, systematic. 6. A man of sound morals and chastened habits.[34] There was no standardization of training, and whereas one preceptor might be very exacting, another would be careless and slovenly in the education of his medical wards. Granted that it had its faults, much that is good could be said for the preceptorial system.

This "living-in" type of apprenticeship was gradually supplanted by the regular daytime-instruction type. Since under the latter system board and room were not furnished and the doctor could not expect much in the way of labor from his apprentice, a regular fee was charged. This was frequently $100 per year. A rough average of this type of apprenticeship was three years. Upon completion of the course the preceptor would issue a certificate. Unless some form of examination was required by law, this certificate, when registered, entitled the holder to practise medicine. If the young physician became a member of a medical society, he was likely to rate a little higher. At times students and young doctors clubbed together and brought in an outside lecturer for two or three weeks' instruction. Men who held the college medical degree were always careful to display the M.D. on their prescriptions and signs. In the absence of data it is hard to estimate, but it appears that prior to 1840 approximately three-fourths of the doctors in the Middle West received their training by means of the apprentice system.[35]

As the idea that "book larnin'" was not necessary and might even be a handicap gave way to the demand for formal training, the preceptorial system was supplemented, then gradually replaced, by the medical school. There is no more interesting chapter in the development of medical education than that provided by the history of the medical colleges in the Middle West. Many of these schools were of the proprietary type, the product of the personal ambitions and dreams of one man or a group of men; often owners, faculty, and trustees were one and the same. This fact, together with jealousies arising from locations, accounts in large part for the many and bitter conflicts which arose.

To Transylvania University at Lexington, Kentucky, belongs the dual honor of being the first university and the first medical college in the West. Until 1837 only the Ohio Medical College of Cincinnati, which graduated its first class in 1821, arose to question Transylvania's monopoly of medical education in the Ohio Valley. The rivalry of the two cities for the distinction of being the "Athens of the West" in medicine as well as in commerce and general intellectual leadership gave rise to many heated individual controversies.

Transylvania University was formed in 1798 by the

amalgamation of Transylvania Seminary, which had been chartered by the Virginia General Assembly in 1780, and the Kentucky Academy established by the Presbyterians in 1794.[36] The Medical Department was instituted in 1799 with Dr. Samuel Brown as Professor of Chemistry, Anatomy, and Surgery; the first course of medical lectures in the West was conducted in 1801 after the addition of Dr. Frederick Ridgely, Professor in Materia Medica, Midwifery, and the Practice of Physic. Dr. Walter Warfield was also appointed to the staff but he appears not to have lectured. A sum of $500 was granted for the purchase of books and equipment.

Evidently the Trustees felt impelled to act as custodians of the morals and manners of the students as well as to keep the institution flourishing, as their record books reveal, April 12, 1799: The Steward "shall keep his doors open until eight o'clock at night, and that after that time his doors shall be shut, and it shall be at his discretion whether he open his house to those who keep irregular hours, unless the student is absent by special permit from the teachers." And April 14, 1810: "Be it ordained that the Professors be required to exact from the students a more respectful deportment; that no student shall be permitted to have his hat on his head in the University in the presence of the Trustees or Professors; that the students, when they leave the hall or room of recitation be compelled to do it in an orderly manner, and to make their respects to the presiding Professors; and when they are reciting at any public examination, the classes must be compelled to stand up without leaning on each other." Perhaps the present-day medical student is not without his historical precedent.

In spite of its auspicious beginnings, this medical school did not prosper until a reorganization had been effected in 1816-17. Its glorious period began with the presidency of Dr. Horace Holley in 1818. Much of the credit for its achievement unquestionably was due Dr. Dudley, the well-known anatomist and surgeon. "Thundering Jove was not a greater autocrat than Dudley was in the management of the Transylvania School." The rejuvenated medical department attracted students, and in 1817-18 had an enrollment of twenty. On the enlarged faculty were Drs. Dudley — Anatomy and Surgery; James Overton — Theory and Practice of Medicine; Daniel Drake — Materia Medica and Medical Botany; James Blythe — Chemistry; and William Richardson — Obstetrics. Such a staff was comparable to, if not stronger than, the faculty of any of the important medical schools of the East. This imposing group graduated one student, John McCullough, of Lexington.

At the end of this first term a part of the intrafaculty tension which had developed was eased by Dr. Drake's resignation. It has been said that Drs. Drake and Dudley "fought before they had well begun, and continued after they parted."[37] The next year (1819) the liberal citizens of Lexington subscribed over $3,000 to guarantee the salaries of faculty additions. In 1820 the legislature voted $5,000 for the purchase of books and apparatus and the city lent $6,000 for the same purpose. Physicians of the South, Kentucky, and Lexington made further subscriptions which brought the total to $13,000. Thus was a financial foundation securely laid. That the faith of the contributors in Transylvania's future was justified is indicated by a survey of enrollment: 1823 — two hundred; 1824 — two hundred thirty-four; 1825 — two hundred eighty-one. To Drake's return in the fall of 1823 might be attributed a part of this increased enrollment, as he was attaining national renown as a medical teacher and leader. During Transylvania's most active period, from 1817 to 1857, 6,456 students sought instruction and guidance; nearly two thousand of these were graduated.

The session of 1827 promised a faculty of six members, a new building seventy-five by fifty feet in size with "spacious lecture rooms, large apartments for library, museum and chemistry laboratory, librarian's dormitory. Immediately contiguous to the anatomical theatre and dissecting rooms." There were "upwards of 3,000 volumes in the library, being increased by periodicals and standard works," of which the students might keep out two volumes at a time. The museum boasted preparations of plaster and wax. All of this was available for $100 specie, with $20 additional for graduation fee.

Transylvania's heyday, however, had waned. From this time on to its final session in 1856-57 internal factional strife and external forces contributed to its decline. By 1836-37 the rise of Cincinnati, Louisville, St. Louis, and other cities as commercial centers, following the development of steamboat navigation, relegated Lexington to a minor position in the West. Recognizing the importance of location on a main thoroughfare, plus the additional advantage of available anatomical "subjects" (a "universal repugnance [is] felt by the entire community against disinterments," said Dr. L. P. Yandell, of Lexington), several members of the Medical School faculty, instigated by Dr. Charles Caldwell, almost succeeded in moving the school to Louisville. A long and full investigation led, instead, to the dismissal of Drs. Caldwell, Yandell, and Cooke, and the dissolution and reorganization of the entire faculty. The resulting instability, when added to the changing external conditions and the rise of competing schools of medicine all over the country, made inevitable the decline of Transylvania. As Dr. Yandell wrote in a personal letter May 12, 1838: "Dr. Dudley's fame may enable Transylvania to vie with the Institute [Louisville] for a year or two; but it cannot withstand everything."[88]

But Dudley's personality and the deep-seated intrigue which seems to have been social, professional, possibly political and religious, as well as personal, had done their damage. In 1837 Dr. James C. Cross, who was brought from the Ohio Medical College, helped secure the services of Dr. John Eberle for Transylvania, but after Eberle's death in 1838 the whole situation flared up again. Cross was ousted in 1844, and there ensued a pamphlet warfare which, aired as it was in the newspapers, it would have been impossible for any school to survive. Phrases and epithets such as "arch traitor," "snarling emissaries of a bastard aristocracy," "scoundrel," "seduction and adultery," "character gangrene," "gross impudent upstart," "hypocrite," "foul ambition," and "Bacchanalian revelries" flew back and forth. Professors appealed to their students as well as their publics; they even quoted poetry at each other. It was not an edifying spectacle, but on the other hand not an unusual one.

Transylvania had made a valiant effort to overcome these odds. In 1839 two of the faculty members made a trip abroad to purchase equipment for their medical department. Dr. Robert Peter reported the purchase of: "Books [bringing the total up to eight thousand] and plates, six thousand dollars; chemical apparatus, two thousand five hundred dollars; preparations for anatomy and surgery, one thousand five hundred dollars; models for obstetrics, five hundred dollars; specimens for materia medica and therapeutics and drawing, five hundred dollars. A total of eleven thousand dollars." Apparatus included a new daguerrotype outfit, which had just been revealed by its French inventor. Said Dr. Peter, "Transylvania will shine. No institution in our part of the world will be able to compare with her in the means of instruction. In fact, I have seen none in Europe that is more completely prepared to teach modern medicine." Faculty members, however, could not be purchased.

In 1850, after the retirement of Dr. Dudley, the winter session was conducted at the Kentucky School of Medicine, which had been formed at Louisville by local physicians and various Transylvania faculty members under the leadership of Dr. James Mills Bush; Lexington retained only a summer school. The winter session was later resumed with only half-hearted interest. The important period of Transylvania's medical school had ended. In 1856-57 the medical department ceased to operate and in 1859 was formally abolished. The Kentucky School of Medicine at Louisville continued, however, until in 1908 it united with Louisville's two other medical schools to form the present University of Louisville School of Medicine.

Simultaneously with the growth of Transylvania, the Queen City was witnessing one of the classic struggles in the history of medical education, the "Thirty Years' War" of cantankerous Dr. Drake to make Cincinnati the medical center of the West. This he intended to do by the creation of an institution which would attain the standards which he deemed essential for producing well-trained doctors, "that our profession may be made to keep pace with every other."

Outstanding among the names of those who participated prominently in the early medical history of the West was that of Dr. Daniel Drake. He has been called a colossal figure, "a man whose fame, as compared with that of his contemporaries will probably be greater a century hence than it is today, and whose name even now should be among the first on the list of the illustrious dead of the medical profession of the United States."[39] Drake, as did Lincoln and others, manifested in large degree what he himself referred to as "the Western Heart." His entire life was a story of struggle — struggle with the wilderness and early poverty, with other medical schools and other men in the same schools, with men in other sections. It was West against East, West against West, regulars against quacks, big minds against small, big minds against big, and sometimes Drake against all. Always there fermented in his mind the exasperating disparity between ideals and reality.

Drake was born in New Jersey in 1785, but when he was only two and one-half years old his parents joined a party of New Jersey farmers who were seeking new homes in the western country. His people were poor among the poorest; when father Isaac Drake arrived in the Kentucky forests his fortune consisted of one dollar, at that time and place the price of a bushel of corn. When five families of the emigrants purchased a tract of fourteen hundred acres of land to be divided among them according to their respective payments, the Drakes' share was only thirty-eight acres.

Young Daniel's early education was received from itinerant schoolmasters, wandering preachers, the woods and fields. Removal of the family to an unsettled region near Mayslick deprived him of even these meager external human sources of instruction, as for two years he helped his father. At the age of eleven Daniel was able to resume his studies at a regular school in the Mayslick district.[40]

In view of his extensive contributions to medicine, it appears as another of those quirks of fate that Drake's medical education developed as it did. When he was about twelve or thirteen years old, his attention was captured by the medical books of his cousin, John Drake, some six years his senior, who was studying with Dr. William Goforth, of Washington, Kentucky. Isaac, though pleased with the prospect of having a doctor in the immediate family,[41] was able to offer little more than moral support. It was intended that John Drake should locate in Mayslick and that Daniel should study under him, but John's premature death spoiled this plan. Had it been carried out, Daniel might have become another country doctor in Kentucky, unheard of by posterity. Making the most of the situation, however, Isaac arranged to have his young son apprenticed to Dr. Goforth, who had removed to Cincinnati. It was decided that in return for $400, a considerable sum for the Kentuckian, Daniel would receive board and instruction for four years.

In 1800, then, young Daniel began his training.

"My first assigned duties were to read Quincy's dispensatory and grind quicksilver into unguentum mercuriale; the latter of which, from previous practice on a Kentucky handmill, I found much the easier of the two. But few of you have seen the genuine, old doctor's shop of the last century, or regaled your olfactory nerves in the mingled odors which, like incense to the God of Physic, rose from brown paper bundles, bottles stopped with worm-eaten corks, and open jars of ointment, not a whit behind those of the apothecary in the days of Solomon; yet such a place is very well for a student. However idle, he will be always absorbing a little medicine; especially if he sleeps beneath the greasy counter. It was my allotted task to commit to memory Chesselden on the bones, and Innes on the muscles, without specimens of the former or plates of the latter; and afterwards to meander the currents of the humoral pathology of Boerhaave and Vansweiten; without having studied the chemistry of Chaptal, the physiology of Haller or the materia medica of Cullen."[42]

Drake applied himself with industry. Upon the completion of his apprenticeship he became the full-fledged partner of Dr. Goforth. Though their business increased rapidly, their cash intake did not add up in like proportion. In letters to his father, Drake spoke of entering from $3 to $6 on their books every day, but expressed doubt of ever collecting twenty-five per cent of this.

"The doctor trusts every one who comes, as usual. I can get but a small share in the management of our accounts, or they would be conducted more to our advantage. I have not had three dollars in money since I came down, but I hope it will be different with me after a while. An execution against the doctor, for the medicine he got three years since, was issued a few days ago, and must be levied and returned before the next general court, which commences the first of September . . . . I am heartily sick and tired of living in the midst of so much difficulty and embarrassment; and almost wish sometimes I had never engaged in partnership with him, for his medicine is so nearly gone that we can scarcely make out to practice, even by buying all we are able to buy . . . ."[43]

There were, however, compensations. Dr. Goforth was a very popular man among the more important people in town and introduced his young student to all — William H. Harrison, General Gano, the Symmes family, Arthur St. Clair, Nicholas Longworth. In this way Drake was able to form many friendships and to awaken and stimulate an interest in public affairs which he maintained throughout his life.

To Drake is accorded the double distinction of receiving the first medical diploma conferred west of the Alleghenies —granted in 1805 by his mentor[44]—and of being the first product of the West to be graduated from a recognized medical school. He had attended the University of Pennsylvania from 1805 to 1806, but did not complete his course and get his degree until 1816. Perhaps no other among the medical leaders of the West achieved notice in such a variety of activities. After 1807 Drake maintained a drug store in which he sold practically everything needed by the residents of pioneer Cincinnati. In it he fitted up in 1816 the first soda fountain in the West. His interest in community affairs was almost unlimited. He was one of the trustees of the Lancaster Seminary, which later became Cincinnati College; he was instrumental in building the first Episcopal church in Cincinnati and in starting a library society, a debating society, a school of literature and art, and a museum for the study of western antiquities and natural history.

"Cincinnati had much to offer, even in the twenties and thirties, in the way of an intellectual nobility, yet many a frontier town numbered groups that would have commanded attention anywhere. . . . Centuries were telescoped into decennia during this rapid development of educational and social movements on the frontiers. And Daniel Drake should be viewed, not only by what he said, wrote, and built up in that fertile period but also by the group which he formed around himself — his enemies and his friends."

He took an active part in furthering various projects for canals and railroads. He attained national renown as a medical teacher and is regarded as the Middle West's most outstanding contributor to medical journalism. His *Notices of Cincinnati, its Topography, Climate and Diseases*, 1810, and its later revisions, attest his accuracy of detail and analysis.

In 1817, upon the invitation of Dr. Dudley, Drake accepted a professorship at Transylvania, but after only a year of lecturing he returned to Cincinnati to plan, in conjunction with Dr. Coleman Rogers and, later, Rev. Elijah Slack of the Lancaster School, a systematic course of instruction for medical students. Because of a clash of personalities this partnership was not successful. Not a few of the disputes were occasioned by Slack, who, though not a physician but a Presbyterian minister, was well versed in chemistry. He was an honest, painstaking man, with character above reproach, but he was also pedantic, deliberate, and tiresome in his lectures. His notorious lack of humor often gave rise to a number of unintentionally informal lectures, such as the one in which he was endeavoring to show before a mixed class the chemical composition of water. Reaching for the pig's bladder, which in those pre-rubber days served as a receptacle, he remarked: "I shall now fill my bladder and proceed to make water." In spite of such peculiarities, he was a very useful man, nearly always found with the winning side, which ordinarily meant that he was opposed to Drake. The triumvirate was dissolved after a short session of four months.

In January of this same year (1819) the Ohio legislature had authorized the establishment at Cincinnati of The Medical College of Ohio, with six chairs. The refusal of Drs. Rogers and Samuel Brown to have anything to do with the institution caused a delay in the opening of the school, originally scheduled for the fall of 1819, until November, 1820. At this time a class of twenty-four assembled on the second floor of the general store of Isaac Drake & Co. Of these students seven were graduated the following April. In the address to the class Dr. Drake pointed out that "Intestive dissentions and jealousies, resemble the morbid actions of a fever which produce debility and delirium." But he was better on a fever than disorders of this type. Faculty strife which had been smouldering soon flared anew. Eleven months later, in March, 1822, Dr. Drake was expelled from his own school. Public action forced his reinstatement, but since his position was embarrassing, he resigned. His school continued in the hands of his rivals, headed by the Rev. Mr. Slack. The next few years were chaotic ones for the Ohio Medical College.

Drake, meanwhile, in 1823 again accepted a professorship at Transylvania, where he remained until 1827, when he returned to Cincinnati to engage in private practice. Never too contented away from schools, in 1831 he eagerly accepted a chair at Jefferson in Philadelphia. Even at that time there must have been hovering in his mind a plan whereby he might once more become associated with medical teaching in Cincinnati.[45] Before the session was over, in spite of his immense popularity Drake resigned and hurried back to Ohio, where the trustees of Miami College in Oxford had announced their intention to open a medical school in Cincinnati for their college.

Drake was accompanied by a party of distinguished teachers, which included Drs. John Eberle and Thomas D. Mitchell, who were to act as professors in the projected school. The Ohio Medical College became alarmed when the prospectus for the new school was issued in 1831, and entered into negotiations with Drake. This resulted in the merging of the two schools, largely on Drake's terms, which included the dismissal of his old enemies, Drs. Slack and Jesse Smith, and his own reinstatement in the Ohio Medical College. That even this reconstruction did not suit Drake was evident by his resignation at the end of the 1831-32 session because of conflict with Dr. John Moorhead. During the remaining years of the first half of the decade, while Dr. Drake retired to private practice, the affairs of the school became more and more hopelessly involved; troubles and wrangles in the faculty and Board of Trustees were a continuous occurrence. The students were at odds with the faculty, and at one time even memorialized the legislature against it. Physicians from Cincinnati and other parts of Ohio presented to the trustees a petition for remedial action. Newspapers added their bit by printing attacks on the profession. The legislature, believing the college had become largely "an arena for local jealousies," refused to help. When the complete collapse of the school seemed inevitable in 1835, Drake was called to try to salvage something from the ruins. He demanded the dismissal of Moorhead, but, notwithstanding the urgency of the situation, so great was Moorhead's popularity that this demand was refused.

Drake followed his earlier plan of fire and backfire; this time he carried out his threat and established another school, the Medical Department of Cincinnati College. Of this school it was said, "This marks without a doubt the highest point ever reached in medical education in the West."[46] During these years Drake was at his peak as a teacher. As described by one of his colleagues, Dr. Samuel D. Gross,

"He was a great lecturer. His voice was clear and strong, and he had the power of expression which amounted to genuine eloquence. When under full sway, every nerve quivered and he could be heard at a great distance. At such times his whole soul would seem to be on fire. He would froth at the mouth, sway to and fro like a tree in a storm, and raise his voice to the highest pitch. With first course students he was never popular, not because there was anything disagreeable in his manner, but because few of them had been sufficiently educated to the import of his utterances."

The distinguished faculty of eight members included Drs. Gross, Landon C. Rives, Joseph Nash McDowell, and Willard Parker. Lack of clinical material was a serious disadvantage, since the Commercial Hospital was completely controlled by Ohio Medical College, and Drake's Eye Infirmary and another small institution which he had fitted up were inadequate. Legislative permission for his students to attend the Commercial clinics was eventually secured, but it came too late to be of great benefit. Shortage of funds and faculty resignations gradually stifled the little school, and it was forced to close its doors in 1839.

During this period, another Kentucky school had started to offer education for doctors-to-be of the West. In 1833, largely as a result of the efforts of Dr. Alban Gold Smith (Goldsmith) the Kentucky legislature authorized the establishment of The Medical Institute of the City of Louisville. Failure to obtain financial backing and difficulties in management, however, delayed the opening of the school. It was finally organized in 1837 through the aid of some of the refugees of the Transylvania faculty. The mayor and city council made an outright grant of $30,000 and a city block to the Institute, and later presented it with $20,000 in cash for a library, apparatus, and an anatomical museum. True it was, as Dr. L. P. Yandell wrote to a colleague, "Louisville *is* the place."

In its first school year, 1837-38, enrollment, representing fourteen states besides Kentucky, reached eighty, with twenty additional students in Medical Jurisprudence. The twenty-four graduates at the end of the first term included three from Indiana, two each from Illinois and Tennessee, and one from Ohio. Despite the general depression throughout the country the institution prospered. By its third session it had acquired a clinical amphitheater, the first west of the Alleghenies. Fifteen thousand dollars of the library and apparatus fund had been spent abroad. Of the twenty-four medical schools in the country at that time, the Institute was surpassed in enrollment only by the University of Pennsylvania and Transylvania. The faculty at various times included outstanding leaders of the entire country: Drs. Drake, Gross, Yandell, Charles Caldwell, Charles Wilkins Short, John Esten Cooke.

For a decade this school ranked with the leading medical schools of the United States. When on April 23, 1846, the University of Louisville was authorized with two departments, Medicine and Law, the Louisville Medical Institute became the Medical Department.[47]

After the collapse of the Medical Department of the Cincinnati College, Drake, worn out and thoroughly disgusted, accepted a professorship at the Louisville Medical Institute, where he remained from 1840 to 1849, teaching, practicing, and preparing his most important work, *The Diseases of the Interior Valley of North America*.[48] This tremendous undertaking had been in his mind for years. The first volume appeared in 1850; the second was so nearly completed at the time of his death in 1852 that it was published only two years later. The two volumes comprise slightly fewer than two thousand pages.

Though Drake's Medical Department of the Cincinnati College was formed primarily for the purpose of exterminating the Ohio Medical College, its actual effect was to stimulate in the latter school a reorganization which proved to be its salvation. Prosperity by the middle forties had again fanned the old fires of jealousy, and bickerings boiled up once more. Drake was called from Louisville for the 1849-50 session, but conditions were so distasteful in Cincinnati that he stayed for only the one session. He returned to Louisville, as he wrote in November, 1850, "the fourth time, in 33 years, that I have entered the state of Ky. as a newly appointed teacher, and I must say that the present reception is the most comfortable of all."[49]

In less than one year subsequent to the beginning of the session 1849-50 there were twenty-five changes in the faculty of the Cincinnati school, only nine fewer than the Medical Department of the University of Pennsylvania had experienced in its sixty years of existence. In 1852 Drake was again asked to come from Louisville to stay the seemingly inevitable dissolution of the Ohio Medical College. Home once more, he wrote in his last letter to one of his daughters on October 5, 1852:

"Our preliminary October lectures were begun yesterday at eleven o'clock. The Faculty honored me with the opening address, which was a mighty offhand affair. The number of matriculates was 25 . . . . We think the prospects very good. Neither of our rival schools has yet had a lecture. I know not how many matriculates they have. I have entered on the care of the medical ward of the Hospital and must continue in that duty, for five months . . . ."[50]

Death in November from arachnitis ended for this old fighter a life of conflicts, but strife within the school did not pass with him. Construction of a new building in this year, at a cost of $50,000, apparently paved the way for a healthier condition, and the competition of rival schools proved stimulating. The school entered upon a period of more stable existence and continued to 1886, when it became nominally the Medical Department of the University of Cincinnati. This arrangement in reality meant nothing, and not until ten years later was a definite relationship effected.

Simultaneously various minor medical schools were developing in Ohio. Willoughby in 1834 established a university which organized a medical department in the next year. In 1847 this medical department was transferred to Columbus and reorganized as the Starling Medical College. The Cleveland Medical College (Western Reserve), founded in 1843, was flourishing under the capable leadership of Dr. Jared Potter Kirtland. Dr. Alvah H. Baker's institution operated after 1851 as the Cincinnati College of Medicine and Surgery. Its first decade was an interrupted chain of internal and external troubles, largely attributable to the selfish and domineering manner of the founder. In 1854 it was the scene of "one of the most fiendish crimes in the history of the West," when one Arrison settled a personal quarrel by the delivery of an infernal machine to a medical student, Isaac H. Allison, which killed him and his wife and nearly wrecked the building.

The warfare among these schools, when added to the strife occasioned by the introduction of the many irregular factions and quack representatives, made Ohio, and particularly Cincinnati, the medical No-Man's Land of the period.

St. Louis, though older than either Cincinnati or Louisville, lagged almost a generation behind in the development of western medical education. In 1840 Dr. Joseph Nash McDowell, brilliant but eccentric nephew of Dr. Ephraim McDowell, with a group of St. Louis physicians organized a medical school under the charter of Kemper College, an institution maintained by the Protestant Episcopal Church. McDowell was born at Lexington, Kentucky, in 1803 and received his medical degree from Transylvania in 1825. After teaching anatomy for a year at Transylvania, he went to Philadelphia, where for one year he taught anatomy at

Jefferson. Returning to the West, he married a sister of Daniel Drake, and from 1835 to 1839 was Professor of Anatomy in the Cincinnati Medical College. When the latter went out of existence in 1839 McDowell moved to St. Louis and organized the Kemper Medical Department.

In 1845, when Kemper College was finding it difficult to keep going, the medical school became the Medical Department of the University of Missouri. When, shortly before the Civil War, the university discontinued its medical department, McDowell's old school became the Medical Department of the Missouri Institute of Science.

The Medical Department of St. Louis University, a Jesuit school, was established in 1836, but did not begin to function until 1842, under the leadership of the erudite Dr. Charles Alexander Pope. He was the son-in-law of Col. John O'Fallon, who had given $80,000 for the establishment of the institution. Pope is said to have donated "at least $30,000 besides." The medical department severed its connection with the university in 1855, when the Know-Nothing movement was at its height, and received a charter as the St. Louis Medical College.

For years there existed between "McDowell's College" and "Pope's College" a rivalry kept alive largely by Dr. McDowell's peculiarities. His dislikes were as intense as his love for anatomy. "Preternaturally cadaverous, he looked as though he had pared his own flesh down so that he might study his own bones." In later years he claimed to have performed the ovariotomy for which his uncle became famous; his surgical skill and anatomical knowledge make this credible. The human body was to him an awful miracle of nature. His lectures and demonstrations were rich with stories; students said he had a different one for almost every muscle, nerve, and bone. "He was an unusually fluent and eloquent speaker, a natural orator and possessed to a pre-eminent degree that rare and wonderful power of adapting himself to any and all kinds of audiences. He literally reveled in antithesis and climax, and as a vivid word-picturer few could equal him. A perfect master of invective and ridicule, never at a loss to entertain any company he might be thrown into." This love for story-telling, when combined with his public eloquence and the bitterness he bore his antagonist, gave rise to sundry interesting episodes. On one occasion he is reported to have said at a commencement, "That by the Grace of God and the permission of the Pope, I expect to lecture here for the next twenty years to come." At another time:

"McDowell, tall and with bushy gray hair brushed back on his forehead, slowly sauntered down the aisle of the amphitheatre with a violin and bow in his hand. Seeing so many students sitting sideways, he commandingly said in his penetrating, high-pitched voice: 'Gentlemen, I pray you, gentlemen, sit straight and face the music.' After scraping off a few tunes he very gravely laid down his violin and bow and said 'Gentlemen, we have now been together for five long months and we have passed many pleasant and delightful moments together, and doubtless some sad and perplexing ones, and now the saddest of all sad words are to be uttered, namely, "Farewell." We have floated in an atmosphere of physiology, we have waded knee-deep, nay, neck-deep into a sea of theory and practice, we have wandered into the tortuous maze and confusing labyrinth of anatomy; we have wearily culled amidst pungent odors and savored the queer elements of materia medica. We have patiently plodded in the crucible of chemicals. Yes, gentlemen, filled with that weariness at times which could have made us sleep sweetly, or snore profoundly upon a bed of flint, and now, gentlemen, farewell. Here we have made the furrow and sowed the seeds. In after years one of your number will come back to the City of St. Louis, with the snow of many winters upon his hair, walking not on two legs, but on three, as Sphinx has it, and as he wanders here and there upon the thoroughfares of this great city, suddenly, gentlemen, it will occur to him to ask about Dr. McDowell. Then he will hail and ask one of the eager passersby: "Where is Dr. McDowell?" He will say: "What Dr. McDowell?" "Why, Dr. McDowell, the surgeon." He will tell him, gentlemen, that Dr. McDowell lies buried out at Bellefontaine. Slowly and painfully he will wend his way thither; there he will find amidst rank weeds and seeding grass a simple marble slab inscribed, "J. N. McDowell, Surgeon." As he stands there contemplating the rare virtues and eccentricities of this old man, suddenly, gentlemen, the spirit of Dr. McDowell will arise upon ethereal wings and bless him. Yes, thrice bless him. Then it will take a swoop, and when it passes this building, it will drop a parting tear, but, gentlemen, when it gets to Pope's College, it will expectorate.' "[51]

His students eagerly entered the battle of the colleges. The main medical hall was designed by McDowell to serve as a fortress, should occasion demand; his residence on the opposite corner was also planned to resist an assault. At one time as many as one thousand four hundred discarded muskets, purchased from the United States Government, were stored in his house and in the college basement. Cannons which the patriotic professor had installed were used, much to the annoyance of nearby dwellers, for celebrating Washington's Birthday and the Fourth of July. Foiled in his ambitions to lead an expedition of students and followers to the conquest of Upper California, McDowell at last enlisted the guns in the Southern cause in the 1860's.

Despite these childish activities, the St. Louis schools managed to provide physicians with training quite comparable to that furnished by the other schools in existence at the time.[52]

The northern Illinois-Chicago area was another center of medical education. The first effort to teach medicine in Illinois came in 1842 with the organization of the Franklin Medical College at St. Charles by Dr. George W. Richards. He was ably supported by a strong faculty which included Drs. Nichols Hard, John Thomas, John Delamater, Edward Mead, and Samuel Denton. Of Dr. Delamater it has been said that probably no medical man ever taught so many subjects in so many different medical schools. He was also largely responsible for the establishment at Jacksonville,

in 1847, of the first state hospital for the insane in Illinois.
Records of this pioneer medical school are almost non-
existent. It is known that the work was carried on in quarters above a store and in the offices of the teachers; none
of the trustees of the school was a member of the faculty.
It was rumored in the community that the students were
"possessed of hyena proclivities." Following dissection of
the body of a Mrs. Runyon, the fear and hatred of the
"resurrectionist" activities of the students led to an attack
upon the school by enraged citizens. Shots were exchanged,
one student was killed, and Dr. Richards himself was so
seriously injured by a ball through one lung and the brachial
plexus that paralysis of the right arm resulted; his death
from a pulmonary infection four years later was traced
to this incident. The school was forced to close in 1849.[53]

The second venture of Illinois in medical education came
in 1843, when a medical school with a faculty of four was
added to the Illinois College, established in 1830 at Jacksonville. A distinctive feature of this school was its gratuit-
ous admission of students who planned to become missionaries. Although it seemingly got off to a good start, the
school passed out of existence in 1848, chiefly because its
leading spirit, Dr. David Prince, was so industrious in procuring cadavers for his anatomy students that this school,
too, engendered community hatred. During its five years of
existence it had more than one hundred students, of whom
forty-three were graduated.[54]

A few weeks after the opening of the Illinois College
Medical School the Rush Medical College of Chicago began
its long life. This, "the first institution of the kind in Illinois or indeed west of Cincinnati and Lexington," as the
Chicago American of March 25, 1837, proudly announced,
had, as the result of the efforts of Drs. Daniel Brainard and
Josiah Cosmare Goodhue, been chartered by the Illinois
legislature in 1837, at a time when the population of Chicago was little more than three thousand. Financial conditions had delayed its opening, although Dr. Brainard had
given instruction to a few students during the intervening

years. As Dr. Brainard's widow later wrote: "When the question of a name for the college was discussed, it was decided to name it after Dr. Benjamin Rush, of Philadelphia, then deceased, in hope of his heirs handsomely remembering it. However, at that time, they received no more than a letter of thanks."

At the opening of the first session in December, 1843, the faculty was composed of four members. Requirements for graduation and fees were similar to those in effect in the other medical schools of the country: three years of study with "a respectable physician"; two courses of lectures, of which one was to be taken at Rush, or two years of practice instead of one of the lecture courses; "good moral character"; twenty-one years of age; a thesis in the student's own handwriting; and special examinations in all courses. For the sixteen weeks' course a ticket cost $60, with an additional $5 for dissecting and a graduation fee of $20. Courses were given in two small rented rooms until 1844, when the college occupied a building of its own.

Rush was quick to adopt new practices. "Laughing Gas" was administered for surgery in 1847 and chloroform the following year. It plunged into the struggle over admission of women to medical schools by permitting Miss Emily Blackwell to attend one session. By 1846 its library contained six hundred volumes, a free dispensary was being operated, and additions had been made to the faculty.

One of these additions, Dr. Nathan S. Davis, who came to Chicago in 1849, is generally regarded as the most active founder of the American Medical Association. He was a strong, aggressive character and advocated the lengthening and grading of the course of instruction. As a consequence of dissension with Dr. Brainard over this policy, Davis, with several other members of the faculty, left Rush ten years later and established a medical department at Lind University. Lind is credited with being the first school to use the graded system of medical instruction. When this institution (renamed Lake Forest University) folded up, the medical department set up independently as the Chicago Medical College in 1863, and this in turn finally became the Medical Department of Northwestern University in 1869.

The dissenters also took away from Rush control of the clinical service at Mercy Hospital, established in 1850 by Dr. Davis as the Illinois General Hospital of the Lakes. Through the skillful management of Dr. Brainard, Rush successfully surmounted this handicap and, in spite of all intervening crises, exists today — since 1924 a part of the University of Chicago — a living monument to its founder, as Dr. Davis prophesied in his opening address, "identified with the interests of a great and prosperous city."[55]

The fourth and last of the early Illinois medical schools was the College of Physicians and Surgeons of the Upper Mississippi, organized in 1848 at Rock Island. It was a part of Madison Medical College, a Wisconsin institution, which by its charter had been given power to create branches in locations other than Madison. Though this school began auspiciously with a faculty of seven professors and an additional demonstrator of anatomy, only one course was given in Illinois. Twenty-one students were graduated in February, 1849. A new charter was secured in Iowa, and the school was moved to Davenport in the autumn. It remained there only one session. In the spring of 1850 it became the Medical Department of the State University of Iowa and was removed to Keokuk.[56]

The history of early medical education in Wisconsin is rather sketchy. In 1847 the Wisconsin Medical College was incorporated, to be located in or near Milwaukee, but little more is known about it. In 1849 Dr. Alfred L. Castleman, who had previously been appointed to confer with the Chancellor of the University of Wisconsin on the possibility of organizing a medical department in the university, reported unfavorably. Because of the meagerness of clinical facilities it was not considered advisable even during the latter half of the century to start a complete medical college in Madison. In 1850 physicians attempted to organize a medical college under the charter of the state university.

Dr. Erastus B. Wolcott, surgeon, was elected president but no further progress was made. A similar lack of success followed a renewed attempt in 1868. In 1864 the LaCrosse Medical College was founded at LaCrosse, but it seems to have had a very short existence.[57]

Such formal education as was obtained by early doctors in Indiana came from schools outside the state. Although Isaac Reed, preacher and traveller, wrote in 1817, "I believe there are more men of public education in the professions of law and medicine, than would be expected abroad, in the State so young,"[58] a widely acquainted Indiana doctor stated that as late as 1825 not ten per cent of the physicians were graduates of medical colleges and not over twenty-five or thirty per cent had ever attended one course of lectures. The need for medical education was recognized as early as 1806, when the legislature of Indiana Territory issued a charter for Vincennes University which authorized it to set up a medical department as well as departments of law and theology, but thirty years elapsed before the medical department was organized.

Not until March 5, 1833, did an Indiana school issue a medical diploma, if it can be counted as such, since the "Christian College" at New Albany, which had been incorporated by the General Assembly only forty days previously, granted this degree under the assumed name of the "University of Indiana." Nor did its questionable activities stop there. Under John Cook Bennett, its first president or chancellor, this diploma-mill began dispensing degrees to the highest bidders, a practice which it continued for a number of years, although the institution actually never did go into legitimate operation. Bennett soon left this school to establish Willoughby Medical College in Ohio, where he remained but a short time before becoming associated with the Mormons.

The Medical Department of Vincennes University was finally organized and announced its first session in September, 1837. Since the records of the University for this year are missing, very little is known of this venture in medical education. According to the contemporary newspapers the lectures "commenced" and were "well attended." Financial difficulties which beset the University at the time make it highly probable that this initial session of the medical school was also its final one.

In 1838 it was "Enacted by the General Assembly of the State of Indiana, That there shall be and hereby is created and established a university adjacent to the town of Bloomington, in the county of Monroe, for the education of youth in the American, learned and foreign languages, the useful arts, sciences (including law and medicine), and literature." The operation of the medical department in this school did not become effective, however, until many years later.

Actual medical-college education in Indiana was begun in the winter of 1840-41, when a charter was obtained from the legislature through the exertions of John H. Bradley, member from LaPorte, for "a school of high rank, to be called the LaPorte University." This charter, drawn by William Andrews, provided for an institution that should have a literary, a medical, and a law department. The medical department, organized in 1842, had a faculty of five, which included Dr. Daniel ("Old Death") Meeker, to whom it owed its existence. The school progressed with a fair degree of success. Its enrollment for the spring terms 1845-46, 1846-47, and 1847-48 was sixty, ninety, and one hundred one, respectively. The spring course of 1848 was given at Lafayette, at the insistence of Dr. Deming, in the hope of the eventual removal of the school to that place. Thirty students were graduated in 1849. During the eight years of the school's existence it enrolled a total of five hundred sixty-five students, of whom one hundred twenty-seven were graduated.

Apparently prospective students were not too much impressed by the promises of Professor Moses L. Knapp in his commencement address of 1847:

"If you are adapted to the people, and the place is growing rapidly — requisites I have insisted on — and you pursue the course I have marked out, and will certainly go into practice, you will possibly have as much professional business as you can do the first summer. One of the first graduates of this school after its reorganization in 1843 obtained practice to the amount of nearly $3,000 the first summer and autumn, settling himself in a country village, in Illinois, where there were four doctors. This is worthy of being mentioned alongside of the far famed success of the celebrated Dr. Lettsom, who amassed nearly $8,000 in the first five months of his practice, on his return from England to Tortulo."

Changes of 1848, including the incorporation of the name "Indiana Medical College," did little to improve the fortunes of the school. Growth of other medical centers all around — Chicago, Ann Arbor, Indianapolis, Lafayette — furnished too much competition for the little college. In 1851 it was consolidated with the Indiana Central Medical College of Indianapolis, the medical department of Asbury University of Greencastle.

Indiana Central had opened its first session in the autumn of 1849. In 1850 it graduated ten students from an enrollment of forty. Even the combination with the LaPorte institution did not materially increase its numbers, nor did early conflict with the Botanics help its progress. Disagreement among the faculty and trustees caused its dissolution at the end of the 1851-52 session. Two of its most notable faculty members were Drs. John S. Bobbs and Livingston Dunlap.

One other Indiana medical school appeared within the period — the Medical College of Evansville, which was organized in March, 1846, but did not open its first course of lectures until nearly four years later, in November, 1849. From the forty-one matriculants, nine were candidates for graduation the first commencement. After five commencements the school suspended operations in 1856 and did not reopen until 1871. During its turbid existence frequent faculty changes were the rule. Moreover, the fact that the school was a product of the religious fervor and temperance agitation of the time did not add to its strength.

"Classes were opened with prayer and lessons in anatomy made more interesting by the interjection of an occasional Bible-reading. Students who promised not to use liquor, tobacco and profane language were admitted without having to pay any tuition. The average medical student found these requirements too exacting. Thus the school soon closed its doors."[59]

In 1817 the Governor and Judges of Michigan Territory authorized the incorporation of the "Catholepistemiad or University of Michigania." One of the thirteen Didaxiim or professorships was the Didaxia of Iatrica or Medical Sciences. It was 1837 before this grandiose paper university was translated into a school. The Michigan medical profession was exceedingly fortunate in having one of its members, Dr. Zana Pitcher, on the University Board of Regents. In 1847 he was appointed chairman of the committee to consider the establishment of a medical school. The medical school as established "was essentially the work of his hands," for only minor changes were made in his recommendations of 1848 and 1849.

The next year, 1850, the school was inaugurated at Ann Arbor with a faculty of five members. Its growth was hampered during the early years by a lack of clinical facilities. This condition was not remedied until over a quarter of a century later, when, in 1877, a one-hundred-fifty-bed hospital was provided. During this period patients were brought to the school by physicians of the state for free consultation, provided they submitted to demonstration before the medical students. The early years of the medical department were filled with conflicts with the homeopaths. Michigan was one of the first schools in the United States to require high qualifications for entrance and longer courses.

The development of hospitals in the West paralleled the rise of medical schools; the two were interdependent. Founders of medical schools early recognized the inability of their institutions to function properly without clinical facilities. Often it became necessary either to open hospitals or to close schools. Sometimes the problem was solved the one way, sometimes the other. Nevertheless, beginnings were made. The contrast between the early hospitals and those of today would probably be more striking than between the medical schools of the two periods.

The pioneer's pride and independence which sometimes made him skeptical of college doctors operated doubly strong against hospitals. The idea prevailed that these new-fangled affairs were essentially charity asylums, in the same category with poorhouses, pesthouses, and insane asylums. This was a natural assumption, since the earliest hospitals often combined these social services. Furthermore, there was the black record of deaths under which the early hospitals labored. In these pre-Listerian days post-operation infections were the rule rather than the exception, and even if the patient miraculously escaped death he would often, as a result of the surgeon's ignorance of asepsis and antisepsis, spend the remainder of his life minus arm or leg. Even after Lister had proved Pasteur's thesis, years were required for doctors as well as patients to accept it. The appearance of "laudable pus" or "God's salve" was regarded by the surgeon as an indication that the healing mechanism of the body had been set in motion and, God willing, the patient would recover. Too frequently doctors sent their cases to the hospital as the last resort, and patients felt that they were committed there to die rather than to live.

The first hospital in Cincinnati was opened about 1815 when the township trustees rented a house for the accommodation of sick and indigent persons. The building was ill-adapted to its purpose, and the institution passed out of existence in 1821 when the "Commercial Hospital and Lunatic Asylum of the State of Ohio," advocated by Dr. Drake as a part of his educational system, was chartered by the legislature. The state was to pay a small sum toward the support of patients, the township to supply the remainder, and the professors of the Ohio Medical College were to be its medical and surgical attendants, with the privilege of introducing their students for clinical instruction. The fees of admission were to constitute a fund for the purchase of chemical and anatomical apparatus, and books for the college. By contract with the Secretary of the Treasury the hospital became also the Marine Hospital of the United States.

Some delay attended the erection of a building, but one was completed in 1823. The hospital became enmeshed in the troubles of the college, particularly after the rise of rival schools which demanded a share in the clinical advantages of the hospital. In 1839 the legislature passed a law which extended its use to the students of all medical colleges. In 1853 the hospital fight became a public scandal when brought to the fore by the Eclectics, rival schools, and even the Methodists who were disgruntled by the failure of Wesleyan University to create a medical department in 1850. The trustees of the hospital, torn between conflicting forces, finally admitted students of the Eclectic Institute to clinical demonstrations. The result was almost daily fights between the two sects, and for nearly a year the clinical lectures had to be suspended. In 1855 the trustees were empowered to sell tickets to students of all colleges, a procedure which seemed to restore temporary peace. The absorption of the Miami Medical College by the Ohio Medical in 1858 also helped to ease the situation somewhat. Drake's "Cincinnati Eye Infirmary," which he had opened in 1827, in later years provided in a very meager and inadequate manner clinical material for his Medical Department of Cincinnati College.

In 1852 the City Infirmary was established. Orphan asylums which had been set up in different parts of the state relieved the hospital from the responsibility of caring for parentless children; the Lick Run, and later the Carthage (Longview), lunatic asylums likewise limited the functions of the old Commercial Hospital. Control in the late 1850's and early 1860's passed to the hands of specialized boards. In 1865 the crowded condition of the hospital was relieved by the establishment of a temporary annex, and, although it was hard to convince the people of the necessity for a new building, one was finally constructed.

The first orphan asylum in Cincinnati was established in 1829 by the Sisters of Charity. In 1852 they opened their "Hotel for Invalids" in the house in which Dr. Taliaferro and others had conducted a private hospital for about ten years. This "St. John's Hotel for Invalids" had as a medical staff professors of the newly organized Miami Medical College. Concurrently with the opening of the hospital the Sisters opened two orphans' homes.

In 1858 another hospital, St. Mary's, was established in Cincinnati by the "Sisters of the Poor of St. Frances" in the building which had housed an orphanage conducted by a German Catholic society. The Sisters also opened St. Elizabeth's Hospital in Covington, Kentucky, within two years; another in Columbus, Ohio, in 1862; and yet another in Quincy, Illinois, in 1866.

Following the outbreak of the cholera epidemic in Detroit, in 1834 a temporary hospital was set up in the building that Bishop Rese had purchased to remodel for Catholic use. The first permanent hospital in Detroit, St. Vincent's, was established by the Sisters of Charity in 1845; five years later it became St. Mary's. Detroit, too, was beginning to recognize the need of special treatment for its mental cases, although as late as 1845 well, sick, and insane had been interned together, and cases of idiots chained in horse stalls were reported.

At Indianapolis, Drs. John S. Bobbs and Livingston Dunlap, with a number of citizens, in 1845 memorialized the City Council for a hospital. This was ordered erected in January of the following year. A smallpox epidemic broke out at this time and the plans temporarily disappeared with it. Four years later the building was completed but not furnished, nor were provisions made to maintain it. In 1860 it was granted to a society of ladies for use as a home for friendless women. During the Civil War it was employed as a military hospital.

Chicago had a number of hospitals and related institutions. The first hospital arose from the desire of Dr. Nathan S. Davis for clinical material for his students at Rush Medical College. Rooms were rented in "The Lake House"; in 1850 the institution became the "Illinois General Hospital of the Lakes." The next year nursing was placed in the hands of the Sisters of Mercy, who obtained a charter for the "Mercy Hospital." When Dr. Davis and his associates left Rush in 1859, they entered into a contract with the Sisters to attend patients free of charge in return for the right to give clinical instruction in the hospital. In 1869 a new building was constructed and Mercy was considered the "finest hospital west of New York."

The U. S. Marine Hospital No. 5 was established in 1852 on part of the Ft. Dearborn reservation. In 1867 a new one was constructed midway between Chicago and Evanston. It was destroyed in the Chicago fire, but was rebuilt on the same site. It was originally intended for sailors in the Merchant Marine.

In 1855 a poorhouse was instituted on the Cook County Farm at Jefferson, about twelve miles from Chicago. The insane were lodged in a small brick building adjacent to it. Admirable as was the idea, contemporary descriptions speak of vermin-infested cells seven by eight feet heated only by stoves in the corridor, of food passed in through apertures, and of meager bathing facilities.

The first city hospital was constructed in 1854, especially for cholera patients. Because of conflict with the homeopaths the new building was not occupied until 1859. Rush physicians at that time leased the hospital from the city and contracted to care for the sick poor at $3 per week for each patient. In 1862 the United State Government took it over for military purposes and converted it into an army hospital, known until 1865 as "Des Marres General Hospital"; it was used for soldiers suffering from eye and ear troubles. It became the Cook County Hospital.

The Isolation Hospital of Chicago was established in 1856 as a smallpox hospital for twelve patients in what is now Lincoln Park. It was enlarged in 1865, destroyed in the 1871 fire, rebuilt, then destroyed by fire again.

Other Chicago institutions established later included: the Chicago Eye and Ear Infirmary, founded by Dr. Edward L. Holmes and others in 1858, which had received its first applicant before a single room had been cleared and furnished, and accommodated one hundred fifteen patients during its first year; St. Luke's, 1864; Hospital for Women and Children, founded by Dr. Mary Harris in 1865; Alexian Brothers, 1866; Deaconess, 1868; and St. Joseph's, 1868, known at first as Providence, and established by the Sisters of Charity of St. Vincent de Paul. It later affiliated with Rush Medical College.

Wisconsin's first hospital of which we have record was St. John's Infirmary, which was opened in Milwaukee, 1848, by the Sisters of Charity of St. Vincent de Paul. The Milwaukee Hospital was founded in 1863 chiefly through the efforts of the Rev. William Paussauant with the aid of other Lutheran pastors and laymen, and the Deaconness Institution.

The first hospital in Missouri was established in St. Louis in 1828 by the Sisters of Charity. Until 1832 they carried on in a log house with two rooms and a kitchen, but a new building was erected just in time to care for some of the cholera victims of that year. In 1843 the hospital was incorporated as the St. Louis Hospital Association. A big "St. Louis Hospital Lottery" was widely advertised in the spring of 1833. Over three thousand tickets were offered and $10,000 in prizes announced. Chances were supposed to be much better than in the Mammoth New York Lottery. The *Illinois Advocate and State Register* later said, "The first day's drawing of this humbug took place . . . tickets to the amount of $12,000 drew in prizes less than $1,500."

The first city hospital in St. Louis was opened for patients in 1846 and was totally destroyed by fire ten years later. The new hospital, which was ready for occupancy by the following year, likewise suffered a violent end in destruction by tornado in 1896.

The Louisville Hospital, chartered in 1817, opened in 1823 to "those engaged in navigating the Ohio and Mississippi rivers [who] owing to the fatigue and exposure incident to long voyages become sick and languish at the town of Louisville where the commerce in which they are engaged sustains a pause occasioned by the falls of the Ohio River." In 1826 it was transferred from the state of Kentucky to the city of Louisville; the Federal Government provided $500 annually for its support. In 1836 another act passed for the promotion of the hospital provided: "That the trustees of the Louisville Marine Hospital may confide the medical department of said hospital to the Institute, and the Mayor and Council of the City of Louisville may confide the medical department of the poor house and hospital to said Institute"; the name of the institution was changed to the Louisville City Hospital. This same year the St. Vincent Infirmary opened; in 1853 it was moved from the Orphanage to a new location and its name changed to St. Joseph's Infirmary. About 1836 Lexington established a City Hospital and Work-House. The Federal Government in 1847 set up in Louisville a Marine Hospital. Various special institutions were opened in Kentucky to care for the blind and the insane.

* * *

Whether the doctor received his early training at the hands of a preceptor or in a medical school, he still had a long way to go before he could be considered proficient in his profession. The few elementary textbooks used in college would soon become partially obsolete and an up-to-date library was expensive and difficult to get. Dr. Gideon Case, who died in 1822 in Hudson, Ohio, had books valued at $32.25 listed in his estate. Some doctors had Bell's *Surgery*, Cheselden or Wistar's *Anatomy*, Boerhaave's *Lectures*, Van Swieten's *Commentaries*, Cullen's *Materia Medica and Practice*, Quinsey's *Dispensatory*, Rush or Senac's *Fevers*,

Hamilton or Smellie on *Obstetrics,* and John Hunter's *Blood, Inflammation and Gun Shot Wounds.* By the late 1820's a western doctor could reasonably expect to find a number of these books, either in stock or on order, in the bookstores of Cincinnati. Fifteen years later similar stores were available in Louisville and St. Louis. Most of the American books came from Philadelphia publishers and dealers, although Boston, New York, and Baltimore shared in the trade. The European center from which most of the importers got books was Edinburgh.

Doctors of the West were making their own contributions to medical literature in the prewar period. Three of the most outstanding were Drs. Gross, Eberle, and Drake. In Philadelphia in 1839 appeared Gross's *Elements of Pathological Anatomy,* regarded as the first attempt to present the subject systematically and coherently in English. For more than a quarter of a century this was the standard authority. Gross's work, *A Practical Treatise of Foreign Bodies in the Air Passage,* Philadelphia, 1854, was likewise regarded as a pioneer in this field. In 1859, also at Philadelphia, Gross published his two-volume *A System of Surgery; Pathological, Diagnostic, Therapeutique, and Operative.* This treatise, the first comprehensive work on the subject, ran through six editions and was translated into several foreign languages. It has been judged "the greatest work on surgery of its day, and probably one of the greatest ever written." Its sixth edition, published in 1882, contained twenty-three hundred pages with sixteen hundred illustrations. "Possibly no book ever written had a greater influence on surgical thought." The last important work of Dr. Gross was his *Autobiography,* Philadelphia, 1887, which is one of the finest of its kind written by a first-rank physician of the Middle West.

Eberle's *A Treatise on the Practice of Medicine* appeared as a two-volume work in Philadelphia in 1830. This study, "comprehensive and original, not a mere compilation of previous or foreign works," passed through five editions and was adopted as a textbook by numerous colleges. For the special use of students he published in Cincinnati in 1834 a synopsis of his lectures, *Notes of Lectures on the Theory and Practice of Medicine, delivered in the Jefferson Medical College, at Philadelphia.* A third edition appeared in Philadelphia in 1840.

In 1850 Dr. Drake published the first volume of his *A Systematic, Historical, Etiological and Practical Treatise, on the Principal Diseases of the Interior Valley of North America as They Appear in the Caucasian, African, Indian, and Esquimaux Varieties of Its Population.* Drake's work was, as he said, "an attempt to present an account — etiological, symptomatical, and therapeutic — of the most important diseases of a particular portion of the earth. . . ." To present such a complete account it was necessary for the causative physical factors of diseases to be studied — the character of soil, climate, temperature, and food in various regions. Likewise habits of the people had to be examined, and finally the prevailing diseases and treatments had to be investigated.

As early as 1822 Drake had sent out an appeal to physicians of the Middle West and South requesting information on geographic and medical conditions peculiar to their particular locality. Questions such as were sent by a committee (Drs. Samuel Brown, Richardson, and Drake) to "Physicians of the Western and Southern States and especially to those of Kentucky" serve as a sample of Drake's early method of coverage:

"1. At what time did the late epidemic commence and terminate? Was it preceded or succeeded by any unusual forms of disease? Did it appear to spare any particular class of persons, or those of a certain age, or sex, more than another?

"2. What were its characteristic symptoms? — Did they vary in the progress of the epidemic? Did they in any instance manifest identity with those of the *Yellow Fever* of our maritime Cities of the West Indies? What were the morbid appearances upon the dissection of those who died?

"3. What was the most successful plan of cure? Was

blood-letting useful? What method of treatment appeared to be prejudicial?

"4. In what situation was the disease most prevalent? Did it chiefly prevail in the country, and the smaller town? Was it more common and violent in dry and elevated situations than in the neighborhood of rivers? Did topographical circumstances vary its type, and the indications of cure? Finally, was there anything in the condition of the season which can throw light on the origin of the disease or account for its extensive prevalence?"[60]

Innumerable duties delayed for many years the beginning of actual observations, but by 1837 Drake was making shorter trips for personal information-gathering. On horseback and foot, by buggy, boat, and railway he covered the whole western country, studying the earth and its waters, the sky and air, plants, animals, and people. As his technique was developed, the investigations were extended. During these years he was credited with travelling "at least thirty thousand miles" and examining "thoroughly a zone of country comprising four millions of square miles . . ."; "from Hudson Bay to the desert lands of the Rio Grande, from the palm groves of Florida to the headwaters of the Mississippi, from the mouth of the St. Lawrence and the great lakes of the North, to the prairies of the far West and to the Sierras of the Rocky Mountains."

The first volume, which was published at Cincinnati in 1850, concerned itself with General Etiology and was divided into three parts: Topography and Hydrography, Climatic Etiology, and Physiological and Social Etiology. The second volume, published posthumously at Philadelphia in 1854, treated of Febrile Diseases: Autumnal Fever, Yellow Fever, Typhous Fevers, Eruptive Fevers, and Phlogistic Fevers — the Phlegmasiæ.

The reception of the work by the profession both here and abroad was gratifying. At the Cincinnati meeting of the American Medical Association in 1850 the chairman of the committee on medical literature devoted the greater part of his report to it, and referred to it as an "achieve-

ment of which every doctor in America should be proud."
Then followed a demonstration and ovation such as few
doctors have received in the annals of American medicine.
When the author was called upon, he was overcome, faint,
and speechless. When he recovered, he said, "I have not
lived in vain," but wished that departed loved ones could
have been there to share the acclaim.

Alexander von Humboldt pronounced *Diseases of the
Interior Valley* "a treasure among scientific works" and
Benjamin Silliman of Yale classified it as "an enduring monument of American genius." The *Edinburgh Review* gave
it favorable notice and the *British and Foreign Medico-
Chirurgical Review* devoted thirty pages to it. Later critics,
evaluating American medical books, stated that, though it
was not possible to make a great list, one could make a
strong one, and on that list Drake's work was among the
strongest.

Since books were often unavailable, medical journals
were the best means by which the doctor could increase his
knowledge and keep abreast of the developments in the field
of medicine. Indispensable as were these professional periodicals, with the possible exception of the minority of general practitioners in the West who had emigrated from
eastern cities, few physicians were subscribers.[61]

True, as with agricultural knowledge, a certain amount
of medical literature was printed in the newspapers. In a
period in which the newspaper was made up largely from
copy lifted bodily from "exchanges," articles from periodicals, British and American, were common property. In
addition to the usual hints on health, recipes, and the like,
newspapers ran contributions, often of a column or more
in length, by local doctors. Sometimes these were continued
through several issues. For instance, in 1821 the Cincinnati
Liberty Hall published a long series by "Hippocrates";
number seventeen was on "Emetics," number eighteen on
"Blood Letting." Others treated of seasonal fevers, epidemics, and wounds. As interest in this sort of thing increased, leading doctors became aware of the need for

periodicals devoted entirely to the subject of medicine.

The first American medical journal, the *Medical Repository*, began as a quarterly in New York in 1797 under the editorship of three physicians, Samuel Latham Mitchill, Professor of Chemistry at Columbia, Elihu Hubbard Smith, one of the "Hartford wits," and Edward Miller. As stated in Smith's "Introductory Address," special attention was to be given to the study of epidemics, connection between climate and health, and diet. As the work progressed, other fields of science including agriculture, geography, and natural history were given space. It was continued, rather spasmodically at times, until 1824. This publication did not have an extensive circulation in the Middle West; in its second year its total circulation was under three hundred.[62]

Other eastern periodicals of varying duration centered in New York, Philadelphia, Boston, and Baltimore.[63] Of these journals western doctors favored the Philadelphia and New York publications. How many were regular subscribers there is no way of knowing, but likely a small number. Not infrequently the subscriber had the issues bound into volumes for reference use.

In the West Cincinnati competed with Lexington and Louisville for first place in publication of medical journals. Chicago, St. Louis, Columbus, and Detroit were minor publishing centers in the pre-Civil War period. Western medical journalism had its beginning in 1818-19, when Dr. Drake issued proposals for a medical journal in Cincinnati, and obtained between two and three hundred subscribers. Other duties at this time interfered with the project, and it was not until 1822, when Dr. John D. Godman issued the first number of the *Western Quarterly Reporter of Medical, Surgical and Natural Science,* published by John P. Foote of Cincinnati, that a medical periodical actually came into existence. After only six numbers Dr. Godman returned East and the work was discontinued. It was intended that Dr. Drake should revive the publication at Lexington, but he was unable to do so.

The first successful and continuous medical periodical

THE

WESTERN JOURNAL

OF THE

MEDICAL AND PHYSICAL SCIENCES.

EDITED BY DANIEL DRAKE, M. D.

LATE PROFESSOR OF CLINICAL MEDICINE IN THE MEDICAL COLLEGE
OF OHIO, AND FORMERLY PROFESSOR IN TRANSYLVANIA UNIVERSITY,
AND THE JEFFERSON MEDICAL COLLEGE.

VOL. VII.

SECOND HEXADE—VOL. I.

CINCINNATI, OHIO.

PRINTED AND PUBLISHED, QUARTERLY, AT THE CHRONICLE OFFICE,
NO. 5, JOHNSTON'S ROW, UPPER MARKET ST.

BY E. DEMING.

1834.

"The natural history of the Mississippi States is a subject of interest, both in a professional and a national point of view; and as there is not in this region, any MAGAZINE devoted to the Physical Sciences, the Editors will be gratified to . . . make public, all kinds of original facts and observations on the Climate, Mineralogy, Botany and Zoology of the States, which lie between the Lakes and the Gulph of Mexico."

in the West began in April, 1826. At that time Drs. Guy
W. Wright and James M. Mason started at Cincinnati the
semimonthly *Ohio Medical Repository of Original and
Selected Intelligence,* which was soon changed to a monthly.
In April, 1827, Dr. Drake replaced Dr. Mason, and the title
changed to the *Western Medical and Physical Journal,
Original and Eclectic,* also a monthly. After one volume
(1828) Drake edited it alone as the *Western Journal of
the Medical and Physical Sciences,* and changed it into a
quarterly after the second volume (1829). His first editorial adjunct was Dr. James C. Finley in 1830; later he
added Dr. William Wood, then Drs. Gross and John P.
Harrison. Its last number was issued in July, 1838.

Dr. Oliver Wendell Holmes as chairman of the American Medical Association's committee on medical literature
in 1848 criticized the medical journals of the period for a
lack of originality. "The same articles have been presented
over and over again . . . in many different periodicals,
each borrowing from its neighbours the best papers of the
last preceding number, so that the perusal of many is not
so much more laborious than that of a single one, as would
be anticipated. The ring of editors sit in each other's laps."
The *Western Journal* was perhaps less deserving of this
criticism than many other periodicals, since it devoted
much space to original materials. Its numbers consisted of
discussions of cases and essays, reviews and bibliographical
notices, and miscellaneous intelligence — analectic, analytical, and original. A study of its contributors reveals many
familiar names — Eberle, Finley, Cross, Caldwell, James M.
Staughton, Landon C. Rives, Joseph Nash McDowell,
Gross, and again and again Drake. Members of the profession in Pennsylvania, New York, Tennessee, and Georgia at
different times made contributions. Fevers, epidemics, surgical discoveries, paralysis, "dyssentery," drugs and their
effects were dealt with at appropriate times. Professional
topics of the day — medical education, the role of the preceptor, quacks, intemperance, were given their due, as were

such items of public interest as spontaneous human combustion.[64]

In 1839 the *Western Journal* united with the Louisville *Journal of Medicine and Surgery,* a quarterly which had been started in January, 1838, by Professors Henry Miller, Yandell, and Thomas H. Bell of the Louisville Medical Institute, but which had suspended after the second number in April, 1838. The new monthly appeared in January, 1840, under the title of the *Western Journal of Medicine and Surgery* and continued until 1855. Drs. Drake and Yandell, its first editors, were later joined by Dr. Thomas W. Colescott. Dr. Drake later (in 1852) stated: "In 1849, my connection with it was dissolved, and also that of Dr. Colescott, since which it has been continued by Professor Yandell and Dr. Bell." This periodical was superseded in 1856 by the *Louisville Review,* which merged the next year with the *Medical Examiner and Record of Medical Science* of Philadelphia to form the *North American Medico-Chirurgical Review.* This journal ran five volumes, 1857 to 1861.

Lexington's contribution to medical journalism was the quarterly *Transylvania Journal of Medicine and the Associate Sciences,* which under the editorship of Drs. John Esten Cooke and Charles W. Short, and later L. P. Yandell and Robert Peter, was in existence from 1828 to 1839. After the Transylvania faculty conflict of 1837 this periodical deteriorated noticeably.

Ohio Medical College added its effort, the *Western Medical Gazette,* a semimonthly, which was published from December, 1832, to August, 1833, by Dr. Eberle, assisted by Drs. Staughton, Bailey, Mitchell, and Goldsmith. It was soon revived by Silas Reed and Dr. Gross as a monthly. In April, 1835, it was absorbed by Drake's *Western Journal.* Two years later, in 1837, Dr. Eberle and various members of the Ohio Medical College — Smith, Moorhead, John Locke, Jedediah Cobb, John T. Shotwell — again undertook a publication, the *Western Quarterly Journal of Practical Medicine,* which issued only the June number.

During this same period, from September, 1835, to January, 1836, Dr. James M. Mason edited at Cincinnati the monthly *Ohio Medical Repository*. In 1842 the monthly *Western Lancet* was begun by Dr. Leonidas M. Lawson and continued until 1859. At that time it combined with the monthly *Medical Observer*, which had been started in 1856 by George Mendenhall, John A. Murphy, and E. S. Stevens, to form the *Cincinnati Lancet and Observer*. In 1873 it was purchased by J. C. Culbertson, who in 1878 acquired control of the *Clinic*, which had published, under the auspices of the Ohio Medical College, fourteen volumes since 1871. This combination was called the *Cincinnati Lancet and Clinic* and within a few years became the *Cincinnati Lancet-Clinic*. After Culbertson's retirement it lost much of its prestige and influence, but in 1907 gained a new lease on life when it came under new managership. It continued to publish until November, 1916.

Dr. A. H. Baker, the founder of the Cincinnati College of Medicine and Surgery, published a monthly journal in the interests of his school, known as the *Cincinnati Medical News; devoted to the dissemination of truth*. It began in 1858 and was suspended in 1863. In 1860 its name was changed to *Cincinnati Medical and Surgical News*. At Columbus was published from 1848 to November, 1864, the *Ohio Medical and Surgical Journal*. It was revived and a new series ran from 1876 to 1878.

The journalistic contribution of Illinois consisted primarily of the *Illinois Medical and Surgical Journal*, which lasted from 1844 to 1889. It was edited by James Van Sandt Blaney in Chicago. After two volumes it became known as the *Illinois and Indiana Medical and Surgical Journal*. Volumes V to XIV were the *Northwestern Medical and Surgical Journal;* from XV (1859) to XXXII it was the *Chicago Medical Journal*.

Michigan's *Peninsular Journal of Medicine and the Collateral Sciences* was begun in 1853 by Dr. Edmund Andrews at Ann Arbor. With volume II, Dr. A. B. Palmer joined the staff, and with volume III, Andrews dropped out and Drs. Zana Pitcher, W. Brodie, and E. P. Christian were added. When in 1856 the *Peninsular Journal* rejected one of his articles, Dr. Henry Goadby, of Detroit, in something of a huff started the *Medical Independent and Monthly Review of Medicine and Surgery.* With the aid of Drs. Edward Kane and L. G. Robertson he kept it going until 1858, when it was absorbed by the older periodical. This consolidation became known as the *Peninsular and Independent Medical Journal, devoted to medicine, surgery, and pharmacy,* and was edited by Drs. Palmer, Moses Gunn, and Frederick Stearns. It continued at Detroit until 1860.

Missouri had as its first medical periodical the *St. Louis Medical and Surgical Journal,* a bimonthly, started by Dr. M. L. Linton in April, 1843. It was enlarged in 1845 and Drs. W. M. McPheeters and V. J. Torgeaud became associated with it. In November, 1861, since McPheeters had joined the army, publication was suspended; it resumed in January, 1864, and continued until 1907. The *Missouri Medical and Surgical Journal* began in May, 1845, with Dr. R. F. Stevens as editor and the faculty members of Kemper College as associate editors. In September, 1848, it merged with the *St. Louis Journal.* Missouri's other periodical, the *Kansas City Review of Medicine and Surgery,* was a bimonthly which originated in January, 1858, under the editorship and ownership of Drs. Theodore S. Case and G. M. B. Maughs. Because of the war it ceased publication in April, 1861.

Iowa physicians had one professional magazine in the prewar period, the *Iowa Medical Journal,* which between 1853 and 1869 published five volumes at Keokuk. Indiana and Wisconsin had no medical periodicals of consequence until the second half of the century. At the town of Hanover, Indiana, in 1836, Dr. Buell Eastman announced the ambitious project of the *Itinerant Physician.* The first number — probably due to premature birth, since it was dated "1736" — seems to have been the last. Its early demise was not caused by lack of an omniverous program — it lacked only subscribers.

In the absence of data regarding the circulation of these western medical periodicals it is impossible even to make an estimate. Editors, though they complained of delinquent subscribers, seldom revealed circulation figures. The free mailing list was large, particularly of the periodicals published by medical schools, copies of which were sent to many newspapers of the region for publicity purposes, as well as to other periodicals. Any but the best-established of these journals probably did well to average three hundred paid subscriptions. As with the general magazines, they had more readers than subscribers, but not so many in proportion. Probably few of them were financially self-sustaining. The supporting income from patent medicine advertising, the chief reliance of most newspapers, was not available to them.

* * *

Dentistry as a profession was only beginning. For the ordinary toothaches there were home remedies aplenty, and when too far gone the tooth was looped with a string and pulled by a friend, or the string was hitched to a springy bent sapling, which, when released, would yank out the offender. At least one case is recorded in which the rugged old pioneer, after holding the sapling for a couple of hours, lost his nerve, got sleepy, so cut the string and went home in disgust. Difficult cases were taken to the country doctor, who, with a torturous crank-like lever known as a "pullikin" or a turnkey, sometimes achieved the desired result. This instrument worked on the leverage principle, the grip increasing with the amount of resistance offered. It could not easily break the jaw, for its main arm pressed down while the loose end, placed under the tooth, lifted. The doctor knew the patient would throw his head the way the iron was turning, hence could prepare by taking a strong arm hold on the patient's head. Later forceps of assorted sizes and shapes were used. When teeth decayed without excessive pain, the dead stumps and roots were, as a rule, not interfered with. Plugs of tinfoil were sometimes used to advantage by fastidious persons, as this substance showed less conspicuously than gold leaf.

Once the teeth were extracted it was impossible for the average person to have them replaced, and toothless gums were common among older folk. Some thought that diseases of the teeth were more common in the United States than in England or Germany. It was recognized at this time that diseases of the mouth were more prevalent in civilized than in savage life. Among the causes assigned was, "It is the law of the animal economy, that the organ oftenest thrown into high excitement, is most liable to disease. Now the civilized state is one of wealth and luxury; it is emphatically an eating state."

Aside from natural wear, tear, and neglect, the salivating effects of the overdoses of calomel, and possibly fevers and constitutional afflictions were no doubt aggravating factors. By the 1820's some itinerant dentists were available in the larger towns of the West. One such travelling practitioner who devoted the seven years between 1830 and 1837 entirely to dental surgery, reported in the (Columbus) *Daily Journal and Register*, December 6, 1837, that he had "travelled between 25 and 30 thousand miles in different parts of the United States."

In 1815, Robert Smether, dentist, informed Chillicothe ladies and gentlemen by notice in the *Supporter* that he extracted and cleaned teeth, removed causes of their decay, and could cure the "scorbutic complaint" of the gums which caused teeth to become loose. The next year "T. Etheridge, Surgeon Dentist" announced in the *Liberty Hall* that he would "tarry a short time" in Cincinnati.

"He cleans, whitens, and separates the Teeth, without the least pain; and when the molares or double teeth, become hollow and useless, he plugs them with gold or tinfoil, which often restores them to their former usefulness: and he inserts ARTIFICIAL TEETH from one to a set, in a neat and durable manner; & when advisable to have them set, warrants them to be permanent."

Itinerant dentists, many of them mere tooth-pullers,

were not always accorded the greatest regard; for example, one writer used more than a column of the front page of the Cincinnati *National Republican and Ohio Political Register,* August 10,1824, to discuss "The Tooth-Drawer," who "is a most savage little animal" and who "desires that the world had but one tooth that he might wrench it out by a single twist! . . . He has the confidence to consider a man's throat as public property, and will intrude himself into his mouth, ransack his jaws, and pilfer him of his teeth, without the least hesitation . . . . He has no time nor inclination to think of anything, save ravishing people of their teeth. A Tooth Drawer is as forward as he is foolish — as important as he is ignorant — and as impenetrable as he is impertinent."

In 1837 in Columbus "Mr. Powell, Operative Dentist" had "on hand a beautiful and well selected assortment of PORCELAIN TEETH, consisting of French and American Manufacture, which, in point of strength, beauty, and durability, is superior to any other material that has ever been used for artificial teeth." By 1840 in Cincinnati was used a "new substance, like clay, [which] pushed firmly in the teeth, hardens in a day or two like the tooth itself." Such a feat in an era of hard times and bank failures called forth the comment from a newspaper editor that it was now possible to mend almost everything except dishonesty.

Dentistry was usually practiced, not as a specialty, but in conjunction with medicine. One of the first opportunities, if not the first, for dental instruction in schools in the West was offered when Dr. John Harris of Bainbridge, Ohio, announced in the Chillicothe *Supporter and Gazette,* November 1, 1827, the opening of his "School of Medical Instruction," equipped with:

"Anatomical preparations and Chemical Apparatus, sufficiently extensive for the exhibition of many important experiments. He will deliver Lectures, during the winter season, at least once a week on each of the following branches, viz.: Demonstrative Anatomy, Operative Surgery and Chemistry; and during the summer season he will devote as much of his time in lecturing on Osteology, Physiology, Materia Medica, Theory and Practice of Medicine and Obstetrics, as his professional avocations may permit; and every possible facility will be afforded to those who may see cause to patronize his efforts. No student will be received who has not at least a first rate English education. Terms of tuition will be reasonable, depending on circumstances. October 25, 1827."

By the same medium, from February 21, 1828, to December 3, 1828, Dr. Harris added further: "From his knowledge of the Medical Profession Surgery and Dental Surgery in particular, he flatters himself that he shall be able to render general satisfaction to all, who may have occasion to employ him."

From 1835 to 1836 Dr. Harris attended a course in medicine and gave dental instruction at Transylvania. In 1836 he tried to obtain a charter for a regular university dental institution in Ohio, but failed. This has been mentioned as the first effort anywhere to obtain legislative permission for a dental school. In the winter of 1839-40 Dr. Chapin A. Harris, brother and student of Dr. John, succeeded in obtaining a charter for the first dental college in the world at Baltimore.

Dr. Chapin A. Harris was the instigator, and became the editor, of the *American Journal of Dental Science,* New York, 1839, the profession's first periodical. The second periodical worthy of note was Dr. James Taylor's quarterly *Dental Register of the West,* published at Cincinnati, under this title, from 1847 to 1865. It became the *Dental Register* and issued its last number in November, 1923.

Dr. Taylor, who had been a student of Dr. John Harris in the School of Medical Instruction, founded a dental college at Cincinnati in 1845, after his efforts to have it as a separate department in the Ohio Medical College had failed. "No funds, no buildings, no apparatus, and with but few competent teachers. However, through patience, labor, and anxiety, which endured year after year, success crowned their perseverance . . . ." The school was chartered by the forty-third General Assembly of Ohio and the college opened in a rented building. Students were required to pay a matriculation fee of $5, $25 to each professor per session, $10 for dissection tickets (optional), and $25 for diploma fee; $100 cash in advance would pay the cost of the whole course. For graduation the candidate was required to: present two full courses of lectures of which the last was to have been in Taylor's institution; be twenty-one years of age and of good moral character; offer two years' study with a reputable practitioner or in lieu thereof one year's study in a medical school; present and defend a "written thesis on some subject relating to dental science, and be subject to a critical examination upon the theory and practice of dentistry." The school offered courses in anatomy and physiology, dental pathology and therapeutics, practical dentistry, and pharmacy. Of the twenty-one students enrolled for the 1845-46 session, eleven came from Ohio, five from Kentucky, two from Indiana, one each from New York, Mississippi, and Arkansas. Of these, six were graduated, each of whom was presented with a copy of the Bible, "a custom which prevailed for many years." From 1845 to 1858 ninety-nine were graduated.

As dentists grew in numbers, they began to organize societies. In 1844 both the Cincinnati Association of Dental Surgeons and the Mississippi Valley Association of Dental Surgeons were formed. At Cleveland in 1857 the Northern Ohio Dental Association came into being and two years later at Springfield, Ohio, was organized the Mad River Valley Association.

Eye troubles received little attention. But few people used their eyes consistently for close work. When vision got bad, various spectacles from the stock of the peddler or general store were tried on until a pair was found to fit. Although astigmatism was discovered at the very beginning of the century and cylindrical lenses were being ground at Philadelphia in 1828, the rudiments of optometry were known by only a few; so spectacles only magnified to take care of "long-sightedness" and "short-sightedness." A few eye specialists began to appear by the late 1830's. Dr. Waldo of Columbus, for instance, announced in his "card" "special attention to Diseases of the Eye. Artificial Eyes inserted." It was probably easier to get a satisfactory glass eye than a satisfactory pair of glasses. Dr. Drake's Cincinnati Eye Infirmary, founded in 1827, pioneered in institutionalized care; this system was adopted in 1858 by the Chicago Eye and Ear Infirmary, and three years later the first Eye and Ear Clinic west of the Mississippi was established in Missouri by Simon Pollack.

CHAPTER IV

"Then thick as locusts dark'ning all the ground,
A tribe, with herbs and roots fantastic crown'd,
All with some wond'rous gift approach the people,
—Lobelia, pulmel, and steam kettle."
—Pope, The Dunciad, *as modified by Daniel Drake.*

The age-old tendency of unscientific ideas to attach themselves to, and operate within, the scope of a recognized science is perhaps best illustrated in the field of medicine. Around its periphery has ever hovered a mass of thought and practice ranging from the merely illogical to the obviously crackpot and superstitious, from sincere assumptions to premeditated fraud and quackery. Nor — keeping in mind that the "valid" science of one period, once discarded, frequently steps down to become the stock-in-trade of the charlatans and ignorant of a later — is it always easy to draw the line. It is hard to deny that often the only difference between regular practice and empirical practice lay in the routine use of merely different remedies. Not always did the disadvantages rest with the irregular. By the law of averages the chances of success of one were about equal to those of the other. "It seems to be one of the rules of the faith in our art," wrote Dr. Walter Channing of Harvard, "that every truth must be helped into belief by some persuasive fiction of the school. And I . . . confess, that as far as I know, the medical profession can scarcely produce a single volume, in its practical department, from the works of Hippocrates down to the last made textbook, which, by the requisitions of an exact philosophy, will not be found to contain nearly as much fiction as truth."

And, speaking of the Babel-like confusion which the public noted in the medical profession at the time of the cholera and which existed regarding other diseases as well, Dr. James Rush, son of the distinguished Dr. Benjamin, said:

"Whence comes all this? Not from exact observation, which assimilates our minds to one consenting usefulness; but from fiction, which individualizes each one of us to our own solitary conceit, or herds us into sects for idle or mischievous contention with each other; which leads to continual imposition on the public, inasmuch as fictions, for a time, always draw more listeners than truth; which so generally gives to the mediocrity of men, and sometimes even to the palpably weak, a leading influence in our profession, and which helps the impostures of the advertising quack, who, being an unavoidable product of the pretending theories of the schools, may be called a physician with the requisite amount of fictions, but without respectability."[1]

So it was in the Middle West, where the art of medicine was still floundering in its swaddling clothes of uncertainty and superstition. Always to be found was:

"The professional buzzard . . . weakly watery-eyed, red-nosed old scarecrow who at some time in his early life has gotten hold of several recipes which he considers valuable and he is therefore induced to give suffering humanity the benefit of them. He has a decided weakness for 'yarb medicines' which he gives in the form of slops and teas. He pours this stuff down his dupes with the same idea, I imagine, that the hired girl pours dish-water down a rat-hole, that of filling a vacuum and killing time."[2]

Although this remark referred to the 1880's, it well describes conditions a generation earlier. In addition to the regular members of the profession, seventeen different kinds of "doctors" were named as practicing: eclectic, botanic, homeopathic, uroscopian, old Thomsonian, hydropathic, electric, faith, spiritual, herbalist, electropathic, vitapathic, botanico-medical, physio-medical, physio-electric, hygeo-therapeutic, and "traveling."[3] Several others might be added, but this inventory will serve as a working list. More than three quacks to every regular were reported in Wisconsin, and early Michigan's high death rate was said to result from their presence. Indiana was adjudged "a sink-hole in medical practice"; Ohio was condemned as a "paradise of the incompetent."

Most prominent and influential among the irregular medical sects were the Thomsonians. Thomsonianism derived largely from aboriginal root and herb healing; in turn it became the point of departure for many minor groups and cults.

Once a man has been labeled as a leader, a certain number of human beings will view with admiration; if he arise from the masses they will add awe and reverence. Such a man was Samuel Thomson, originator of the "steam system" of Botanic medicine, which swept the country, particularly the West, in the 1830's and 1840's.

Thomson was born in 1769 at Alstead, New Hampshire. In modern parlance, he would be termed a "natural," for at the tender age of three, while driving the cows and minding the geese, he might have been found, he says, "very curious to know the names of all the herbs which I saw growing, and what they were good for; and to satisfy my curiosity was constantly making enquiries of those persons that I happened to be with, for that purpose. All the information I thus obtained, or by my own observation, I carefully laid up in my memory, and never forgot." Of particular persistence was his early unpleasant contact with the emetic lobelia, which in later years was the basic element of the Thomsonian materia medica.

Formal education, except for one month, he lacked, for the rigors of living in uncleared New Hampshire during this early period left little time for more than the struggle for existence. Although at sixteen he offered himself to study under a root doctor, he was turned down as deficient in education. In 1796 when the doctors had practically given up as hopeless the case of his daughter who was ill of scarlet fever, Thomson tried his first steam cure and was convinced that it saved the child. As his growing family required frequent medical service, he applied his self-taught vegetable treatments. His successes and a general distrust of the contemporary medical practices and ethics, combined with "a very strong aversion to working on a farm," led Thomson in 1805 to adopt the healing profession as his own. It remained merely "to fix upon some system, or plan for my future government in the treatment of disease."

With Nature (and probably earlier herbals) as his guide and experience as his instructor he conceived and brought forth "the only correct theory" of treatment: all disease is the effect of one general cause, and may be removed by one general remedy. All animal bodies are formed of four elements: earth and water, air, and fire (or heat), the cause of life and motion. In a state of health a definite balance is maintained among these elements, but a change in any one of them naturally upsets the equilibrium. Cold, or lessening of the power of heat by the obstruction of perspiration, causes all diseases, for it is simple knowledge that no person ever dies of heat; he always gets cold first. *Post hoc* — to prevent death one has merely to prevent the departure of the heat; to restore health one has to return heat to its natural extent. When this has been done, it is necessary for the system to be cleared of all obstructions and to have restored a natural perspiration. The stomach can then digest the food taken into it, and as a result the whole body becomes nourished and invigorated and its heat or health can be maintained. This system is applicable to all diseases in all mankind, for the only differences the doctor meets are individual variations in temperaments of the constituent elements.

To cleanse the stomach and to aid in raising heat and promoting perspiration Dr. Thomson found *Lobelia inflata,* the "Puke Weed," most useful. Another concoction, con-

Man in whom the "four elements" have failed to maintain the required "definite balance."

tents secret and known to his followers in later years as "No. 2," was effective in maintaining the heat in the stomach until the body could be cleared of obstructions, whereas "No. 3" was best for removing "canker" from the alimentary tract.[4] Other supplementary preparations had similar uses. Experience in the yellow fever epidemic of 1805 in Alstead and Walpole had proved the efficacy of parboiling the patient to restore his natural heat. After much experimenting Dr. Thomson decided that the best method was to:

"Take several stones of different sizes and put them in the fire until red hot, then take the smallest first, and put one of them into a pan or kettle of hot water, with the stone about half immersed — the patient must be undressed and a blanket put around him so as to shield his whole body from the air, and then place him over the steam. Change the stones as often as they grow cool, so as to keep up a lively steam, and keep them over it; if they are faint, throw a little cold water on the face and stomach, which will let down the outward heat and restore the strength — after they have been over the steam long enough, which will generally be about 15 or 20 minutes, they must be washed all over with cold water or spirit and be put in bed, or may be dressed, as the circumstances of the case shall permit."

This treatment with certain modifications was effective in cases of dropsy, cancer, humors, mortifications, "fellons," dysentery, consumption, rheumatism, "scalt" head, venereal diseases, and fits. In his treatment of an old maid "much disordered for many years and very spleeny," complications of a serious nature almost developed, for so speedy was the woman's recovery that she immediately acquired a husband, who ungraciously accused Dr. Thomson of using love powder. Steaming might be supplemented at times by the use of an electrical machine for external applications. Perhaps this was the Perkins influence.

Dr. Thomson's cures naturally brought vociferous criticism from the regular members of the profession. In 1809-10 he was charged with murder after the death of a patient, supposedly from use of the "screw auger" lobelia. Fortunately for our story, if not for his patients, he was acquitted, perhaps much better off for the resultant publicity.[5] A few years later a petition for a law against quackery, specifically naming him, was sent to the New Hampshire legislature. But the Law giveth as well as threateneth to take away, for in March, 1813, the United States Patent Office granted a patent to Dr. Thomson — the first of a number which it was to issue to various "doctors" in ensuing years. This gave him the exclusive right to administer six concoctions, "No. 1," "No. 2," etc., in the healing of specific diseases. Ten years later this patent was replaced by a fourteen-year right, which before its expiration was renewed for another fourteen-year period.

The system, having now been perfected and legalized, was ready to be propagated. Not that the law mattered much, for Thomson, not content to confine his practice to the range of a horseback-travelling doctor in New England, had moved from Beverly to Boston, where he opened an office and infirmary and had, since 1806, with the aid of authorized agents, been selling "Family Rights" which admitted aspirants into the ranks as full-fledged members of the "Friendly Botanic Societies." Members were sworn to secrecy regarding the intricacies of the Thomsonian cures.

In 1821 he published a pamplet slightly longer than its title: *A Brief Sketch of the Causes and Treatment of Disease, Addressed to the People of the United States; pointing out to them the Pernicious Consequences of Using Poisons as Medicine, such as Mercury, Arsenic, Nitre, Antimony, and Opium. Designed as an introduction to a full explanation to be published hereafter, of the system of practice discovered by the Author.* The next year, assisted by Elias Smith, a Universalist preacher of Boston, he published *A Narrative, of the Life and Medical Discoveries of Samuel Thomson, ... To which is added an introduction to his New Guide to health or Botanic Family Physician.* An engraved certificate which came with the *New Guide* served as a diploma, and conferred upon the purchaser the right:

"Of preparing and using, for himself and family, the Medicine and System of Practice secured to Samuel Thomson, by Letters Patent from the President of the United States; and . . . is hereby constituted a member of the Friendly Botanic Society, and is entitled to an enjoyment of all the privileges attached to membership therein. . . . All Purchasers of Rights can have intercourse with each other for advice, by showing their Receipt. All those who partake, or have participated, in stolen rights, or what is virtually the same, have bought them of those who have no right to sell, can show no receipt, either from me or any of my agents, and are not to be patronized by you

or any honest man, as they are liable to sixty dollars fine
for each and every trespass. Hold no counsel or advice
with them, or with any who shall pretend to have made
any improvement on my System of Practice, as I cannot be
responsible for the effect of any such improvement. 'Resist
the devil, and he will flee from you!' "

Though the price was $20, the book became a best seller.
Under one title or another it ran through thirteen editions
— the later ones mostly published in Ohio — and according to its author, sold over one hundred thousand copies.
The fourth edition was translated into German for would-
be practitioners of Pennsylvania and eastern Ohio. The
New Guide or Family Physician was also published separately in several editions.

From 1822 to 1837 Thomsonianism enjoyed a popularity more extensive than that of any other of the unortho-
dox systems. From its New Hampshire birthplace it spread
to the rest of New England and to New York; from New
York it moved southward as centers were established in
New Jersey, Maryland, central Virginia, and Georgia.
Westward it migrated to eastern Pennsylvania and into
northern Ohio. After 1821 Charles Thomson, son of the
founder, spent much time working in Ohio. In 1825
Charles Miles was made general agent for Thomsonian promotional sales at Columbus; within a year and a half he
sold five hundred rights. Horton Howard became con-
troller of western headquarters at Columbus and in three
and a half years sold four thousand rights in Ohio and
neighboring states.

In 1832 was started at Columbus the *Thomsonian Recorder, or Impartial Advocate of Botanic Medicine,*[9] with
Thomas Hersey as editor; he was succeeded two years later
by Dr. Alvah Curtis. "In no period has the Botanic cause
spread so successfully as it has since the *Thomsonian Recorder* began to command an extensive circulation," wrote
the editor in October, 1833. A few months later:

"Two years ago a man did not dare to come out boldly
and avow himself in favor of the Thomsonian plan of

curing disease, unless he wished to be ridiculed; but now a majority of the people of my acquaintance do not use any other remedies. There is much sickness in our country and the greatest demand for Botanic Medicines I have ever known."

The amount of sickness could not be appreciably increased, but the demand for Botanic medicines could. Now developed a high-powered sales promotional system which anticipated by years that of the sewing machine companies. Agents were dispatched "By different directions, Eastward and Southward, et cetera, and in their several routes, to have an opportunity to give all their principal Agents, and many others a personal call." These agents were authorized to sell the "System" to any and all who could be persuaded to buy. According to lists in the *Recorder,* Ohio and Tennessee led with the largest number of agents, but Indiana, Illinois, and other states were well represented. It is not clear under what financial arrangements these agents operated, but it was probably on commission. Some of them gave lectures as well as sold books and rights. At Cincinnati, for instance, in 1829 Dr. Samuel Robinson delivered "A Course of Fifteen Lectures, on Medical Botany, denominated Thomson's New Theory of Medical Practice; in which the various theories that have preceded it, are reviewed and compared." Tickets were 25 cents for individual lectures or $1.50 for the course. These lectures were later (1829) edited and published by Horton Howard of Columbus; subsequently five other editions were issued at Columbus and Boston. Among the Botanic medical works this publication was surpassed in sales only by Thomson's *Narrative and New Guide.* Thomson stated in his *Narrative* that "Those lectures were delivered without my knowledge, being at the time a thousand miles from that place. Horton Howard obtained them, while acting as my agent, paid for them out of my money, secured the copy right in his own name, and printed an edition of them, which he sold for his own benefit. This book gave a great spread to the sale of rights. I have since secured the copy right in Boston, and printed an edition of two thousand copies, which are selling from fifty to sixty-two and a half cents a copy. They contain much information relative to the practice of medicine as taught in medical colleges, and found in medical authors; not to be found elsewhere in so small and cheap a work." "He is entitled to much credit for this service done the system."

The success of the Thomson and Robinson books led to spontaneous publication of a small deluge of Botanic medical works. Among others, Miles, who had been selling Thomson's books, published his own *New and Improved System of Medical Botanical Practice* at "Cleaveland" in 1829, in which he made no mention of Samuel Thomson.

Horton Howard published a three-volume *An Improved System of Botanic Medicine* at Columbus in 1832. Two more editions followed. A one-volume edition was published by J. Kost of Cincinnati in 1852. Meanwhile J. Kost, M.D., wrote, and published at Mt. Vernon his *Practice of Medicine according to the Plan Most Approved by the Reformed or Botanic Colleges* etc. etc.[7] These books drew upon Rafinesque and others for plant illustrations and were of much more elaborate content than the original Thomson. Without illustrations, but with seven hundred pages and two hundred thirty "valuable vegetable remedies" plus a dispensatory was J. E. Carter's *The Botanic Physician or Family Medical Adviser*, published at Madisonville, Tennessee, in 1837. There were many others.

Even printers ran off anonymous Botanic manuals. At Norwalk, Ohio, in 1835, for instance, S. and C. A. Preston set up and distributed the thirty-page *The Medical Instructor, or the Cause and Cure of Disorders, expressed in Plain, Easy Language, and Intended for the Great Benefit of Mankind.*

Botanic medicines were widely advertised, not only in Botanic publications but in general newspapers as well. They were dispensed both wholesale and retail in such centers as Cincinnati, Louisville, Indianapolis, and St. Louis. Directions given in Thomson's book for preparation of the medicines recommended were quite general and indefinite; he warned his followers that the most efficacious remedies were manufactured by establishments which he either owned or controlled. The largest of these, located in Cincinnati, to a great extent supplied the western territory.

The need for medicines was apparent if the Thomsonian recipes were to be followed. For instance, for a dyspeptic patient who had suffered seven years was recommended a treatment of Composition No. 6, Spice Bitters, and Nerve Powders every two or three hours for several days, "then I carried him through a full course of medicine." Since he sweat but little in a steam bath,

"I gave him the warming medicine very freely, such as Nos. 2 and 6, *Composition*, &c. I rubbed the surface of the body freely with cold water, vinegar and salt, mixed—repeating these applications several times, while over the steam. After about an hour I applied cold water and vinegar, by means of a towel—then dressed and put him to bed, gave him an emetic, repeating the dose till I had given him twelve large tea spoonsful of the Third Preparation. It operated slowly after several hours. I then resumed the use of medicine first prescribed. I gave freely of Nos. 2, 3, 4, 5, and 6; Nerve Powders, Stomachic Bitters, Conserve of Hollyhock, and Golden Seal. I prepared bitters of equal parts of Golden Seal, Columbo Root, Nerve Powders, Unicorn Root, Balmony, Poplar Bark, with enough Bitter Root to obviate or remove costiveness, and Cayenne sufficient to make the medicine quite warm. This course I pursued, using alkalies, such as Pearlash, Sal Aeratus, &c, . . . I proceeded afterwards to take him through another full course of medicine, then resumed the treatment with tonics and stimulants as before."[8]

Or for a child bitten by a spider:

"I commenced by giving it, in the first place, a teaspoonful of bear's oil. I then administered an injection, prepared with Nos. 2 and 3, in which I put two tea-spoonsful of the Third Preparation of No. 1; immediately after I sponged it with No. 6 and Tincture of Lobelia. After waiting an hour and a half, I administered another injection, in which I put one tea-spoonful of the Third Preparation of No. 1, and one of the Tincture. I then steamed it and gave it a tea-spoonful of the Tincture of Lobelia. The medicines failed to operate, and its fits continued hard, and became more frequent. Seeing that the medicine I had already given it failed to operate, I concluded that I would give it no more; but, being overpursuaded by the family, I administered a third injection, prepared like the second, steamed and sponged it again, and gave it another teaspoonful of the Tincture No. 1 of Lobelia. Its system then became relaxed, and vomitting followed. Its fits ceased — it then being about midnight — by sunrise next morning, it could not have been discovered that the child had ever been sick, and has done well ever since."[9]

In 1835 the Botanics maintained that half of the people of Ohio relied upon their system; the regular doctors conceded one-third. Even the Governor of Mississippi stated publicly that one-half the people of his state were adherents. Wrote the editor of the *Thomsonian Recorder*, March 1, 1834: "The practice is every day gaining a stronger hold in the minds of the American people. Not less than one million and a half of our fellow-citizens now believe in it, and adopt it solely in their families. And never was the System progressing with more rapid strides. We have an opportunity of knowing, and speak advisedly. Within the last twelve months, the demand for rights and medicine has increased in ten-fold proportion — far beyond our ability of supplying." By 1839 Thomson claimed three million followers in the United States. Of one thing he was positive: "that I have been the cause of awakening a spirit of enquiry among the people of this country, into the medical practice and the fashionable manner of treatment in curing disease, from which great benefits will be derived to the Community." With equal modesty Dr. Alvah Curtis said, "The Thomsonian system in forty years has saved more millions of human beings from a miserable life and a premature grave than the whole United States contained in the days of Washington."

The reasons for the great popularity of Thomsonianism are fairly obvious. The relative simplicity of the system made a wide appeal; it linked up closely with the Indian herb practice, belief in which was deep-seated in the minds of many people. Persons who viewed with dread the mysterious prescriptions of the regulars were inclined to feel confidence in medicines with which they were familiar. The Thomsonian system offered a solution to the problem of the shortage of doctors, particularly in those regions where the population was growing more rapidly than the number of regularly trained doctors. Any one could practice Botanic medicine without previous experience or training. That it was profitable — at least to promoters — goes without saying; $20 for a book and license was much cheaper than medical school or the cost of several years of preceptorial training.

The Botanics also cashed in upon a certain prejudice, prevalent in the popular mind, against the regular doctors. Not only were the latter accused of disseminating poisonous medicines and of bleeding their patients, but of bleeding their pocket-books as well. Furthermore, the regulars promised no certain cure; the Botanics did. The latter were sure they had the "peculiar blessing of the Almighty" upon their side. Even in the treatment of cholera, which nonplused the regulars, their success was amazing. Dr. Curtis reported only one death among two hundred patients who had received Botanic treatment, and several of these had been in a state of collapse when the treatments began. It is no doubt possible, as the regulars suggested, that the Thomsonians extended their cholera diagnoses to include almost everything from hives to whooping cough. But on the other hand there was the record of a Boston doctor who had given "over 1500 courses of medicine to more than one thousand patients in almost every state and stage of disease" and but one death occurred.

More difficult to explain was the death of Horton

Howard and most of his family from cholera. The editor of the *Hamilton Intelligencer*, August 31, 1833, who claimed to have had considerable faith in the Thomsonian system, said that this was "not so good." For this statement he received two columns of hot reply and resolutions from what he called the "Friendly Botanic anti-any-thing-else-than-Lobelia-No. 6-and-Hot Brick Branch Society of Hamilton and Rossville."

Another advantage, not an exclusive privilege with Thomsonianism, however, was that the system existed "by authority"; that is, it was guaranteed by the Government, possibly by the President himself, who, it would be supposed, would recommend nothing that he had not tried on himself and believed useful for the people. Such was the power of a patent.

Certainly not least among the appeals of Thomsonianism was its democracy. As its founder pointed out, man had three great interests: religion, government, and medicine. In the past these subjects had been controlled by three classes of men: priests, lawyers, and physicians. But those days of darkness "are done away." Scriptures were translated and the people had been taught to read. In government the "common people" had discovered the secrets of democracy. Likewise, medicine, which had in a great measure been concealed behind a dead language, was now being revealed to them. Quackery was being destroyed by the knowledge of its dangers being diffused among mankind.

"The application of some dashing, unmeaning, foreign, difficult name to a simple medicine, or to a simple, common disease is calculated to strike an unlettered person speechless; and fancying that he is no more able to understand the preparation of the medicine, or the nature of the disease, than he is to comprehend its unintelligible technical name, he is readily induced to give over the study, as one beyond the reach of his intellect. The practice of encumbering the science of medicine with difficult, classic, technicals has hitherto secured to the faculty a privilege, which the Romish priests have lost; — viz: the exercising a despotic sway in controling all matters that pertained to their art. But the time has arrived when the impartial and intelligent will read and study for themselves; and the daw in borrowed feathers will be stripped of the foreign gaudy plumage with which learning had dressed her. 'Tis true, some of the faculty are as much disturbed about the reformation in medicine, as Demetrius and the craftsmen of Ephesus were at St. Paul's preaching in that city. And the cry is heard through every land, 'Great is Diana of the Faculty, whom not only the mercurial-mongers of America, but all the world worship.' "[10]

These ideas fitted in perfectly with the rampant spirit of the times sometimes labeled "Jacksonian Democracy." Many people had an innate distrust of "book larnin'," whether in their "public sarvints," their preachers, or their doctors. The "riglars," with their Latin and all, too often were thought of as being vested interests. The "call" was more important than the training. After all, wasn't every man as good as everybody else — and possibly just a little bit better? As Dr. Drake said, every quack is indeed a demagogue and relies for his success upon the same arts as his political and religious kinsmen. He convinces his followers that he is one of the *people*, whereas those who have spent their lives in acquiring the knowledge handed down by the great physicians of the past "are not of the *people*, but arrayed against the *people*, and bent on killing them off with rats bane . . . . Thus it is that the *people* allow themselves to be *charmed*, till they lose their senses, and crawl into the serpent's mouth. Would you arrest them, you thrust yourself between a snake and a fool — to be hissed into wonderment by the former, and brayed into silence by the latter."

Naturally such a good thing as Thomsonianism — financially, at least — found it difficult to maintain its integrity. Heresy breeds heresy; there threatened to be as many prophets as followers, as many "schools" of Botanic medicine as individual Botanics. Old Samuel's despotism — he was a good example of the not infrequent type which, while preaching the advantages of democracy, practices the arts of dictatorship — was resented by many of his followers, even his own sons. The ranks began to break as early as 1827, when Dr. Wooster Beach of New York organized the "Eclectic," or "Reformed," system of Botanic medicine. Another faction, headed by Horton Howard of Ohio, had in 1832 established themselves as the "Improved Botanics," but with the death of their leader in the cholera epidemic of 1833 this offshoot began to disappear. One cause of contention was the question of schools. Since Dr. Thomson thought that formal education was a handicap in the practice of his medicine — and might also cut into his sales — he was opposed to the establishing of schools. As Dr. Thomas Cooke, whose *Botanic Medical Reformer and Home Physician* (Philadelphia, 1839) was a competitor of the Thomson books, said: "We have also always expressed favorable sentiments in regard to the establishment of Reformed Botanic Schools and Colleges; but we cannot see wherein the Thomsonian system requires a College to elucidate more particularly the ideas of Dr. Thomson on Medicine. The Book has it all. Go beyond that, and Dr. Thomson himself says: 'He knoweth it not!'"

In September, 1832, Thomson issued in the first number of the *Recorder* a call for a "United States Thomsonian Convention" of delegates from the various Friendly Botanic Societies. This convention, which met at Columbus, Ohio, in December, was to exchange ideas on medicinal plants and remedial procedures, and promote the general progress of the cause. It was a combination pep-meeting, love fest, and pressure-group midwife. Between resolutions to state legislatures regarding medical legislation — the Ohio legislature a few weeks later repealed the law which restricted the practice of the Botanics and Alabama extended them equality the same year — the delegates listened to amazing written testimonials of the effectiveness of Botanic cures from those who could not attend.

The second annual convention, held in Pittsburgh, attempted to create a permanent organization. It also aspired

to found a "National Thomsonian Infirmary" at Baltimore, but this project failed to secure legislative sanction.
Nevertheless various infirmaries were established in the
eastern states, as well as one at Columbus, headed by Dr.
Alvah Curtis; shortly the *Recorder* was reporting impressive statistics of cures in these institutions. There was Peter
R. Jones, who had been "bound hand and foot nine days
literally dissected by the British surgeons," then transferred
to the Massachusetts General Hospital, where another dissection was recommended. To this he "preferred the *loss
of life*." He was cured at a Botanic infirmary by four
courses of medicine. There was also the case of "A Lady
—deplorable state of mental derangement—attended by
the *celebrated* Dr. Shattuck, and by him pronounced *beyond the reach of medical aid*, and advised that she be immediately removed to the Insane Hospital or *Mad House*,
Pepperell, Mass.—cured in one week, and married in three
months." Thousand-dollar rewards were posted for anyone
who would prove the contrary.—But back to the convention.

A "Test Resolution" was adopted which prescribed the
line for true Botanics: no practitioner was to use as medicine any animal, mineral, or vegetable poisons; bleed or
blister; or use or sell any compounds the component parts
of which were kept a secret, or any other article contrary
to the principles laid down by the founder of the system.

All this in vain. As the year 1837 approached, and with
it the expiration of Thomson's patent, the controversies
between the factions began to multiply. Already schools
for training in Botanic medicine had been opened in Georgia, Virginia, Tennessee, and Massachusetts. These naturally favored the new, or "Reformed," Botanic system in
opposition to the original Thomsonian brand. Likewise
the dissensions of Drs. Curtis, Howard, and Beach, were
becoming more open and aggressive. The formal parting
of the ways did not occur, however, until the Philadelphia
convention of 1838. Thomson was apparently aware of the
fact that matters were getting out of hand. In his annual

convention address he summarized the work of the various conventions, spoke of their difficulties, expressed his displeasure with some of its followers, then concluded: "With these considerations and with no other object than the permanent good of us all, so far as my System of Practice can contribute to that end, I ask that this Convention may be forever dissolved." The convention did not adopt this recommendation, but divided. One group, headed by Dr. Curtis, formed the "Independent Thomsonian Botanic Society," and the old guard organized itself as the "United States Thomsonian Society." Thereafter each organization, of course, regarded itself as the true society and branded the other as the heretic.

The United States Thomsonian Society held its first meeting in New York in 1840, but the attendance was small. Only the state society of Delaware expressed its loyalty to the old system. Though Dr. Thomson tried to keep the organization intact, the heyday of his power had passed. Neither he nor his sons — he died in 1843 — were able to hold the old following together. For a while after Thomson's death three main groups of Botanics were apparent: the True Thomsonians, the Physiomedicals, and the Reformed Botanics, or Eclectics. The True Thomsonians, realizing that the name of their founder no longer carried the magic of earlier years, soon dropped his name from their societies and called themselves simply Botanics. Many of their better members deserted to one of the other factions; by the time of the Civil War the Botanics, as an organization, had practically disappeared.

Meanwhile Dr. Curtis with his Independent Thomsonians had been assuming the domineering characteristics which he had so deplored in Dr. Thomson. He tried to channel his followers' beliefs into a definite system which he called Physiomedicalism. Whatever the differences between this brand of Botanic practice and the older ones, they must have existed largely in the mind of Curtis. Like Thomson, he believed heat to be "the manifestation for life, the cause of fever, and cold an effect or obstruction, the cause of diseases." His agents were "lobelia, nervine, slippery elm, cayenne, bayberry, gum, myrrh and the like, with plenty of water, of a temperature suited to the cases, properly applied and judiciously selected, as to time, quality and manner." In pointing out the merits and distinguishing features of his system, Curtis said: "it counts irritation, fever and inflammation as so many modes of *manifesting* an interruption of the free action of the vital force,— of course, *not disease, but a sanative effort.* Secondly, it never seeks to diminish the *power to produce* the symptoms, but always to remove what prevents an equilibrium of vital action, whether that obstacle be a positive substance, as in retained secretions or excretions; or a mere condition, as in cramp, tetanus, the contraction of the surface in the incipient stages of fever, etc." Emphasis was placed upon "natural medication," or cure by the exercise of physiological laws.

Dr. Curtis has been described as "very able but gushing, fussy and erratic; a host in himself, tremendously energetic, well educated, a good talker and reasoner and by nature a fighter." He was certainly one of the better educated among the Botanic leaders and advocated the use of schools in the training of Botanic physicians. In 1835, while he was still nominally a follower of Dr. Thomson, he had begun to instruct students in his own house and had followed this by an application to the General Assembly for an Act of Incorporation. Announcements for the school which appeared in the papers in the autumn of 1837 stated: "We wage an uncompromising and relentless warfare against quackery of all kinds, against every species and description of medical poisons and of direct processes for the reduction of the vital energies. The Science of Medicine, in our view, is that system of truths which indicate the means, and teach the art of aiding all the organs of the body, in their efforts to remove every obstruction to the full, free and universal action of the vital principle." Fees were $25 for five months. Prospects were considered good for a large class. "We are even informed that we shall be *honored with the presence of several M.D.'s. This is right and proper,* and will by no means offend us." Not until March, 1839, was the "Literary and Botanical-Medical Institute of Ohio" incorporated, with the powers of a university.

Its medical department was opened at Columbus the following autumn as The College of Physicians and Surgeons. In 1841 it moved to Cincinnati, where some years later it underwent certain changes in organization. The medical department became the Physiopathic College of Ohio. In 1859 the Physio-Medical Institute was organized and existed as such until it was finally suspended in 1885; its last five years, after the death of Dr. Curtis, were unimportant.

The *Thomsonian Recorder,* which in 1837 changed its name to the *Botanico-Medical Recorder,* apparently moved with Curtis and the College to Cincinnati, where he continued to edit it until 1852. In that year it became the *Physio-Medical Recorder,* which lasted until 1880. In addition to his editing Dr. Curtis wrote, among other books, *Lectures on Midwifery and Diseases Peculiar to Women and Children,* 1846; Synopsis of a Course of *Lectures on Medical Science* (as delivered at the College), 1846; and *A Fair Examination and Criticism of All the Medical Systems in Vogue,* 1855.

If by the 1830's the story of the Botanics seems to become somewhat confused, so it was. For instance, there were the Botanico-Medicals, whose origin and life history are not clear. They had neither a Thomson nor a Curtis to advertise them. In 1830 their strength was confined largely to three central-Atlantic states and Ohio. A few years later they were prominent also in Indiana. The Bloomington *Medical Investigator,* apparently intended as their organ, ran for a spell in 1847. It reported the organization of various county societies, one with more than sixty members. Their system differed from that of the other Botanics in little more than name; it embodied the usual impossible remedies garnished with a few sprigs of common sense.

By their own admission their cures constituted "the best means for the restoration of . . . health ever yet promulgated to the world."[11] Even a regular could find little fault with the profound observation that "severe suffering, colic, writhings, and crying in children generally follow a hearty meal of boiled or fried cabbage, crout or pickles."[12] At the same time, the most thorough-going Thomsonian would have had difficulty in objecting to Tincture of Lobelia, "an excellent remedy in phthisic, croup, whooping cough, bad colds and all catarrhal affectations, and is perfectly safe in its effects on all ages and conditions of persons." The method of preparation was thus: "Fill a jar with the green herb, well bruised and pressed, and for every quart which the jar will contain, add three or four pods of common red pepper; then pour on good whiskey enough to cover the herb, and let it stand for use. The longer it stands, the stronger it will become."[13] And hardly anyone, regular or otherwise, could dispute the merits of the following "simple apparatus," did he believe in the hot bath:

"Make a false cover for your tea-kettle of tin or sheet iron, pierce it with two holes, one small enough for a thumb screw, — the other large enough for the insertion of a short pipe or tube. Get a small trap of iron — make it crooked to suit the shape of the inside of the tea-kettle, have it punched in, or near the centre for the reception of the thumb screw which is intended merely to hold the cover to its place. Have two elbows made to suit the size of your pipe — say 1½ inches in diameter; then get four, five, or six tin pipes so made that they will slide into each other, — that is, have them smaller at one end than at the other, and each succeeding piece suited to the size of the preceding. This completes the apparatus, and you may sit in your chair before the fire, or lie in bed and take your bath at your pleasure. The whole apparatus costs about 75 cents."[14]

If neither this gadget nor sitting in a chair on top of a washtub filled with boiling water generated enough heat, and particularly if one were a bit jaundiced in addition, one might:

"Take a double handful of Wild-cherry tree bark — of the roots; — the same quantity of Yellow Poplar bark of the roots — or sarsaparilla roots — of the bark of the red Sumach roots — half the quantity of bitter root . . . . Boil these ingredients in two gallons of water until it is reduced to half a gallon; — pour off and strain the liquid. Then boil or simmer down to one pint — add this to one gallon of *hard cider*; — shake it well — then add two ounces of garden Madder, or Madder of the hops. Commence with half a wineglassfull three times a day, increasing the dose gradually to half a teacupful or even more in bad cases. When you have drank half — add another half gallon of cider."[15]

If, in spite of — or possibly, one might add, because of — such treatments, a violent case of insanity should develop, "I endeavor to keep up a perspiration, by all the usual means which I can apply in the case — vomiting freely, once or twice, or even four times, in twenty-four hours, . . . where there is long continued . . . fever, I keep the patient constantly under the influence of lobelia and skullcap . . . ."[16] In the absence of evidence to the contrary we may have to take the word of the Botanico-Medicals: "We tried the remedies and were relieved; 'Go thou and do likewise.' "[17]

"Eclecticism," or the "Reformed" system of Botanic medicine, is somewhat easier to identify, if not to explain. It stemmed largely from the Dr. Wooster Beach schism of 1827. At an early age Beach had become interested in medical and theological research; later he fell under the influence of a Dr. Ferris, who was much interested in botany, and Dr. Jacob Tidd of New Jersey, with whom he studied and practiced. After attending a course of lectures of the College of Physicians and Surgeons in New York while Drs. Philip W. Post, David Hosack, Valentine Mott, and other distinguished men were professors, he located in New York in 1825, but soon found himself in disagreement with the theory of practice held by the regulars. He had sought to acquire knowledge of the best medical ideas of the Indian doctors, female practitioners, and Botanics, as well as those of the regulars. When a friend to whom he was expounding his theory of combining the good features of all these into a "reformed medicine" called him an "Eclectic," the Beach system was named.

It should be noted that the term "Eclecticism," as self-applied by those of the Beach persuasion, was a narrow and specific use of a general term. Eclecticism literally means the practice of exercising choice among a number of doctrines or systems. The regular doctors generally so used the term when they applied it as a sort of epithet to all the irregular followings. Rafinesque in 1828 described eclectic physicians as those who selected and adopted in practice whatever was most beneficial, and who changed their prescriptions according to exigencies and acquired knowledge. All too frequently eclecticism meant different things to different persons.

In its narrower sense Eclecticism, organized as a movement of protest against the practices of the regular doctors, was without definite positive concepts, but gradually some specific tenets were formulated. Dr. Thomas Vaughan Morrow, one of the pioneer leaders in the movement, said: "Our College [Eclectic Medical Institute of Cincinnati] will be strictly what its name indicates — ECLECTIC — excluding all such medicines and such remedies as 'under the ordinary circumstances of their judicious use, are liable to produce evil consequences, or endanger the future health of the patient,' while we draw from any and every source all such medicines and modes of treating disease, as are found to be valuable, and at the same time, not necessarily attended with bad consequences." In the meeting of the National Eclectic Medical Association in 1852 the Eclectics pledged themselves to "maintain the utmost freedom of thought and investigation"; to use only such medication as should help Nature in effecting a recovery, the "safest, speediest and most efficient" though not exclusive method for which they believed to be a vegetable materia medica; and to exclude all "permanently depressing and disorganizing agencies . . . such as bleeding . . . and mineral poisons . . . [which] under the ordinary circumstance of their administration are liable to injure the stamina of the human constitution."

The early use of crude and bulky vegetable remedies in treatments, some so distasteful and repulsive that the sensitive patients found them beyond their powers of endurance, often served to restrict the general acceptance of Eclecticism. These various unpleasant experiences of the patients led to experimentation with more palatable modes of administering cures. The Botanics had at a comparatively early date made use of the process of concentration, but the Eclectics did not find a satisfactory substitute until the discovery in 1847 by William S. Merrell of Cincinnati of the extractive principle. After successfully experimenting upon himself with the effects of the resin of the mandrake, he submitted his results to the Eclectic Institute, where they were received with acclaim; this principle laid the foundation for the establishment of a "scientific" pharmacopoeia. A complete outline of his many observations and discoveries was first given in John King's *American Eclectic Dispensatory*, 1858. The next step in Eclectic practice was the development of a series of concentrated fluid medicines, either "Officinal Tinctures" made by dilutions of the tinctures of vegetable substances and alcohol, or "beautiful and efficient Medicinal Syrups" with dilutions of simple syrups.

Dr. Beach had early recognized the value of publicity for the furtherance of his reforms. His three-volume work, *The American Practice of Medicine* (1833), which he sent with compliments to the rulers of England, France, Prussia, Holland, Saxony, and Wurtemberg, and even to the Pope, had resulted in much publicity for him, as well as medals, decorations, and honorary fellowships in many foreign medical societies. He furthered his cause by the publication of two periodicals, the *Telescope* (New York, 1824-29) and, later, the *Ishmaelite*.

Eclectic education began in Beach's Reformed Medical Academy of New York, which he established in 1827.

Since this school lacked the legal sanction of a legislative charter, he began to look for a new location. A number of applicants to the New York school had come from the West; thus it was most natural that Beach should turn his eyes, and send his circulars advertising for a site for a reformed medical college, to this region. One of these came into the hands of Col. James Kilbourne, founder of Worthington, Ohio, who saw therein a means of salvation for the Worthington College, which, though at one time thriving, had met hard times. The Board of Trustees, at Kilbourne's request, issued Beach an invitation to use their charter and building for his proposed medical school in the West. Necessary charter amendments were made in 1829 and by the following December the Worthington Reformed Medical College was opened for students. According to a graduate of the school, its equipment included excellent chemical apparatus and an anatomy room well lighted and equipped like an amphitheater. Long announcements or advertisements were sent out to the newspapers regarding the course of study and admission requirements. Students upon entering were to become honorary members of the Reformed Medical Society of the United States. Editors who ran the notice fifty-two times were to receive free tuition certificates or $150 worth of medicines and advice from any member of the Society.

Other means of publicity were also utilized. In November, 1833, the *Ohio State Journal* published a letter written by five students of the "Reformed Medical Department of Worthington College" to President Morrow. They asked the differences between their system and others; whether the Reformed system ever used calomel or any mercury preparation, arsenic or antimony; and why they were frequently referred to as quacks and steam doctors. Morrow's three-column reply was in effect a prolonged sales talk for the Reformed system.

Dr. John J. Steele was commissioned to establish the school but, since certain of his habits seemed to conflict with the moral sense of the community, he was succeeded by Dr. Thomas Vaughan Morrow as president. In the fall and winter term of 1839 were offered: Anatomy and Physiology for $12; Chemistry and Medical Jurisprudence, $12; Theory and Practice of Medicine and Midwifery, $12; Surgery and Diseases of Women and Children, $10; Botany, Materia Medica, and Pharmacology, $10. The charge for spring and summer sessions was only $5 per ticket. There was an optional $5 dissection fee; the fee for graduation was $10. Five daily lectures were given for five months in the fall and winter term; in alternate springs a three-months' course was offered. The summer sessions were devoted to botanical field trips.

Nine years of growth and prosperity followed the opening of the school, but the lifting of cadavers from a neighboring graveyard led to the formation of an infuriated mob which wrecked Dr. Morrow's home and practically demolished the college. He then moved to Cincinnati, where in 1840 he organized the Reformed Medical School of Cincinnati "to effect a permanent and salutary form of the Healing Art in the most enlarged and liberal spirit of Medical Eclecticism." In the beginning this school, like the earlier New York establishment, operated without a charter, but as enrollment increased from a single student for the first term to thirty in 1845, the mayor and more than a thousand citizens sent a petition to the legislature. A charter was granted to this institution as the Eclectic Medical Institute of Cincinnati. The school, of course, was vigorously opposed by the regulars, one of whom was so satisfied with his professional state that he declared, "Medical science does not need, nor is it susceptible of further improvement or reform." During the first three years of existence as the Institute, enrollment was greater than in any of the schools of the regulars. Attendance for the first ten years showed a gradual growth, a reflection of the rapid increase in popular acceptance of Eclecticism. Dr. Beach lectured at the Institute only one year, 1845-46.

In keeping with the spirit of the times as well as the place, The Eclectic Institute became involved in numerous rounds of faculty bickering and wrangling. In fact, it would have been remarkable, considering the nature of Eclecticism, had this not been the case. Drawing for ideas and materials as the faculty did upon the whole field of Botanic practice as well as that of the regulars, each instructor was inclined to become a system unto himself. One can imagine the complications which might result from using Eberle's *On the Theory and Practice of Medicine,* a standby of the regulars, and at the same time including lectures on the elements of homeopathy. Besides there was the inevitable rivalry which resulted from certain of the professors' promoting and selling their own medicines.[18]

Kentucky Eclectics, noting the flounderings of the Cincinnati Institute, chartered the "American Reform Medical Institute" at Louisville in 1849 and opened it the following year. After several terms of "excellent promise," with activities which included a publication, the *Medical Era,* under Dr. Johnson M. Jordan, this school failed to develop as the Eclectic center of the West, and closed rather abruptly.

In addition to the troubles mentioned, a new problem presented itself at the Cincinnati Institute. Although the announcement for 1851 listed fees at $100 for a full course of lectures, $15 for graduation, and $5 for demonstration, the proposal of free lectures was adopted, to the Dean's notion, "in accordance with the Free-School movement." Other Eclectics, somewhat more candid, thought that such a step might compel the suspension of competing Reformed colleges and thus leave the field open to the Institute. This would be doubly beneficial; propagation of Eclectic ideas, as they of the Institute saw them, would be guaranteed, and also the resultant increased enrollment at the Institute would yield a larger income through additional extra fees, and through the sale of the professors' books — an idea which may sound vaguely familiar to present-day students. This plan for "free education" met with a storm of protest from other members of the profession, both irregular and regular, and failed to attract the anticipated increase. After a few years it was abandoned. (Some years later the Medical Department of the University of Michigan tried a similar experiment. Their hopes were even higher; through the adoption of free tuition they anticipated an annual revenue of $300,000 for the state treasury, and expected Ann Arbor to eclipse even Philadelphia as a medical center. Needless to say, this, too, failed.)

Dr. Morrow, whose ability as a practitioner and teacher of medicine was recognized by his contemporaries of even the regular school, died in 1850. Conditions in his institution did not improve with his passing. A faculty reorganization the next year failed to help much. The mild-mannered members resigned one by one, leaving only the more bellicose, who seemed about equally proficient with words and fists. Personal animosities, financial mixups, and professional jealousies resulted in one general melée, with several smaller fights on the side. When dissatisfaction with some of the new professors developed among the students, Dr. L. E. Jones in the involvement criticized Dr. Joseph Rodes Buchanan. Buchanan, who since Morrow's death had been head of the school, was not of a disposition to accept criticism. Personal charge and countercharge flew thick and fast and the trustees finally expelled Dr. Jones. Undaunted, he, with Dr. A. H. Baldridge, another former faculty member, thereupon set up a rival school, the American Medical College, which, with a faculty of eight, began instructing an "encouraging attendance" in a two-year term similar to that of the parent institution. Ironically enough, the remnants of Jones's new school were, a few years later, to join Buchanan's new school after Buchanan, in turn, had been expelled. In 1856-57 the American Medical College published the *American Medical Journal* which then merged with the *College Journal of Medical Science* published by the Eclectic College of Medicine. The journal ceased in 1859.

The main fight at the Institute revolved around Drs. C. H. Cleaveland and R. S. Newton, leaders of two opposing factions. Newton was a staunch "Eclectic Concentrations" man. When Cleaveland made fun of these remedies, Newton called him a heretic and a wolf in sheep's clothing. Newton and a colleague, Dr. Zoheth Freeman, got into a squabble with Dr. Buchanan over the way he ran the *Eclectic Medical Journal,* the publication of the school. In addition, Newton took on Dr. John King, his editorial partner in the recently issued *National Dispensatory.*

Dr. Cleaveland hoped to get control of the new Board of Trustees which was to be elected in 1856, but he was unable to purchase the controlling balance of stock held by Dr. L. E. Jones. No doubt the Institute, with the resultant sales of medicines recommended by it or its professors, was of sufficient financial importance to be worth fighting for. Lawsuits and injunctions followed, but Dr. Cleaveland was unable to oust his opponents. Remembering the other nine points of the law, he seized the building of the school and barricaded every door and window. The Newton-Freeman forces attacked and the Cleaveland army was forced to retire. But not for long, for they rallied and in a counter attack which lasted two days and two nights pistols, chisels, bludgeons, blunderbusses, and other weapons were flourished, if not used. "On the principal staircase Newton stood erect inspiring his little host like Leonidas at Thermopylae. Buchanan and Cleaveland were bravely leading the attack, but each time they were repulsed by the Spartans under Newton and Freeman. This surely was a case where doctors disagreed." The "six-pound" cannon which the defenders had planted in the hall was too much for the offense to overcome. The historic siege was ended when the mayor and police arrived. Dr. Cleaveland and his legions took up winter quarters in a separate building, which they declared to be the real Eclectic Institute. During its life of one term this school graduated twenty-one students.

In the court decision which came out of *quo warranto* proceedings Dr. Newton won. Whereupon Cleaveland, Buchanan, *et al.,* set up the Eclectic College of Medicine in the same building in which Daniel Drake twenty years earlier had started his college to fight the Medical College of Ohio. The new school had a strong faculty and offered the Eclectic Institute keen competition. Although it absorbed Dr. Jones's previously established offshoot, and embarked upon what seemed to be a successful career of its own, it rejoined the Institute in 1859.

The Institute had up to this time graduated eight hundred fifty-one students. An important part of the school had been its clinical department. The Civil War brought confusion and misfortune, but in 1862, when it seemed definitely headed for the rocks, Dr. John M. Scudder, a man of marked ability, both medical and executive, took the school in hand. He said, "Dr. Beach's shoes do not fit me and I do not know why I should wear Dr. Morrow's coat if I can get a better one." Scudder was a big enough man to rise above the usual petty wranglings and personal jealousies. Besides managing the school in a business-like way, he found time to publish the *Eclectic Practice of Medicine* in 1864, a reference-book on domestic medicine, and a few years later *The Principles of Medicine, Diseases of Children,* and several other works. In these books the organized theory of Eclectic practice was crystallized and most clearly presented. The fundamentals were not materially different from those of the regulars. For instance, Scudder believed the proposition that the action of medicines to be curative must be opposed to the processes of the diseases to be so obvious that it required no presentation of the facts in proof. Under Scudder's guidance the Eclectic Institute became the leading medical college of Cincinnati in the 1880's.

By the time of the Civil War Eclecticism had travelled far from its original parentage. While on the one hand, under the leadership of the Cincinnati Eclectic Institute, the movement had developed along lines which, if not convergent with, were at least closely parallel to those of the regular medical beliefs, on the other hand the disorganized elements had fanned out into the most heterogeneous group of practitioners of the medical world. From Eclecticism to eclecticism was but a short step. The divergent factions of the Botanics had never been able to get together. About all they had in common was their opposition to the regulars. Ordinarily none too certain of their chemistry, anatomy, or physiology, they were proud of their Botanic orthodoxy — as was the old doctor who assured the newcomer from a regular medical college that he never administered any mineral medicine whatsoever except the iron in the "cast steel" soap from which he made his pills.

Dr. Morrow, following an earlier example of Dr. Beach, had attempted to organize the various factions of Botanics, Reformed and otherwise, into a united front against the common enemy, the regulars. Early in 1841 he tried to enlist the support of all Botanics in the East and South for this union, and also for the founding of a National Reformed Medical University at some central point in the Union, but met with no success. Since much of the opposing medical legislation in the various states had, by 1845, been set aside, once again an effort to combine was made, this time by certain physicians of New York and Pennsylvania. Their cue was immediately taken up by Dr. Morrow, who opened correspondence with the cults of reformists. Meanwhile, an additional stimulus had been supplied by the creation in 1846 of their rivals' American Medical Association. The first convention of the Reformed practitioners of medicine met in Cincinnati in May, 1848, and effected a permanent organization, the American Eclectic Medical Association, which, as the National Eclectic Medical Association, continued until 1857 when internal troubles caused its dissolution.

Simultaneously an attempt was made to organize Reformed state societies. The Ohio Eclectic Medical Society was formed in 1858 and held regular meetings until the Civil War. There was also the Union Society of Clermont County and the Cincinnati Eclectic Medical Society, which became the Cincinnati Academy of Eclectic Medicine. In Indiana the Eclectic Medical Association was organized at

Indianapolis in 1857, and in the same year a society was begun in Marshall, Illinois. Most of these organizations soon went out of existence, to be revived or replaced in the new upsurge of Eclecticism in the postwar years. Organizations in Michigan and Wisconsin did not come into being until this later period. In 1870 the American Eclectic Medical Association was revived. By 1890 organizations existed in most of the states and in 1893 at the Columbian Exposition in Chicago a sort of World Congress of Eclectic Physicians and Surgeons was held. That the Eclectic or Reformed practice lasted longer than any of the groups formed after the demise of pure Thomsonianism may be directly traced to the quality and training of its leaders.

In medicine, as in politics and religion, the period of the 1840's and '50's was one of flux and transition. It is impossible to keep track of the schisms, mergings, and crossings-over. Thomsonians not only became Eclectics, Physio-Medicals, and Botanics; some joined the regulars. In the records of the regular medical schools of the period are occasional references to applicants who had previously practiced the "steam and puke" system. Others went over to the water-cure system and a number took up homeopathy. On the other hand, so severe at times was the competition of "the People's Doctors" that the regular doctors were forced to adopt their methods or lose their own practice. Far more regulars became irregulars than one would realize from reading the formal medical histories of the period. Perhaps the eclectics had the right idea after all; they were the true democrats in the field of medicine. They pretented to be familiar with all the irregular systems, and a really elastic eclectic included the regular system as well. The patient—or if he were too ill to vote, his friends or relatives—was permitted to name his own poison; the eclectic would administer it. Considering the variety of choices—since hydropathy, vitapathy, homeopathy, and other practices soon had their followings—one is forced to admit the versatility of these accommodating doctors.

MEDICAL ODDS: ANIMA TO ZOOTES

CHAPTER V

"They shall have mysteries—aye precious stuff
For knaves to thrive by—mysteries enough;
Dark tangled doctrines, dark as fraud can weave,
Which simple votaries shall on trust receive,
While craftier feign belief, till they believe."

*B*y 1840 the Middle West had developed a distinct spirit of regional self-consciousness, proud of its history, its way of life, and its prospects; resentful of outside criticism and distrustful of eastern and European ideas and products, whether in government, education, or special brands of religion. This attitude did little, however, to limit experience to the merely provincial when it came to disease and medical systems. In these matters the regional taste proved both cosmopolitan and omniverous. Whatever the West took, whether Asiatic cholera or European homeopathy, it took hard.

* * *

The system of homeopathy was formulated by young Samuel Christian Friedrich Hahnemann. His studies in the medical schools of Vienna and Leipsic, followed by

Erlangen, from which he was graduated in 1779, had not instilled in him a complete respect for the profession as it then existed. The discrepancies and contradictions within the theory and practice of medicine which he encountered after his graduation furthered these doubts. Regardless of the merits or demerits of the medical system which he established, due credit must be given him for his early advanced thoughts of reform: he insisted that drugs must be pure to be effective; he disapproved of purging and venesection; he demanded decent treatment for the insane, cleanliness in obstetrical cases, quarantine and public sanitation, preventive medicine, pure air, proper clothing, and hygiene. In these beliefs he was more than half a century ahead of his time. His, however, was merely another of those voices crying in the wilderness. Failing to get the cooperation of fellow doctors in establishing these reforms, he voluntarily retired from the profession to give his time to research.

Hahnemann's first idea of the homeopathic rule of practice is said to have occurred to him while translating Dr. Cullen's *Materia Medica* in 1790, but not until 1796 did he offer these beginnings to the public in the form of an "Essay on a New Principle." In this he advocated a partial application — that is, to some chronic diseases — of the results of his experimentation in ascertaining the effect of different medicines upon persons in good health.

Further experimentation as to the effects of a multitude of inorganic substances upon himself as well as other subjects gradually gave definite shape to a system of medicine new and somewhat remote from his earlier concept of a reformed medicine. He developed three basic tenets: 1. Diseases are curable by particular drugs which produce similar pathologic effects upon the healthy body; that is, cinchona would cure malaria because it would produce in a person not infected with the disease symptoms comparable to those exhibited by a malarial patient. 2. The dynamic effect of drugs is increased by giving them in very small doses, diluted even to a decillionth of the original

strength. 3. Chronic diseases are manifestations of a sup-
pressed "Psora," which in society not too polite might be
called simply an itch.

These were not original ideas. Paracelsus (?1490-1541)
had propounded the theory of "similia similibus curantur"
— like cures like — but had directed his attack toward the
causes of disease rather than toward the symptoms exhibited, as did Hahnemann. Even earlier, Hippocrates and
Galen had advocated the use of "Helleboris which causes
mania, to cure mania," and the alchemists had anticipated
his dilution theory by several hundred years when they set
forth their belief in the efficacy of small dosage, such as the
use of a maximum of three drops of gold or tincture of
gold to be taken in beer or wine to cure the most serious
of illnesses.[1]

By 1805, when Hahnemann published his *Medicine of
Experience,* all his earlier restrictions were abandoned, and
homeopathy was definitely launched as a system unlimited
in applicability. By means of an extensive program of
writing and lecturing, the attention of the general public
rather than that of the medical profession was focused
upon his developing theory. This program was further
popularized by the admission to his classes of students
without previous medical training. The publication in 1810
of the homeopathic bible, *Organon der Rationellen Heil-
kunde,*[2] supplemented in 1811 by *Pure Materia Medica,*
embodied the fundamentals as conceived by Hahnemann.

A distinctive technique was developed during Hahnemann's sixteen years of experimentation. Since "Every
medicine exhibits peculiar actions on the human frame,
which are not produced in exactly the same manner by
any other medicinal substance of a different kind . . . .
medicines on which depend man's life and death, disease
and health, must be thoroughly and most carefully distinguished from one another, and for this purpose tested by
careful, pure experiments on the healthy body for the purpose of ascertaining their powers and real effects, in order
to obtain an accurate knowledge of them, and to enable us

to avoid any mistake in their employment in diseases, for it is only by correct selection of them that the greatest of all earthly blessings, the health of the body and of the mind can be rapidly and permanently restored."

The substance on trial — cinchona, mercury, or any of the sixty-two others enumerated in his *Materia Medica* — was given in common or minute doses to a healthy person. Every possible sensation, each movement of mind or body exhibited by the subject within succeeding hours or days he thought was unquestionably a result of the drug administered, "even though the experimenter had observed, *a considerable time previously,* the spontaneous occurrence of similar phenomena in himself." These were carefully recorded, preferably in the exact words of the person being examined. From the records "everything that is conjectural, all that is mere assertion or imaginary should be strictly excluded; everything should be the pure language of nature carefully and honestly interrogated."

It was necessary for the examiner to have "especial circumspection, tact, knowledge of human nature, caution in conducting the inquiry and patience in an eminent degree." Furthermore, the person being examined "must during the whole time of the experiment avoid all over-exertion of mind and body, all sorts of dissipation and disturbing passions; he should have no urgent business to distract his attention; he must devote himself to careful self-observation and not be disturbed whilst so engaged; his body must be in what is for him a good state of health, and he must possess a sufficient amount of intelligence to be able to express and describe his sensations in accurate terms." He must be "a person who is a lover of truth, temperate in all respects, of delicate feelings, and who can direct the most minute attention to his sensations . . . ."

In the proving, medicines should be given to both males and females "in order also to reveal the alterations of the health they produce in the sexual sphere," and to subjects "varying in their corporeal and mental constitution." Hahnemann thought it best for subjects to assume various positions in order to determine the possibilities of the medicines; that is, whether the postural changes affected the symptoms exhibited.

After thorough and painstaking research he found that the least powerful of his dosages excited ninety-seven symptoms, a negligible number in comparison to the 1,491 effected by the most potent. Another careful researcher produced upon himself 1,349 symptoms by administering one-decillionth of a grain of salt. A child in Gloucester County, Virginia, years later, however, lacking these powers of discernment, unknown to the family, consumed at one sitting, $8 worth of medicine, the entire family supply for a year, and failed to notice any symptoms at all.

Acetate of lime, according to Hahnemann, produced in the subject, "after stooping some time, a sense of painful weight about the head upon resuming the erect posture; an itching, tickling sensation at the outer edge of the palm of the left hand, which obliges the person to scratch." Muriatic acid caused catarrah, sighing, pimples, and "after having written a long time with the back a little bent over, violent pains in the back and shoulder-blades, as if from strain; dreams which are not remembered, — disposition to mental dejection, — wakefulness before and after midnight." More than fifteen years later this procedure of observing and reporting was still being continued, as his *Treatise on Chronic Diseases,* 1828, shows: "After dinner, disposition to sleep; the patient winks"; then nine days after taking remedy: "After dinner, prostration and feeling of weakness." The remedy proposed was oyster shell.

Hahnemann finally concluded that whichever medicine was found to "contain in the symptoms observed from its use the greatest similarity to the totality of the symptoms of a given natural disease will and must be the most suitable, the most certain homeopathic remedy for the disease." He believed that the action of a single dose did not fully display itself in some cases until twenty-four or even thirty days after it had been taken; since its good effects were not exhausted until towards the fortieth or fiftieth day, it would be absurd and injurious to administer a new remedy during this period. The true homeopath never mixed his drinks.

The proper drug for use in treatment of any disease once having been ascertained, the next problem confronting the doctor would quite logically be that of determining the proper amount of the medicine to be used. Here again Hahnemann carefully evolved another principle of his system. Attenuation and dilution, according to the second homeopathic essential, were necessary to bring into play in a most effective manner the curative properties of the drug to be used: "the best dose of the properly selected remedy is always the very smallest one in one of the high potencies (x), as well for chronic as for acute diseases." To attenuate the drug, he advised that:

"A grain of the substance, if it is solid, a drop if it is liquid, is to be added to about a third part of one hundred grains of sugar of milk in an unglazed porcelain capsule which has had the polish removed from the lower part of its cavity by rubbing it with wet sand; they are to be mingled for an instant with a bone or horn spatula, and then rubbed together for six minutes; then the mass is to be scraped together from the mortar and pestle, which is to take four minutes; then to be again rubbed for six minutes. Four minutes are then to be devoted to scraping the powder into a heap, and the second third of the hundred grains of sugar of milk to be added. Then they are to be stirred an instant and rubbed six minutes,—again to be scraped together four minutes and forcibly rubbed six, once more scraped for four minutes, when the last third of the hundred grains of sugar of milk is to be added and mingled by stirring with the spatula, six minutes of forcible rubbing, four of scraping together, and six more (positively the last six) of rubbing, finish this part of the process.

"Every grain of this powder contains the hundredth of a grain of the medicinal substance mingled with the sugar of milk. If, therefore, a grain of the powder just prepared is mingled with another hundred grains of sugar of milk, and the process just described repeated, we shall have a powder of which every grain contains the hundredth of the hundredth, or the ten thousandth part of a grain of the medicinal substance. Repeat the same process with the same quantity of fresh sugar of milk, and every grain of your powder will contain the millionth of a grain of the medicinal substance. When the powder is of this strength, it is ready to employ in the further solutions and dilutions to be made use of in practice."

Once the drug had been attenuated, there remained yet, before it could be used, the triturition or dilution of it. This process was to be accomplished by combining it with a liquid, preferably alcohol. A grain of the attenuated powder was to be covered over with a hundred drops of alcohol; the container was to be slowly turned for a few minutes until the powder dissolved, then two shakes given it. Hahnemann said: "A long experience and multiplied observations upon the sick lead me within the last few years to prefer giving only two shakes to medicinal liquids, whereas I formerly used to give ten." The more the vial was shaken the more highly "potentized" the medicine became. Also the effect of the dose increased with each addition of the fluid in which it was dissolved; hence the preparer of the concoction had to exercise extreme care lest he create, unwittingly, a medicine too powerful for even the strongest of patients, not to mention his more sensitive sufferers. For experimental purpose Hahnemann once "dissolved a grain of soda in half an ounce of water mixed with alcohol in a phial, which was thereby filled two-thirds full, and shook this solution continuously for half an hour, and this fluid was in potency and energy equal to the thirtieth development of power."

The process of dilution was carried on in the same manner as that of attenuation. Each successive dilution with alcohol reduced the medicine to a hundredth part of the quantity of that which preceded it. In this way the dilution of the original millionth of a grain of medicine contained in a grain of powder could be carried successfully to the billionth, trillionth, quadrillionth, quintillionth, and very often much higher fractional divisions. Dr. Oliver Wendell Holmes once figured that if a pharmacist were to utilize a whole drop or grain of medicine, in compounding he would use enough alcohol to fill a million lakes two miles in circumference, yielding a supply for every individual of the whole human family, past and present, with more than five billion doses each. These figures were computed for only "Potency IV," or the twelfth dilution. Hahnemann later concluded that the thirtieth dilution was the most efficacious, though some substances were diluted to the "x" degree. The power of a "Potency" increased with each three dilutions. The first dilution contained 1/100th of a drop or grain of the original substance, the second 1/10,000th, and the third 1/1,000,000th or "Potency I"; hence "Potency II," after the sixth dilution would contain 1/1,000,000,000th and "Potency IV" 1/1,000,000,-000,000,000th of the medicine. One unkind critic of the dilution principle of the Hahnemann system said it was about as sensible as to expect even a German to be able to detect beer at the mouth of the River Spree after a glass had been spilled several miles upstream. Almost as thin was the recipe recommended in Indiana in 1850: hang two starved pigeons in the kitchen window so that their shadow falls into a ten-gallon pot on the stove. After the shadow has boiled ten hours over a slow fire, give to the patient one drop of the mixture in a glass of water every ten days.

Hahnemann found that one sugar globule the size of a poppy seed, soaked in the diluted medicine (about one three-hundredth of a drop), when laid upon the tongue was often a very satisfactory treatment, and "If it be necessary, in the case of a very sensitive patient, to employ the smallest possible dose and to bring about the most rapid result, one single olfaction merely will suffice." In fact, he discovered that smelling first with one nostril then the other was efficacious, even when the patient had no sense of smell. In Cincinnati years later Professor Joseph Rodes Buchanan found that symptoms and results were produced by holding the medicinal substances in the hand, carefully shielded from any direct physical contact. If in any case the patient failed to show improvement, the doctor could be fairly sure that the dose administered had not been small enough. A dosage homeopathically selected could never be so small "that it shall not be stronger than the natural disease." Since the ultimate dilution theoretically would make a deadly poison of any medicine, one wonders what would be the effect of taking none at all.

Strange substances as well as quantities were included in the Hahnemann materia medica, such as *lachryma filia,* the tears of a young girl in great grief and suffering, to be used for great grief and suffering in young girls; *flavus irides,* the yellow ray of the spectrum; extracts of three kinds of *pediculi,* or lice; extracts of all the body glands then known.

The third great tenet of homeopathy, though a result of twelve years of labor by its founder, was abandoned almost immediately, even by confirmed followers of the system. According to it, "Psora" was a miasm, or evil spirit, which pervaded the body and ultimately manifested itself on the body surface in the form of an eruption or itch. Diseases of excesses — of too much food, lack of food, severe physical impressions, and the like — were regarded as "generally only a transient explosion of the latent psora." External treatment was thus dangerous, since local symptoms were not the true source of trouble and might be cured while the psora yet existed as dangerous as ever. Even cancers, Hahnemann thought, should not be removed.

These were the fundamentals of homeopathy, a mixture of the obvious and the ludicrous. Ridiculous as were certain of its principles, it must be conceded that some of its methods were sound, such as the scientific or experimental approach. Its widespread acceptance indicated that the ailing public was eager for any system which provided an escape from the heroic treatments then in use by the regulars. If, as it was said, "the patients of the homeopaths died of the disease, and the patients of the allopaths died of the cure," things were in a bad way. Homeopathy gave an impetus to reform and improvement in the field of regular medicine.

The doctrine of homeopathy was introduced into New York in 1825 by Hans Burch Gram, a Bostonian Dane, who had adopted it while studying medicine in Copenhagen. So great was his enthusiasm for this science of littles that soon he, too, was busy gaining disciples for Hahnemann, even from among the regulars. Ferdinand L. Wilsey is credited with being, in 1826, the first convert to this theory in the United States. The effectiveness of the simple cures of the homeopaths, particularly in those cases in which the regulars had failed, loomed large in the public mind. Dr. Gram's successful treatment, by the use of a mustard-seed-sized pellet of sugar, of a patient suffering from a toe set at right angles to his foot because of a contracted tendon, was only one example of the many which were recorded. Evidently the homeopaths were regarded as a threat to the medical profession, for they were barred from membership in the county medical societies, hence deprived of the opportunity of receiving license to practice.

Meanwhile troubles and unrest in Saxony had led to the migration of a group of physicians to Northampton County, Pennsylvania. These men, influenced by books and medicines sent to one of them by a pupil of Hahnemann, and perhaps also by the homeopathic accomplishments with which they came into contact, formed the nucleus for the first of the American homeopathic schools, the Allentown Academy. This school, chartered in 1836, was organized by Dr. Constantine Hering, one of Hahnemann's ablest converts, who had returned from the University of Leipsic. Later, in 1848, Hering established the Hahnemann Medical College and Hospital at Philadelphia, with requirements for graduation practically identical with those of the older regular medical schools.

Hering added to homeopathy his own twist known as "isopathy." By this practice disease should be treated by products of the disease; that is, tapeworm heads should be given those suffering from tapeworm, gonorrheal pus to those suffering from gonorrhea. The pioneers, incidentally, had been practicing this theory via the jug long before it was given scientific formulation by doctors or economists.

It was also in 1836 that the first of many homeopathic practitioners in the Middle West, a Dr. Cope, was reported near Plymouth in Richland County, Ohio. Dr. Cope, whose treatment consisted of a single dose, repeated in two weeks in "radical" cases, was reputed to have had remarkable cures and a large practice. Soon a German doctor began practicing in Delaware County, Ohio, giving to his patients "very little pills," and in typhoid cases administering one dose, then returning at the end of a week "to see how it was working." Cincinnati's first homeopathic doctor was Dr. Wilhelm Sturm, a personal student of Hahnemann, who set up shop there in 1839. He is said to have acquired a large practice and much fame throughout the Ohio Valley. The next year one of the founders of the Allentown Academy, Dr. Joseph V. Pulte, came to Cincinnati.

The tremendous growth of homeopathy in Ohio between 1840 and 1856 may well have been largely due to the collapse of Thomsonianism. The new system took hold most strongly in those areas where Thomsonianism had been most firmly established in the decade of the 1830's— eastern Massachusetts, southern Vermont, the eastern part of the Mohawk Valley in New York, eastern Pennsylvania, north, central, and southwestern Ohio, and southern Michigan.[3] There are believers, however, who maintain that homeopathy stood on its own merits.[4]

As in the earlier case of the Thomsonians, much of the popularity of homeopathy arose as a result of its seemingly successful coping with the dread cholera which again swept over the region in epidemic proportions in 1849. Drs. Pulte and Benjamin Ehrmann, of Cincinnati, published claims for their treatment of 1,116 patients, of whom sixty to seventy were in a state of deep collapse when first reporting, with only thirty-five deaths. Whereupon Dr. Samuel A. Latta, editor of the *Methodist Expositor,* issued a special brochure, "The Pretense of Homeopathy," in which he claimed gross misrepresentation in these figures. After the homeopaths replied, a city committee carried on an investigation which vindicated them of certain of the charges, which the editor was asked to correct. During the course of the epidemic some of the practitioners were brought into court by the health board for failure to file proper reports, but were not convicted, since the board was adjudged to be illegally organized. The publicity obtained in these and subsequent attacks served to place the homeopaths before the people. Newspapers of the period were filled with the controversy, pro and con. The free dispensary for cholera victims established in Cincinnati by Edwin C. Wetherell and Dr. F. A. Davis did much to further the cause of Hahnemann in Ohio. In 1855 Dr. Pulte, now nationally known, was the leading speaker at the Buffalo meeting of the American Institute of Homeopathy, the centennial celebration of Hahnemann's birth.

To Dr. Storm Rosa, of Painesville, was given the honor of being the first homeopathic teacher in the West when in 1849 he was called to occupy a chair in the Cincinnati Eclectic Institute. So convincing was his course of two lectures that about one-third of his Eclectic students and even two faculty members, Drs. Benjamin Hill and H. P. Gatchell, were converted. At the end of the term six students received both homeopathic and Eclectic diplomas. The Eclectics, fearing further complications, abolished the chair the next year.

Among the aims of the Homeopathic Society of Cincinnati which came into existence this same year were: "to petition the General Assembly of 1849 for an act establishing a homeopathic college; to promulgate the lectures delivered by Dr. Rosa; to organize a college in Cleveland in 1850."

The last of these objectives was achieved in the autumn of 1850 when the Cleveland Homeopathic Medical College was opened, with an attendance of sixty students the first year. As with regulars and Eclectics before them, the methods of obtaining anatomical materials brought down upon them the ill will and violence of the townspeople, who almost wrecked the school. By 1852 the homeopaths were back in the good graces of the citizens, and some of the townsfolk even made contributions for the reestablishment of the school in a new location. The addition of leading doctors to the faculty, including Dr. Pulte of Cincinnati, aided in placing the school on a more solid foundation. In 1855-56 the school became the Western College of Homeopathy.

By 1851 homeopatic converts in various other centers of the state—Norwalk, Elyria, Pomeroy, Steubenville, Newark, Urbana—had become so numerous that the need was felt for a state society; a meeting accordingly was called in Columbus for the purpose of organizing one. Between 1849 and 1852 the Homeopathic Society of Cincinnati reported a membership of one thousand. One homeopathic physician, Dr. Daniel H. Beckwith, was said to have "rung more silver doorbells in Cleveland than any other doctor." Believers had been present in sufficient numbers to justify the opening in 1845 of a homeopathic pharmacy in Cincinnati and one the following year in Cleveland. In 1856 was instituted the Cleveland Homeopathic Hospital.

Among the books on homeopathy by Ohio doctors those by Dr. Pulte were outstanding. His *Homeopathic Domestic Physician*, published in 1850, and *Woman's Medical Guide*, in 1853, were well known. The former was reprinted in 1852 with anatomical plates and "Special Hydropathic directions." The *Cincinnati Journal of Homeopathy*, begun in 1851, had a brief career, as did Pulte and Gatchell's *American Magazine of Homeopathy and Hydropathy*, started the next year.

A number of homeopaths were practicing in Kentucky in the late 1830's. When in 1840 Dr. I. G. Rosenstein published his *Theory and Practice of Homeopathy*, at Louisville, he received letters of approbation from several local doctors, but he stated that "the whole *west* and *south* is still a barren field." Drawing upon the various works of Hahnemann, Rau, Torelle, and other European homeopaths, Rosenstein presented a concise and clear exposition of homeopathic theory and practice. He emphasized that medicines possessed no direct healing power in themselves. By administering a medicine which would produce in the diseased organs an "affection similar to the complaint," the complaint would temporarily be increased—"homeopathic aggravation"—but the reaction of the organs, supported by the consequent opposite secondary effect of the remedy, would remove the disease. "The original disease then yields, because it is overpowered by the artificial disease caused by the remedies: and this, on the discontinuance of the medicines, is, in turn, speedily overcome by the powers of the constitution. . . . The more violent a disease, the less is the susceptibility of the system, for heterogeneous, and the greater it is for homogeneous influences."

Guidance was given to young practitioners in the classification, diagnosis, and treatment of diseases. Symptoms affecting the patients' moral tendencies and intellectual faculties were to be heeded as well as those connected with "his organic economy." The section on "Regimen"—diet, bathing, exercise, and fresh air—contained much sound advice. "How many pains, and dollars, and disappointments, might have been saved, if patients, instead of going to *Dr. Bolus* and *Dr. Pill,* had only taken, three times a day, half an ounce of common sense with *quantum sufficient* of gymnastics." Especially were girls likely to get insufficient exercise. Exercise could even overcome the hypo. Walking, dancing, skating, and riding were recommended.

The chapter on "Drugs and their Abuses" well set forth the case against them; *pharmaco-mania* in itself might almost be classified as a disease. Rather exceptional was the author's comment on bleeding:

"*Bleeding,* impartiality constrains me to say, cannot always be dispensed with, especialy in inflammations of the lungs and heart; but in most cases we fear that nervous irritation is mistaken for inflammation, in which bleeding and purging very often destroys life."

Warning was given against the use of blisters, setons, and cauteries, especially on young children and in certain diseases. "The time is passed when a judicious practitioner can ever think of such a thing as doing any good by a prolonged suppuration." At the end of the book was a set of instructions by which patients at a distance, afflicted with chronic diseases, might communicate their cases to a homeopathic physician by letter. No cure was guaranteed.

Rosenstein's book antedated Dr. Pulte's first book by ten years. How widely it circulated is not known. Like many of the books on domestic medicine, it was not rigidly confined to one system. Whatever the difference of opinion regarding Rosenstein's facts and theories, anyone familiar with the old-fashioned country schoolroom in early spring will be inclined to agree that 1/481,000,000,000,000,-000,000th of a cubic inch of asafoetida still smells like asafoetida. It is doubtful whether even the atom-smasher can change that.

Homeopathic growth in Illinois radiated from St. Louis in the south and from Chicago in the north. The practice sprang up in the former region in the middle and late 1840's. In the northern area (present Cook County), where in 1857-59 forty per cent of all the homeopaths in the world were said to have been located, the movement owed much of its success to Dr. George Elias Shipman, reputed to have been "without doubt the ablest defender and scholar the cause of homeopathy ever had in the West." He championed the cause by publishing in his *Northwestern Journal of Homeopathia* (1848-52), October, 1850, the following letter and enclosures:

"DR. SHIPMAN:

During the session of 1849 and 1850 I attended a course of lectures at the Rush Medical College in Chicago, and was desirous of attending the ensuing course, and receiving the honors of the College, as I should have been entitled to do had none but the ordinary tests of qualification been applied to me. But wishing to have the matter fully understood previous to securing tickets for another course, I addressed the following to the Secretary of the faculty, and received the accompaning reply:

ST. CHARLES, Ill., September 12, 1850.
DR. N. S. DAVIS—
Sir: I am a homeopathist from a conviction of the truth of the principles and the efficacy of the practice of homeopathia. With these views, will you graduate me if I comply with the ordinary requisitions of the faculty?
Yours, etc.   M. DANIEL COE.

CHICAGO, September 16, 1850.
MR. DANIEL COE—
Dear Sir: I am directed to inform you that the faculty of Rush Medical College will not recommend you to the trustees for a degree so long as they have any reason to suppose that you entertain the doctrines, and intend to trifle with human life on the principles you avow in your letter. To do so otherwise would involve both parties in the grossest inconsistency,
Very respectfully yours,
N. S. DAVIS, *Secretary to the Faculty of Rush Medical College.*"

Believing in the strength of union, Dr. Shipman at a preliminary meeting in June, 1851, introduced a resolution which proposed the formation of a western homeopathic association of "Those present . . . who have conformed to the existing medical institutions of the country, or who have been engaged in the practice of medicine five years (being avowed believers in, and practitioners of the homeopathy) or who shall have passed an examination before the committee." The resolution was adopted the next day and the Western Institute of Homeopathy came into being.

One of the major desires of the Chicago homeopaths was to establish a school for the propagation of the faith. The first attempt proved abortive, for the charter of the proposed institution which was sent to the legislature in 1853 was carelessly mislaid by the representative. Failure to locate the missing document led to the formulation of a new one, in the law office, says tradition, of A. Lincoln. In January, 1855, the Hahnemann Medical College was incorporated, but no faculty was organized until five years later.

Coinciding with the efforts of the homeopaths to establish the school was the foundation of other institutions necessary for their practice. Obviously a special pharmacy for the dispensation of homeopathic dosages was an essential. The first one was established in 1844 at the office of Dr. David Sheppard Smith. Ten years later a hospital was created by popular subscription secured by Dr. Shipman after a gift of $1000 annually for its maintenance had been promised by a Mrs. H. Knight. Financial difficulties forced the suspension of the hospital in 1857. During the twenty-eight months of its existence, according to its reports, this institution set an enviable record of only nine deaths among the three hundred twenty-one patients admitted.

In 1857 began the open hostilities between the homeopaths and the regulars. Trouble arose as the result of a petition to the Common Council by leading Chicago citizens who requested use of a portion of the newly created City Hospital for the treatment of patients according to the homeopathic school of practice. The regulars objected strenuously, both to the ruling of the Council which allotted the use of one-fourth of the hospital to the homeopaths, and to the name "Allopaths"—literally "other diseases"—given to them to distinguish them from their rivals. A war of pamphlets ensued in which everyone denounced everyone else. The board took refuge in inaction, and as a consequence the City Hospital remained unprovided with furniture as well as physicians. Eventually the regulars indirectly won the struggle by obtaining a lease on the building in 1858. They established a public institution, cared for the county poor, and gave clinical demonstrations, principally to students of Rush Medical College. In 1863 the building was confiscated by the Federal Government and was used as a hospital for the treatment of eye and ear cases among soldiers.

The first homeopathic dispensary was opened in 1859; in the course of three months one hundred thirty-five patients were treated. Later its successor was placed in the general charge of the Hahnemann Medical College. There the first course of clinical lectures on homeopathy delivered in the Northwest was given.

Doubtless much of the success achieved by homeopathy in Illinois during this early period can be ascribed to its leadership. The work of Shipman has already been described. David S. Smith, a convert from the regulars, became a national figure and the "Father of Western Homeopathy." Another proselyte, John Taylor Temple, later founded the St. Louis School of Homeopathy, and was the first to perform an autopsy and give medico-legal testimony in Chicago.

Homeopathy made its appearance in Michigan with Dr. S. S. Hall, who was listed in 1843 as the first of the followers of Hahnemann in Detroit. Homeopaths were reported in various localities during the next ten years. Their sucess in the cholera epidemic of 1849 did much to increase the popularity of the movement. Although their numbers were small, their aggressiveness was unlimited. In 1851 the homeopathic doctors of the state sucessfully petitioned the legislature to repeal all restrictive legislation. Their request to have a homeopathic professor added to the faculty of the state university, however, was denied. In 1855 a motion was presented to the courts for a mandamus to compel the Board of Regents of the University of Michigan to appoint a professor of homeopathy or to show cause, but the court held that it would not issue in a case where the public good did not require it. It went further and enumerated as reasons why it would not interfere, even though it had power: there was no pressing necessity apparent, delay in appointment had not been unreasonable, and interference would be disastrous. The agitation for a professorship at the university continued for a quarter of a century; success finally came in 1875.

In spite of the lack of legal sanction, perhaps spurred to greater activity because of its absence, homeopathy gained practitioners and followers. One doctor reported in 1862 that for fifteen years his office prescriptions had averaged seven thousand annually and that he had had from thirty to forty daily professional visits. This was an exceptional case, for in pre-war Michigan homeopaths formed only a small percentage of the total number of practicing physicians.

In Indiana homeopaths offered little real competition to the regulars in the pre-Civil War period; there are only a few scattered references to early practitioners there. Dr. Samuel G. Mitchell, of Indianapolis, in 1837 became a convert to the system of similars and littles as a result of business trips to New York. "He tried to practice it here, but it was not popular at that time. People did not think they were getting enough for their money," reported a local historian. Dr. E. J. Ehrman, who came from Pennsylvania to Evansville in 1845, was the pioneer homeopath there, with an extensive following among the German settlers. After an early struggle against the existing prejudices the success of his cures had become so well known that ten years later he hired an assistant. Dr. R. G. Coe, "Homeopathic Physician and Surgeon," in the *Western Sun* of July 31, 1857, advertised "A sure specific for Chills and Fever, and all other bilious diseases, Dyspepsia cured; all diseases cured without the use of calomel, quinine, or any other poisonous drugs." Regulars treated these practitioners with contempt. Said one, "Well, whosoever employeth a homeopathic doctor and is holpen thereby hath confessed hysterics already unto condemnation." Instances of their incompetence were played up prominently by orthodox practitioners.

In the *Cincinnati Lancet and Observer,* 1858, one Fort
Wayne doctor reported the case of a patient who had lost
his eye by inflammation under homeopathic attention, and
another doctor related his experience on an emergency
obstetrical case in which the patient, after having been
informed by the homeopath in charge that birth was not
possible, was delivered of not one child but twins. Still
another regular criticized: "It is a marvelous mystery what
can be the content of those cases [chests containing homeopathic medicines] daily advertised at prices varying from
$10 to $15 each, accompanied by books of directions,
which cost from twenty-five cents to four dollars." One
packet of nostrums was even advertised for $25. He con-
tinued: "The success of homeopathic practitioners is entirely due to nervous folks, whose only ailment is laziness;
and to dyspeptic people, who suffer from wrong feeding."
The homeopaths, said he, were like the numbers of their
doses: one figure of little value followed by a perfect bat-
talion of ciphers. Still, this caustic critic credited one of
his enemies with curing a hypochondriac who imagined
himself a goose and, procuring an egg, proceeded to "set."
" 'Like cures like' . . . it takes a goose to cure a goose!
He ordered a pair of feather breeches to be worn by the
patient and a dozen eggs. The spell and the eggs were
broken together, and the patient was himself again. Very
eggstraordinary, was it not?"

A Wisconsin doctor said of homeopathy, "He who
actually believes it, is an ignoramus. He who does not
believe it and practices it is dishonest." Another regular
charged: They "amuse their patients with inert doses of
medicines; they depend wholly upon rest or exercise as
the case may be, dietary restrictions, and upon the natural
resources of the system." Perhaps this was not as devastat-
ing as it was intended. The "therapeutic nihilism" of the
homeopaths did its part in forcing drugs to prove themselves.

* * *

One of the rivals of homeopathy for public favor was

hydropathy. Although hydropathy did not attack the West with such virulence as it hit in the East, nevertheless, it became prevalent in scattered localities. In England in the early 1700's had appeared a book on *Psychrolousia, or the History of Cold Bathing, both Ancient and Modern;* in Silesia in 1738 J. S. Hahn published *The Healing Virtues of Cold Water.* It was a Silesian peasant, Vincent Priesnitz, who, having cured his broken ribs by cold water treatment, about 1829 originated the modern hydropathic, or water-cure system, which in the 1840's spread to England and the United States. Hydropathy was known in America much earlier, however, as is witnessed by the publication at Philadelphia in 1723 of the American edition of John Smith's *The Curiosities of Common Water,* followed two years later by *The Curiosities of Common Water: or the Advantages thereof in Preventing Cholera.*

Hydropathy was popularized in the United States largely through the efforts of Dr. Joel Shew, who in his establishment in New York City developed a distinctive technique for treatment. Water, he found, was an extremely versatile and potent substance. It could be given as treatment orally for hiccups, toothache, skin eruptions, palpitation of the heart, and fatigue. Swallowing ice lumps was excellent in cases of gastric haemorrhage. His patients were cautioned against drinking water unthinkingly, lest dangerous results occur. The use of this liquid as an enema was highly recommended.

Water functioned best as a healing agent when it was administered gradually through the skin, by the process known as "transudation." Although there were different ways of effecting such a treatment, the use of the wet sheet was the generally approved technique. A sheet of cotton or linen, dipped in cold water, was spread on several thick woolen blankets. An attendant first wound the sheet around the patient, then the blankets, and secured all with large pins and tapes. Over the whole was thrown a fat feather bed. The patient remained in his cocoon from twenty-five minutes to several hours, depending upon the seriousness of his condition. The wet sheet was useful for reducing all fevers, for toning up the body generally, and for whitening the skin of the ladies. For patients to whom such a treatment was impracticable or impossible, the wet dress, a gown with extra wide sleeves, was suggested, though the excellent results obtained from the wet sheet could not be guaranteed in such circumstances. Patients in either case were warned against drinking water.

Almost all persons using the water cure resorted to the water girdle. This was made of toweling three yards long, soaked every three hours in cold water, and worn for varying periods during the day. In extreme cases, it was kept on for twenty-four hours continuously. The weak-lunged patients wore wet jackets above their girdles, and for local infections and inflammations the compress, in addition, was found to be helpful.

Then there were the baths. The shower was the most powerful and not generally advised. Even the milder douche was to be used with greatest caution, and the patient should keep in a crouching position throughout, for water falling on the head could be extremely dangerous. The head-bath was found excellent for treatment of deafness, loss of taste or smell, delirium tremens, and inflammation of the brain. Prolonged insanity was best treated by the plunge or cold-air bath. The most popular was the sitz bath, which employed water just deep enough to cover the abdomen. Only the part of the patient actually immersed was bare; otherwise he was clothed. With his head, trunk, arms, and legs at strange angles, the patient stayed in the sitz from twenty to thirty minutes, or as long as his acrobatic talents permitted.

The baths were at first given out-of-doors in natural streams of running water, cascades, and waterfalls, but soon Dr. Shew set up inside rooms and vessels which simulated these conditions. There were other varieties of baths: the towel bath (this, Dr. Shew thought, was the neatest of all, as the skillful wielder of the towel could bathe completely from a single quart of water without doing any damage to the carpet); the dripping sheet with which one or more attendants scrubbed the victim vigorously for five minutes; the sponge; and the bath by affusion.

Truly much water had flowed since earlier years when the bath tub had been opposed by ministers, doctors, and good Americans as being immoral, dangerous hygienically, and foreign and un-American.

Water curists over the country were kept up to date on the latest treatment by means of various journals: Dr. Shew's *Water Cure Journal and Herald of Reform* and his *Water Cure Manual,* which he reedited and reissued every year; Mrs. Shew's *Water Cure for Ladies;* hydropathic cook books, and similar publications.

The West had no elaborate and luxurious sylvan bathing centers. In 1849 Dr. H. T. Seeley established a water cure hospital in Grand Rapids, Michigan, where he catered to a number of clients; another was opened at Centerville, Indiana, "the first in the State." Later several were organized in Ohio—combination community settlements, rest havens, and modern bath sanitoria. At Columbus in 1857 W. Shepard, M. D., advertised a "Water Cure and Infirmary for Ladies Exclusively. . . . The subscriber continues to treat at his Institution, near Columbus, Ohio, invalid females exclusively. Such as are confined to the bed will be taken, and no pay called for unless and until they are enabled to walk, go up and down stairs, and wait upon themselves with care and safety. Open at all seasons. . . ."

Although hydropathy was supposed to be a bit complicated for home practice, the prosaic fact seems to be that most natives continued to get their treatments there, or in the nearby "crick." Some regular doctors who added the wet-sheet technique, especially in the treatment of fevers, and others who emphasized the importance of cleanliness in the handling of their cases were accused of being hydropathists. The whole subject lent itself to facetious treatment, and the newspapers had a lot of fun with it. Many of the hydropathists of the Ohio-Michigan region gradually took up Grahamism and amalgamated their system with it.

Dr. Sylvester Graham, a temperance lecturer in the East in 1830, began to observe that intemperance was not confined to the use of liquid nourishment. By 1835 he had made the startling discovery that whereas alcoholism was causing the death of only fifty thousand people annually, folly in dress brought destruction to eighty thousand, and downright gluttony doomed one hundred thousand. To counteract these existing evils he advocated a hygiene cult, based on the belief that if the doctors were unable to find a way for the salvation of mankind it was high time the laity was doing something about it. This redemption was to be brought about by vegetarianism, the use of whole wheat products, Graham bread and crackers, bathing, fresh air, sunlight, dress reform, sex hygiene, and exercise. In order that man be made aware of these means at his disposal Dr. Graham held lectures, at some of which he had more than two thousand people in attendance. He wrote and sponsored books, pamphlets, health papers, Ladies' Physiological Reform Societies, and Men's Graham boarding houses which catered to his followers by providing Graham bread and three baths per week. His lectures, plus many pages of testimonials, were published in Boston in 1839 as *Lectures on the Science of Human Health*. Undoubtedly this movement contributed much toward the development of health and physical education. Although it centered in the East (Boston and New York), it attracted much attention in western papers. Even though it resulted in no important midwestern medical cult, many doctors in time advocated its principles. There is no evidence that the proposal of some of the New England extremists in 1832, to found a "Society for the Suppression of Eating," received any considerable backing in the West.

* * *

Though phrenology can hardly be classified as a system of medicine—perhaps it was a disease—it did get involved with medical practice. The hypothesis that traits of character can be determined by the configuration of the skull was first set forth by the Austrians John Gaspar Spurzheim and François Joseph Gall. These men were expelled from Vienna in 1802 by order of the Austrian government, after their teachings had been adjudged dangerous to religion and morality. For five years they did well in Berlin, then went to Paris, which they liked so well that they sought to settle there. Napoleon referred their request to the French Institute, which reported adversely, and the "Doctors" were sent on their travels. London, Edinburgh, and Dublin, having read the report, offered a poor welcome, so the travellers returned to Berlin. The Bourbon restoration made them again acceptable for a time in Paris; here Gall died in 1827 in comparative obscurity. Spurzheim was given a new lease on life by an invitation to visit the United States.

Ten years before Spurzheim's arrival phrenology had been brought straight to the Middle West by Dr. Charles Caldwell of Transylvania's Medical Department, who in 1821 had gone to Europe with $10,000 to buy books and equipment for the school. In Europe he had taken up phrenology and upon his return began promoting it from Lexington, Louisville, and Cincinnati. At one of his lectures, according to Dr. Samuel Gross, he said, "There are only three great heads in the United States, one is that of Daniel Webster, another that of Henry Clay, and the last," pointing to his own, "modesty prevents me from mentioning." In December, 1822, the Lexington *Kentucky Reporter* advertised a lecture by Professor Rafinesque: "A discourse by request on Phraenology, Craniology and the Analysis of the Human Mind, on this evening at 7 o'clock in the Medical Room. Admission Fifty Cents. Tickets may be had of Mr. McNitt, at the lecture room and at Mr. Deveins." The same year Cincinnati papers carried notices of lectures by "Dr. Cranium." Soon the newspapers were splattered with advertisements, testimonials, and notices of meetings. Caldwell, "The Zealous Phrenologist of

America" and "The American Spurzheim," published his
Elements of Phrenology at Lexington in 1824; a second
edition appeared in 1827. Many people agreed with Sir
Charles Bell, the distinguished Edinburgh anatomist, that
phrenology was "The most extravagant departure from all
legitimate modes of reasoning . . . ever encountered."
But Caldwell rose to its defense against all criticism.[5]

In 1839, at Springfield, Illinois, and elsewhere, a Doctor
Sewall advertised his lectures with a column of testimonials
from such men as Daniel Webster, John McLean, John
Sergeant, and John Quincy Adams. Adams's testimonial
was something of a boomerang to the phrenologist; he
classified phrenology with alchemy, judicial astrology, and
augury. Like Cicero, he could not understand how two
augurs could meet and look each other in the face without
laughing.

The average citizen probably got most of his phrenology by way of the almanacs, which often—in addition to
signs of the zodiac, sundry household hints, and remedies
—contained the phrenological chart with full explanation,
as well as busts of some of the famous followers of the
"science."

Phrenology in the United States received a big impetus
with Spurzheim's arrival in 1832. Yale received him with
open arms and put him on the commencement program.
There he dissected the brain of a child and felt the bumps
of distinguished alumni, faculty, criminals, and lunatics—
at all times being able to tell which was which. This
remarkable feat won him the friendship and following
of Governor Trumbull and President Day, as well as the
support of Benjamin Silliman, the eminent scientist. At
Harvard he performed before Phi Beta Kappas, and began
a course of lectures for the Medical faculty. Only the State
House was large enough to accommodate his popular lectures. This beautiful start was cut short by Spurzheim's
death; having survived the cholera, he died from a gastro-
nomic upset. Refusing to be cheated out of their find,
Harvard removed the heart and brain of "the Prophet"

to have and to hold. They also kept the skull. The rest of Spurzheim went to the cemetery, escorted by presidents, deans, ministers, and citizens.

Princeton, somewhat piqued at having failed to get in on the premier, looked up Spurzheim's record and found it wanting. Besides being something of a fraud, he was not straight on the hereafter. These findings were duly reported in the *North American*. Much fun was had at an Amherst debate where Henry Ward Beecher first demolished, then defended phrenology. When his friend Orson Squire Fowler found that Beecher's bumps of Power of Thought, Eloquence, Splendor of Diction, and Benevolence were far more impressive than those on any of the charts, the boys were converted. Beecher went into the ministry, where he never ceased to pay his respects to phrenology, and Fowler and his brother went on a phrenological tour of New England and New York. Lectures, demonstrations, and private consultations taught the art to any and all who had the price. Parents could feel the bumps of Destructiveness and Combativeness on their children's heads and prepare accordingly. Old maids were told how to make themselves attractive to men, and housewives how to select good servants. Readings of the crania of the students of Mrs. Willard's Female Academy at Troy and of the Siamese twins at New York were good publicity, but it was the inspiration of the Fowler brothers to visit Washington and read the heads of the truly great that made phrenology a national fad.

Soon Phrenological Cabinets were set up in Philadelphia and New York; Boston stayed in the race by virtue of Spurzheim's pickled brain and the phrenological charts of Dr. Samuel Howe. "Professors" were instructing and entertaining the people from one end of the country to the other. Best known of these was the Scotsman George Combe, who spent two years, 1838-40, lecturing in the eastern cities. He came West only to see Dr. Caldwell and William Henry Harrison, but his lectures were followed by western papers. His two-volume report on his travels, *Notes on the United States of North America During a Phrenological Visit,* is better known for its description of the country than for its phrenological data.

For twenty years phrenology flourished. Serious followers expanded its possibilities to the control of personality —even crime might be eliminated when the science was mastered—but the general populace was not entirely convinced. In 1849 "A Skeptic" was advising, "Go everyone and get your heads examined."[6] Many did.

The story of mesmerism, or animal magnetism, is somewhat more exciting as well as complicated. Anton Mesmer had been banned from Vienna earlier than Spurzheim, had found refuge in Germany, and had then gone to Paris, where his seances and researches in high circles aroused considerable interest. Benjamin Franklin concurred with French scientists when they reported that mesmerism was a fraud. This did not bring about the demise of the new art, however, for many famous Frenchmen, including Lafayette and Charles X, kept in active touch with it.

Mesmerism came to the United States in installments. Charles Poyen, a Martinique Frenchman, cooperating with John Greenleaf Whittier in New England in the mid-1830's, found that he had something in his system more exciting than an essay against slavery. He claimed to have been cured of a lung affliction by magnetic treatment when a medical student in Paris. After a few years of hobnobbing with New England prominents, he became both a "Marquis" and a "Doctor"; numbered among his friends, patrons, and supporters were John Neal, Silas Wright, and President Francis Wayland of Brown University. Even Col. William L. Stone, of the New York *Commercial Advertiser,* whose crusade against mesmerism had supplanted his *exposé* of monastic derelictions in Montreal, became a convert. His brother-in-law, President Wayland, and the faculty of Brown pronounced mesmerism a more important science than phrenology. When Mrs. Cora Ogden Mowatt, "Nineteenth Century Glamour Girl," began converting hundreds by her beauty and demonstrations, mesmerism was well on its road to crowding out phrenology.[7]

In the popular mind phrenology, mesmerism or animal magnetism, faith-healing, and the galvanism of Mr. Samuel F. B. Morse were all confused. Western newspapers in the 1840's were filled with strange goings-on. "Professors" made the legs of dead frogs jump, communicated with persons in adjoining rooms, "read minds," and put people into trances in which they sometimes remembered seeing things which they had never seen before. Dr. Phineas Parkhurst Quimby, who in New England was treating his patients by trance therapeutics, had his imitators in the West. Quimby discovered that there was present in man a "higher power" or principle of which man himself was only a medium. Disease itself, according to Quimby, was only an erroneous belief. If one would just think himself in perfect health, he would be in perfect health. On the one hand Quimby's ideas furnished the basis for one of America's most important inventions in religion, and on the other supplied material for the quacks and eclectics in the borderline field between medicine and psychology.

As with other oddities, mesmerism, which appealed particularly to mystics and those with leanings toward the supernatural, contained a quantum of validity. It employed the power of suggestion and stimulated the development of hypnosis, both of which play a part in modern medicine. On the other hand it offered a perfect opportunity for the Cagliostros and Perkinses, with their seances and metallic tractors, to bedizen the public. Perhaps the fun offered outweighed any possibilities of damage. In 1837, when the Columbus Theatre ended its program with the laughable farce "Animal Magnetism," a good time was had by all.

It remained for Joseph Rodes Buchanan, energetic and original son of Kentucky, to tie together phrenology, animal magnetism, and medicine, into an incoherent system, which at one time or another he labeled neurology, anthropology, and therapeutic sarcognomy.

Buchanan's father was a professor of medicine at Transylvania. At the age of six, according to his biographer, young Buchanan began studying geometry, astronomy, history, and French; at eleven he took on sociology; a year later he started the study of law. For a while after the death of his father he was a printer and teacher, but when his health failed, he began the study of medicine at the University of Louisville, from which he was graduated in 1842. The same year appeared his pamphlet of one hundred twenty pages, entitled *Sketches of Buchanan's Discoveries in Neurology*.

From 1846 to 1856 Buchanan was one of the main spirits in the Cincinnati Eclectic Institute, where he held the chair of the Institutes of Medicine and Medical Jurisprudence and, for one year, 1848, was president of the National Eclectic Medical Association. During the Civil War he manufactured salt in Syracuse; from 1867 to 1881 he was professor of physiology in the Eclectic Medical College of New York. He later opened the American University in Boston, founded the Buchanan Anthropological Society, and edited *Buchanan's Journal of Man*. He finally moved to California, where he died in 1899.

Although Buchanan published *Outlines of Lectures on the Neurological System of Anthropology* (Cincinnati, 1854) and *Therapeutic Sarcognomy* (Boston, 1884),[8] the essentials of his system were outlined in the pamphlet published in the year he was graduated from medical school. Few medical students have figured so prominently in national discussion at the beginning of their careers. Eastern newspapers such as the *Newark Daily Advertiser, New York Watchman,* and Washington *Globe,* as well as Boston, Philadelphia, Cincinnati, and Louisville papers, carried letters, editorials, and news accounts. Buchanan stated that in a few minutes he had ascertained more nearly the true physiology than had hithertofore been acquired by all the labors of all the physiologists and pathologists who had ever worked on the subject. While the ink of this statement was yet wet, he contemplated it; though he viewed it with strangeness, he still believed it to be but "a naked statement of a *portion* of the facts."

Buchanan accepted the phrenological doctrine that every part of the brain maintained a particular relation to the body, that every portion of the body had a specific relation to the brain, and that through the brain all phenomena of life are modified and controlled. But whereas Spurzheim and Gall failed definitely to locate the bumps of the external senses, Buchanan provided all these, and demonstrated ninety-one distinct functions. Early in his experiments he discovered a means by which he was able in some instances to control both the minds and bodies of his patients. By manual manipulation or the use of "a galvanic or galvanoid fluid" he perfected the technique of exciting at will any portion of the brain and consequently any organ of the body.

"Thus I make my subjects alternately laugh and weep; reason profoundly of moral truths, and then, without any reason, draw the fist to strike; express the deepest humility, or self-sufficiency and levity; sit for hours with the greatest patience, or leap up with passionate restlessness; express the finest moral sentiments, or assume the manners and feelings of the miser and thief; indulge in eating, and drink strong liquor, or assume a moral dignity, despise sensuality and speak of food with loathing; feel the most exalted moral and religious sentiments, or indulge in levity with an inclination to be vulgar; concentrate the thoughts, by an irresistible impulse, upon some objects before them, or scatter them in utter confusion and wandering; extend their reminiscence back to their earliest days, reviving the memory of almost forgotten circumstances of infantile life, or recall them to the present, and reach on to the future, without the power of looking back to the past; reason, moralize, inquire, or feel an utter vacuity of intellect, and show an almost idiotic expression of countenance; rise with a stern, piercing eye, in the attitude of angry defiance, loll in the most indolent good nature, or sink under an oppressive humility, with eyes continually downcast obey with reverence every request that I may make, or become impatient, contradictory, and indignant, without any reason which did not exist during their humility; display a monomania of calculation, their whole attention being engrossed in calculating every thing which can be counted—the number of their steps, the stripes of the carpet, the keys of the piano, or whatever attracts their attention; and, when the influence is changed, suddenly suspend their counting and refuse to proceed, however they may be entreated."

Among the specific therapeutic effects produced were lengthening and shortening the range of vision, including restoration of partial vision to a person six years totally blind; inducement of drowsiness and sleep; relief of partial deafness; increase of sense of touch in either hand; increase of the electricity of the system, "causing the fingers and toes to stand apart like the filaments of a feather"; stimulation of the sense of smell in both nostrils or singly; cure of all cases of toothache; increase of muscular strength, or great debility and clumsiness; modifications of the circulation; relief of dyspeptic pains in twenty minutes; urination "produced sometimes in three—sometimes in fifteen minutes"; relief of mental dullness; and "general invigoration and reanimation of the constitution."

Since "phrenology" signified merely the science of the mind, Buchanan had to find a better name for his revolutionary system. As "anthropology" was sufficently comprehensive, but not sufficiently specific, and "cerebrology," though sufficiently specific, was not sufficiently comprehensive, he therefore lighted on "neurology" as sufficiently both. Among the fourteen general laws of neurology which followed from the basic principle that the brain governs every corporeal function were the following:

"The functions of the brain are indefinitely subdivisible, and are arranged harmoniously in accordance with the laws of the 'sympathy of contiguity' and the laws of antagonism.

"The various sympathies of the viscera, and the various concentrations of morbid phenomena in disease, may be explained by the positions and sympathies of the various cerebral organs. Physiological sympathy is chiefly the effect of the contiguity and the antagonism of cerebral organs.

"The nervous or cerebral influence, or fluid, is radiated from the brain to the pathognomic lines of the organs and is also efficiently conducted by the human hand. To demonstrate the independent existence and transmissibility of a nervous fluid, establishes an important point in Physiology. I have often performed a very simple experiment, by which it may be clearly established. By taking hold of a metallic rod, (knife, pair of scissors, poker, or whatever happens to be convenient.) we may transmit the nervous fluid through this conducting medium, and produce striking effects upon the person who holds it by the other extremity. The subject should be of an impressible constitution, and should keep the arms relaxed, while the operator grasps the rod firmly, making some muscular exertion. In a few minutes, something like an electric aura is felt, passing up the arm, and it becomes gradually benumbed from the hand to the shoulder. If continued, the influence is diffused over the whole system. I have mentioned this experiment to others, who have repeatedly performed it with entire success.

"This influence is susceptible of being transmitted from one person to another of the proper susceptibility; and in some cases the action of all the intellectual and affective organs may be thus transmitted, reproducing in the subject, the sensations, emotions, and thoughts of the operator. This transmission may be made either through the hand, or by direct radiation from the head.

"The phenomena of Animal Magnetism, are nothing more than peculiar displays of the cerebral functions, and of the laws of the nervous fluid which are established by Neurology."

The medical profession, thought Buchanan, stuck too rigidly to mere material and chemical forces, to the neglect of the psychic. "Alas, if the whole tale could be told of the destruction of health and life by false and narrow medical theories, it would rival the horrors of war." Therapeutic Sarcognomy, "a knowledge of the flesh . . . of the physiological and psychological parts which belong to each part of the body in health, in excitement and in disease, . . . an understanding of the correlation of soul, brain and body" covered all. Life is a Spiritual Power; all Life comes from INFLUX; food, a lower influx, is subordinate to the higher influx of the Spirit. Love and Life are correlative. Health in a negative sense is freedom from injurious and disturbing influence; positively it means the preponderance of the vital, which resists injuries, over Sensibility and Excitability, which succumb. The seat of health or normal perfection lies at the shoulder blades, or "posterior region of the chest." On a clear night it should be protected against the planetary interspaces with which it is constantly exchanging radiation.

Since therapeutic operation on body, brain, and soul was not simple, elaborate charts and definite instructions were provided. "Refreshing dispersive passes" with the hands could do much to keep the patient under the influence of the upper zone of the body and brain—sometimes even restore harmony between discordant husbands and wives.

"If the patient has any selfish, morose or gloomy qualities, or is lacking in the enjoyment of kindly emotions and elevated views of duty, the hands should be applied on the upper surface of the shoulder and the chest as far down as the nipple, the effect of which will be soothing and pleasant as well as beneficial to his moral nature, and will assist in the restoration of health. This is the remedy for bad temper, selfishness, gloom, and domestic discord.

"If the patient is nervous, restless or melancholic, one hand may be placed in the armpit at the region of Cheerfulness, while the other is on Health, or both may be applied at Cheerfulness."

Or a battery and current might be used, with one pole placed on the site of Health and the other at the spot needing stimulus. Medicine even could be used by soaking it in a sponge, applying the sponge, and sending the current through it. Decision as to the respective merits of the Buchanan and Doc Carter cures for hypo are left to the reader.

But all this was merely the lower form of treatment; electricity itself was only an adjunct. The higher treatment lay in the nervauric and psychic power, through which in many cases the operator could affect the patient with therapeutic influences, independent of physical contact. "To what extent the mere presence of the healer may be a substitute for all other healing agencies depends upon his personal endowments." He would have to enter the sick room in a state of glowing health, never in a state of hunger, fatigue, or depression; otherwise he would absorb the malaria of the sick chamber and the nervauric emanations of the patient, and lose power. Ozone would destroy the malaria of human transpiration and a "congenial stimulant" would exalt his powers. Linen clothing should not be worn: it was too good a conductor; silk and wool better conserved the nervaura of the healer; best of all was a silk cap.

Ordinarily patients were more impressionable when lying down. Sex, habits, education, and cranial development were also influencing factors. "The most perfect and interesting exhibitions of Impressibility occur among the most lovely and charming people"; those in love responded particularly well. But those with proud, heroic, and combative elements of character were antagonistic to impressibility and tended to destroy it. "To pour forth hope, joy, love or zeal to cold unresponsive souls is an exhausting experiment, and to sit sympathetically in company with them produces more depression in ourselves than exaltation in them." The refining influences of nervauric practice should not be wasted on coarse, immovable temperaments; such creatures should be willingly abandoned to the heroic treatment of cathartics, emetics, stimulants, narcotics, epipastics, and sudorifics.

Dr. Carter had his hypo, Dr. Thomson his lobelia inflata, the homeopaths their decillionth parts, and the regulars their calomel. Dr. Buchanan had the organ of Sensibility; of all the bumps it was his favorite. From it developed his doctrine of Impressibility and around it to a large degree centered his nervauric system. This organ, discovered while he was still a medical student, lies between the eye and the upper ear in the region of the temple. Here Sensibility, Impressibility, and Somnolence came together. The lower part governed sensations of heat, cold, dryness, light, and sound; in the upper portion centered Modesty and Ideality. A few passes of the hand on this spot, or on the region between the sternum and the umbilicus, and a "thorough Sensitive" would in a few minutes be brought into a somniloquent trance and behave sympathetically under the influence of the operator's constitution.

In this state the subject was in such rapport with the operator that he served as a delicate recording instrument of the psychic and nervauric emanations. *"Since each vital function of the body is expressed at the surface,* and . . . for every function there is an external locality at which it may be reached," the subject might be made to register everything indicated on the chart. If he touched the mirth bump of the operator, provided it were well developed, he would laugh uproariously; if it were subnormal he would merely giggle. By touching the proper spots he would become brave or cringing, amative or combative, cautious or impetuous, cheerful or morose, calculating or reverent. By keeping in contact with the health locality of a healthy person he would absorb energy; if he felt the disease spot of a sick person he would register pain and illness. It might be inferred from the chart, that if he lightly spanked anyone he would become both hostile and violent.

Really good subjects could serve as psychometers on others than the operator, on perfect strangers even. The thoughts, characters, propensities, and talents of anyone could thus be analyzed and measured. Nor need the person under examination even be present: from the handwriting the sensitive subject could detect the delicate nervauric impulses of the writer. Or from a corpse, since death did not destroy the nervaura, he could reconstruct the "facts of history and biography never before obtainable, or even dreamed of."

The possibilities of this technique were limitless. Not only did Buchanan anticipate lie detectors and the aptitude tests of vocational psychologists, but the processes of the "new type" biographers and historians as well. No longer necessary would be such tedious and dry impedimenta as documents. In the field of diagnosis any subject could discover, if not cure, any disease. Best of all, almost anyone could learn to practice this useful art. In fairness to amateur operators one caution was issued. The operator should be careful not to get too familiar nervaurically with a subject whose nervaura was tougher than his own; personalities might become amalgamated to such an extent that unscrambling them would be impossible.

Since Buchanan's system explained the exact source of all the functions of the mind, it followed that "we are enabled to control these functions for every purpose that may be desired, and to act upon mind and body as we please . . . ." It had immense power "for *hygienic and medicinal purposes*—for the *treatment of Insanity*—for the purposes of *Education*—for promoting the *general social happiness*, by a due regulation of the passions—for the *reformation of criminals*, and for the *philosophical re-organization of the science of medicine.*"

Psychometry alone "will guide mankind hereafter into more profound science and philosophy than has ever before been conceived—carrying us into all the mysteries of physiology, pneumatology, paleontology, astronomy, geology and antiquity." The only limitation he put on its possibilities was that in northern climates only a portion of the people were subject to nervauric influences.

"The number is far greater in proportion to the mildness and warmth of the climate, the refinement of character, the cultivation of the gentler emotions, and the effeminacy of the mode of life. In many cases, however, we find the impressibility so moderate as to render it more tedious, expensive and laborious to treat diseases in this manner than by medicines, and unless some measures are adopted to increase the impressibility, there would not be sufficient encouragement to induce one to persevere in manual treatment."[9]

Buchanan thought to carry beyond Psychometry and Sarcognomy, and explain anthropology through its mathematical key Pathognomy, "the law of linear direction *which governs all life in all worlds.*" His chapters on "Cerebral Harmonies, or Laws of Co-operation" and "Mathematical Relations of Man to Man" in his *System of Anthropology* set forth the laws of antagonism, cooperation, and contiguity, with diagrams. The pathognomic lines of the organs which would interfere, clash, and produce antagonism when two heads faced each other, would run parallel, coincide, and produce sympathy when they faced the same direction. One gathers that if all persons faced the same direction at all times, their relations would ever be pleasant. So with nations, with planets even. Had Buchanan given science a whole volume on this subject, as he promised to do in his *Therapeutic Sarcognomy,* it is possible the world might have been spared much trouble. Dr. Buchanan rightly predicted that he would not live to see the triumph of his contribution, to see it revolutionize medicine and life. This failure would be due in part to the "engrossment of ambitious minds in their immediate environment" and "to our systems of education, which utterly fail to develop invention, originality, and power of independent reasoning."

Though Buchanan's ratiocinations resulted in the foundation of no new school of medicine, they radiated "nervauric" influences in infinite ramifications. Before dismissing his theory of nervauric influences too lightly, it might be well for one to read some of the investigations of recent scientists in the field of telepathy, clairvoyance, and measurement of electrical brain waves, or to compare it with the ideas of Dr. Alexis Carrell (*Man the Unknown*).[10]

Buchanan's curious mind ranged over a wide field from Anima, the spirit of life, to "zootes" of the dubious realm. Few things escaped it. One chapter in his *System of Anthropology*, for instance, dealt with "Bletonism," or Water Witching. As he said, the subject had been neglected by the scientific. Although this chapter contained a number of demonstrable errors—"it is very easy . . . to change its [the divining rod's] direction by the unconscious movement of the hand of the holder" (certainly not true when the V-switch ends are held in pliers, or when the switch actually twists off above the grip)—it at least offered an attempted explanation, which is very rare in the voluminous literature on this subject. He also correctly observed that far more persons are "sensitive" in this respect than is currently thought. To anyone familiar with this subject, apparently no more understood by the scientist than by the ignorant, Dr. Buchanan's theory, "The whole cause therefore, of the facts and phenomena must be found in the constitution, capacities and peculiarities of the individual," appears as good as any. Perhaps some people may be able to get the influence of a medicine by merely holding a bottle in the hand. Peculiar as it may seem, he apparently made no effort to find out whether he was a "sensitive," or "witch," with the divining rod.

Other possibilities of the Buchanan system are left to the imagination of the reader. Perhaps the first impression of the *Louisville Journal* of December 1, 1841, gives a fair evaluation:

"What a feast of wonders should we have to spread before old Cotton Mather, of Witchcraft memory, could he, at this day, revisit this breathing world. He would, it is true, miss his witches, his phantom-ships, his ghosts, and hobgoblins; but still, we think, he would be at no loss for materials for another volume of his 'Magnalia'. At least if he would happen along this way about these times, Dr. Buchanan could show him some things which would throw almost any chapter of his book of 'wonderful things' into the shade. He would confess, on attending one of the Doctor's lectures, and witnessing some of his wonderful experiments in 'neurology', (as he styles the science,) that there were yet things in heaven and earth, which had not been dreamt of even in his philosophy.

"We would not exactly class the Doctor's science with witchcraft and hobgoblinism, though it seems to be quite as marvelous as either; for the fact of his having made converts of some of the most intelligent of our citizens, would dispose us, aside from our own observations, to believe there is something in the matter worthy, for its novelty at least, the attention of the curious."

* * *

Possibly John Bunyan Campbell of Pennsylvania, who, after the Civil War, opened the American Health College in Cincinnati, had read some of Buchanan's works. At any rate he founded Vitapathy, and built up a considerable following. Although his school did not fare well at the hands of the Ohio State Board of Medical Registration and Examination, it seemed to prosper otherwise. Largely a one-man affair, the school granted diplomas, but not M.D.'s; taught how to "pull out poison and rabid bites" with a special engine, practice obstetrics, treat diseases of women and children, lockjaw, cancer, and so forth, all without laboratory, dissection, or drugs. Graduates of this school of "vitapathic physicians and ministers" were empowered to heal the sick, give the vitapathic breathing prayer, administer the milk-sacrament, and emanate higher spiritualization.

This whole cult was based upon the presence everywhere of "Vita," a therapeutic agent which could be introduced into the body of a sufferer if handled by a properly qualified vitapathic physician. In order to facilitate this introduction, since "The higher wisdom and spiritual power comes in at the top of the head," and since "Hair is a nonconductor," according to Campbell, "the hair must be parted there to let the spirit in." Students of Campbell were made to pronounce a terrible oath that they would not speak of the contents of his books or show the books to anyone. Secrecy and monopoly were further guaranteed by "United States Right, by State Charter and by the Highest Divine Right," according to the title page of his *Encyclopedia of Vitapathic Practice*. His literary and healing talents were further evidenced by his book on vitapathic materia medica, which contained a portion of the quack-nostrums and household remedies of all ages and climes.

Campbell was referred to in 1909 as "the Cagliostro of Medical Cincinnati," whose "citadel of infamy still stands in Fairmount, a mute witness of iniquity unspeakable." The only question in the minds of some was whether he should have been confined in a state prison or an insane asylum.

The regular doctors felt this way about most of the irregulars.

WHO IS A DOCTOR?

CHAPTER VI

"Who shall decide when doctors disagree?"
Pope, Epistle III.

*I*n the period in which medicine was making the transition from a very uncertain art to a more or less exact science the internecine warfare in the profession was not only prolonged but open, and, like politics and religion, a matter of important public knowledge and concern. Although the main battle line was drawn between regulars and irregulars, with many participants and followers on both sides refusing to wear uniforms for fear of identifying themselves too certainly with what might be the losing army, there were innumerable battles and skirmishes within the ranks of each host.

By mid-century the old one-idea disease and cure systems —those of Brown, Rush, Cooke—were well on the way out as far as regular medicine was concerned. The rise of the French school—Bichat, Louis, and others with their statistical studies and checks—as well as the chemical discoveries

of the early nineteenth century, were important contributing causes.[1] But so was the rise of Botanic, Eclectic, and
homeopathic practices. In relation to the decline of the
one-idea systems they stood as both cause and effect. In
their attacks upon the heroic treatments of the bleed-purge
doctors they helped overthrow the monistic concepts;
having done so, they in turn emphasized their own one-
treatment method and became the haven of refuge of both
doctors and patients who still believed in such simple solutions. It was a process of attack from without, as well as
boring from within. For instance, homeopathy in the
beginning was "as much a part of regular medicine as
any other system, and . . . contemporary studies recognized it as such."[2] Eclecticism, on the other hand, started
from without, yet found its path converging towards that
of regular medicine. These chaotic years in which the older
remedies were being undermined and cast aside with no
immediate certainty of new ones to take their places,
practically coincided with the pioneer period of medicine
in the Middle West.

However uncertain the regulars were regarding tenets
of their own faith, they did agree on two things: the
first, that medicine constituted a body of knowledge which
required some little time and effort to assimilate; and the
second, that the integrity of the profession should be
defended against any and all who sought to break it down.

To them most irritating and obnoxious, because most
numerous and aggressive, were the Botanics. The Botanic
contention that the mineral medicines of the regulars were
poisons and that the patient was overcharged was bad
enough, but the idea that humanity was being bettered
by the administrations of every blacksmith or peddler who
got a copy of Thomson, threw away the tools of his trade,
and set up doctoring, was demoralizing. And in medicine,
as in other fields, the task of combating ignorance with
knowledge was a difficult one. Belief in the efficacy of
charms and superstitions did not pass with savagery;
vestiges remained with man in every situation, though

they became weaker with the advance of sound education.

"In despite of every exertion to illuminate the mass, many dark and impenetrable spots will remain; so that society, in its best composition, must continue to display enough of credulity to render it ridiculous. From the depths of ignorance, with its overshadowing superstitions, — when the hopes of the sick rest upon spells and coscinomancy,— the first step taken, is to blend with these *supernatural*, a variety of *natural* means, resting the efficacy of the latter, on the occult influence of the former. The next advance, leaves the mummeries of the sorcerer behind; but clings to amulets, seventh-sons, 'yarb doctors,' and vagabonds. This brings us to our own age — than which, with all our boasted elevation in learning and philosophy, no other has ever been presented a greater *variety* of barefaced and abominable quackeries. To eradicate them would be more difficult, than to root out the sour dock and Canada thistle of our fields, while the soil continues to favour its reproduction. Planted in the ignorance of the multitude, warmed by its credulity, and cherished by their artful and unblushing authors, these impostures are fixed upon us, as the 'poison oak' encircles the trunk of the noble tree, whose name it has prostituted. True it is, they are not always the same. The stupidest intellect at last comes to perceive their absurdity, and throws them off; but the impostors—

" 'New edge their dulness and new bronze their face,' and speedily invent fresh draughts for the gaping and thirsty populace.

"When one of these quackeries is inoculated into a community, nothing can arrest its spread, or limit its duration. Every dog has its day, and so has every nostrum. The gulping is universal; not extending, it is true, to every individual, but to all classes. The propensity to be cheated is not confined to men or women, the old or young, the poor or rich, the unlearned, or (we are sorry to add,) the learned; but displays its workings in the weak-minded and credulous of all. Like the small pox it prevails till all the susceptible are infected, and have gone through the disease. A moment of common sense may, perhaps, succeed to the period of suffering; as natural fools have sometimes spoken well from the shock of a violent blow. The desire to be cheated, however, returns apace; but not earlier than the desire to cheat—"[8]

So the cry was "down with the regulars."

"If not the greatest impostors, they cheat us out of most money, and kill us to boot.—They bleed us to fainting, blister us to wincing, stupify us with opium, vomit us with tartar instead of lobelia, salivate us with mercury, in place of the panacea, or the 'stone mason's balsam,' and, purge off with calomel all kinds of phlegm, but that which encumbers our brain! Let no one be over nice. The end sometimes justifies the means. Suffering humanity cries aloud, and must be rescued from the keeping of science and skill and professional charity. The world has been in error four thousand years; and the path of medicine may be followed back by the carcasses of its victims. *Doctor* Thomson, and *doctor* Swaim, and *doctor* Rafinesque have received new 'gifts,' and are ready to distribute them. Push aside the 'riglar' Doctors!—Conceal all their cures, and publish all their failures! Go among their patients, and labor to overthrow a long established confidence! Brand them with ignorance of the human system! Stigmatize them with cruelty! Denounce them as mercenary! and Libel them as infamous! Break down the *aristocracy* of learning and science! Give the people their rights: let the drunken and lazy among the tailors, and carpenters, and *lawyers,* and coblers, and *clergy,* and saddlers, and ostlers, now rise to the summit level, and go forth as ministering angels! Become their patrons, and snuff up in turn the *steams* of their incense; sustain them against the professed Doctors; lecture them into notoriety: mould them into form as the bear licks her shapeless pups into beauty: turn jackals and procurers lest they might want business: stand responsible for their success: newspaper abroad their pretended cures; and handbill away the proofs of their murders!"⁴

Dr. Thomas D. Mitchell, of Cincinnati, who was somewhat addicted to writing poetry, treated the subject with a lighter touch, in his poem, "The Cobbler turned Doctor":

> "*There lived a man in* Tinker-town,
> *Whose name was Doctor Wen;*
> *A Wondrous man, of great renown,*
> *As e'er was one in ten.*
>
> "*His story would you like to know,*
> *And how he got his fame?*
> *If e'er he read a book or no,*
> *Or simply stole his name?*
>
> "*I'll tell you Sir; this Doctor Wen*
> *A cobbler was by trade;*
> *Who oft had heard how other men*
> *By chance were Doctors made.*
>
> "*He could not read a single line,*
> *Nor even write his name;*
> *Yet thought by hanging out his sign,*
> *He soon would ride to fame.*
>
> "*So then, resolved to change his trade,*
> *His kit he thus addressed,*
> *And in the short harangue he made,*
> *His shopmates kindly blessed.*
>
> "'*Farewell my awl and wax-ends too,*
> *My lap-stone and my seat,*
> *No more "old cobbler how d'ye do,"*
> *These ears again shall greet.*
>
> "'*I've mended soals full long enough,*
> *And hence my Constant care*

Shall be with Charms *and* Doctor Stuff
Sick bodies *to repair.*

"'So fare ye well my worn out tools,
My shopmates all farewell;
Hence 'tis my lot to work for fools
With charms or magic spell.*

"'For tho' a shoe I ne'er could make,
To fit a foot on earth;
Yet thousands will my nostrums take,
And loudly praise their worth.*

"'In vain long stitches have I tried
My daubing to conceal;
But Doctors faults the grave will hide,
Nor one mistake reveal.*

"'Be Physic then my last resource,
For here I cannot miss;
The Quack must business get of course,
He never fails in this.*

"'I'll purge but little; less I'll bleed,
My plan shall be to charm;
It may not always quite succeed,
But then 'twill do no harm.'*

"This Doctor then his course began,
And quickly gained a name;
For very soon his charming plan,
Spread far and wide his fame."

The regulars pointed out that it was certainly a stretch-ing of the intent of the patent law of 1793 to take advan-tage of its words "or composition of matter" to include drugs and methods of curing disease. Also that there was absolutely nothing new or original about the Botanic system; that plant remedies, some good, some otherwise, had been in use for ages; that steam baths had their points, as well as stimulating medicine, in certain diseases, but might be fatal in others; and that strong medicines were not all minerals; deadly poisons came from the vegetable world as well.

The hands of the more conservative and modest of the regulars were tied somewhat by the "ethics of the profession."[5] Not all possessed the pen and daring of a Daniel Drake. Often help was received from the press. Said the *Edwardsville Spectator* in 1821, "It is one of the severest curses to a new settlement that quacks of every description find refuge there, but none do more mischief to society than the self-dubbed doctors, who in numerous herds deal death and destruction in the shape of pills, powders, tinctures, etc."[6]

Examples of the price paid for "quackery" were constantly printed and circulated. The "hot-stone steam system" received its share of blame for needless sacrifice of life. For instance there was the case of a child with a bean fast in her throat. She was given heat-producing medicines and steam baths to produce perspiration, then cold water was thrown on to produce a cold. The cold was supposed to bring on a cough and the cough bring up the bean. It did not work out according to theory; the vinegar thrown on the hot limestones to induce the perspiration produced carbonic acid gas and suffocated the child. "When a few of them shall be convicted of murder or manslaughter and find their way to the halter or state's prison, the practice being found unprofitable, may be laid aside."[7]

The suggestion was followed up a few years later when the "City and County of New York" indicted and tried Dr. R. K. Frost, who, "not having the fear of God before his eyes, but moved and instigated by the devil," did, in 1837, "feloniously and willfully make an assault . . . and administer unto . . . Tiberius G. French into the body and bowels of him . . . a certain noxious and injurious clyster . . . of cayenne pepper and lobelia . . . and did . . .

willfully apply unto and upon the breast, stomach, belly, and back, head, legs and arms of him . . . a certain noxious and injurious hot vapor called steam . . . and willfully caused to be swallowed by him a certain noxious and injurious drug or herb, to wit: lobelia"—all of which resulted in the said Tiberius G. French's dying or being killed "contrary to the form of the statute in such case made and provided and against the peace, government and dignity of the state." In this famous case, in which the medical faculty were arrayed against the Thomsonians, testimony was heard for three days; among other expert witnesses was Dr. Wooster Beach, founder of Eclecticism. The judge charged the jury to "Pursue common sense as your guide . . . and render such a verdict as will justify you to the prisoner, to your own conscience, your country, and your God." After four hours' deliberation, the jury returned a verdict of guilty of manslaughter in the fourth degree, with a recommendation of mercy. An arrest of judgment was moved, consideration of which was postponed until the next term of court, and the prisoner was given his liberty.

A few days before the trial Samuel Thomson wrote Dr. Frost condoling with him over his persecution, and compared it with his own. "I have been thrust into prison and bound in chains—I have suffered every species of wrong and oppression, and yet I have outlived the venom of my enemies . . . . I have used my medicines for nearly half a century, and I solemnly and unequivocally assure you that I *never* knew them to produce deleterious results. Many accusations, it is true, have been brought against me; but these have invariably originated with the medical faculty, and were founded in malice. I have been bitterly and inhumanly persecuted, for no other reason than because I healed the sick, and that too very often without any compensation, and when they could obtain relief from no other source. I have expended Twenty four thousand Dollars in the State of New York in defending my system . . . ."

A somewhat different kind of trial was that of Col. M. Jewett of Columbus, Ohio, who, in 1835, was tried before a Methodist Church Court on four counts of falsehood. The trouble all began over a testimonial of John Miller in *Jewett's Advertiser* regarding the cure of daughter Nancy's severe case of *Scald Head*. Testimony, charges, defense, citizens' letters, and poems occupy about a hundred pages in the account by Thomas Hersey, which was published in Columbus in 1835, under the title *Clericus, Esculapius, and Scepticus, vs. Col. M. Jewett, and His Chemical Preparations*. The trial committee by unanimous vote pronounced the dispenser of botanic remedies guilty on all four counts, and he was expelled from the church by the minister, E. W. Sehon. Of this "nefarious trial" Hersey said that in the history of persecutions the world had never presented a "blacker scene, a more exceptionable course than has been pursued by a certain coalition of professors, physicians and infidels, to effect the prostration of a man of distinguished and honorable standing, extensively known in the United States for his enterprise, hospitality and christian integrity, who, through a long, active and useful life, has sustained an unblemished reputation."

A sense of humor, itself a critical sense, was an effective weapon, but most doctors were too worked up over the irregulars and "quacks" to use it; they could not see anything funny about the situation. Homeopathy, of course, with its doctrine of infinitesimals, affected the risibilities of pioneer wits, to say nothing of hydropathy, phrenology, vitapathy, and the like. Ironically enough, even "quacks" attacked "quacks." Anthony Hunn of Kentucky — he who had seen jawbones fall out like horseshoes as a result of too much calomel — appealed to the medical profession to supply information to the mass of the people so that they would no longer be prey to quackery. "Quacks, conjurers, Faith-doctors, Indians, Negroes, Cancer-women, etc., will be preferred only by a people bedizzened by ignorance and prejudice, and at war with their own dearest interests."[8]

As for himself, he used "analeptic equalizers," let his patients alone, and had eminent success.

More difficult to handle was the general providential-humanitarian-uplift approach of the irregulars. Not only did Samuel Thomson have a "Call from Providence, and a degree from the God of nature," but hydropathy, phrenology, mesmerism, Grahamism, and to a certain extent homeopathy, got inevitably intertwined with the aurae of democracy, associationalism, eclectic love, and free-soulism. Though the followers of many of the more strenuous of these urges allowed themselves plenty of right-of-way on either side of the straight and narrow path of orthodox religion, they were never loath to call attention to the fact that their enemies were heathen and atheist. So with the irregular medicos. Dr. Samuel Robinson, formerly a clergyman, did it very well in his *Lectures*:

"I know some physicians distinguish between the rational soul and the vital principle of animal life. . . . But in animals, besides vitality, we perceive *thought, reason, memory, design,* and perseverance, with a great number of the noble passions which animate man — *love, gratitude, affection, friendship, grief and bitter woe* . . . . This was the true sentiment and doctrine of the ancient philosophers — the presence and Superintendance of the Deity everywhere."

Contributing to the common belief that the regular faculty were frequently unbelievers was the practice of dissection, considered by many as a desecration of God's highest work — the human body, the temple of man's soul. Having explored its innermost and sacred secrets, they had "searched in vain for the appropriate habitation of the soul, in the cellules of the brain, or the more extensive apartments of the stomach, where later opinions seem to have supposed her residence to be, and have thence inferred, that there was no such inhabitant, and that man was no more than an organized body without a soul."

Since effective state approval of dissection and provision for adequate anatomical specimens were still half a century in the future, medical schools and doctors were hard pressed for cadavers. But where there is a market there usually will appear an entrepreneur.

"Resurrectionists" were both amateur and professional; as among athletes, the dividing line was somewhat hazy. When medical schools were few and scattered, students and professors maintained their own services of supply. Not all who stood around the new grave in the vicinity to witness the farewell ceremony were mourners. Some may have had the advancement of science, the art of healing, or their own careers in mind. "In the eternal fitness of things, many a man or woman was given a chance to redeem by such post-mortem service the emptiness of all the years which preceded the final march to the grave."[9]

Many were the adventures and yarns which collected around this activity. Professor John T. Shotwell, of the Medical College of Ohio, acquired a new name, "Wellshot," in addition to a lasting limp, from one of his nocturnal visits. Dr. Joseph Nash McDowell, a spiritualist as well as a brilliant anatomist and surgeon, and as eccentric as they came, had thrillers enough in his own right without those added by his students. When returning from a night expedition, he was driving the covered wagon and its cargo leisurely into town. When it began to rain and thunder, McDowell, who didn't like thunderstorms, grew nervous. Suddenly a shot rang out. When he turned, he saw the body sitting up, and in its bony white fingers a pistol. This was too much; he got away from there. The next day, when he told his class of being attacked by a cowardly assailant and pursuing the rascal a great distance, he received an ovation. This he acknowledged with grateful smiles and bows.

As medical colleges became better established it was no longer necessary for the professors to take such risks, though the students — according to some, saturated with a special form of depravity — continued to enjoy their ghoulish activities for many years. Early in 1832 students of the Medical College of Ohio memorialized the legislature for redress against a ruling of the trustees by which they were forbidden to make "post mortem examinations." The trustees, in a lengthy defense of their action, stated that some members of the faculty had been exercising this privilege on all who died in the hospital, regardless of status. They pointed out that their ruling still left plenty of bodies, since it affected only thirteen of sixty-seven which became available in the previous year. An agreement was finally reached between the faculty and trustees.[10]

By the 1830's professional body suppliers were carrying on their unromantic vocation in the vicinity of Cincinnati, Louisville, and other medical centers. Their standard price for a cadaver was $10. As long as they confined their excavations to potter's fields, they were seldom bothered. Sometimes mistakes were made — or else malicious plants — as in 1878 when a searching party found, dangling at the end of a rope in the cadaver chute at the Medical College of Ohio, the body of former congressman John Scott Harrison, son of William Henry Harrison. The ensuing furor did much to bring about passage of the Ohio law of 1880 regarding dissection.[11] The whole subject of "Resurrectionism" was one darkly hinted at, but seldom discussed in the open.

The charges regarding the morals and religion of the regular faculty were harder to meet than the criticisms of their medicines. When in 1824 Dr. Charles Caldwell of Transylvania defended the medical profession on the basis of natural religion, as important and as God-given as revealed religion, his address was considered heretical, that of a freethinker.[12]

One of his colleagues, Dr. Thomas D. Mitchell, stated the defense in poetry:

> "Madmen may charge us with immoral views,
> Our creed despise, our arguments abuse,
> Yet pleasure springs from this delightful theme,
> We dwell on Nature and explore her scheme;"

As frontier communities settled — often promoted by land boomers — lawyers and doctors of doubtful qualifications hurried in; sometimes the doctor and preacher were brought in by the promoters as an additional talking point. Though these "Unlicensed Doctors, alias Quacks" might be "the pest of regular practitioners, the tools of knaves, and the bane of society," as the more intelligent people were aware, the majority often defended them on the same grounds as they opposed legislation which required stock owners to fence in their animals. Such legislation was class legislation in favor of those who owned improved bulls, and the services of free scrub-bulls were better than no bulls at all. So with medical regulation; it would protect a vested interest.

The problem of regulation of doctors was an old one. The Code of Hammurabi as well as other codes of ancient times contained provisions regarding fees and malpractice. The Salic Law of the Franks provided that "If any one have given herbs to another so that he die, he shall be sentenced to 200 shillings (or shall surely be given over to fire)." And again, "If any one shall have dug up and plundered a corpse already buried, and it shall have been proved on him, he shall be outlawed until the day when he comes to an agreement with the relatives of the dead man, and they ask for him that he be allowed to come among men. And whoever, before he come to an arrangement with the relative, shall give him bread or shelter — even if they are his relations or his own wife — shall be sentenced to 600 denars which make xv shillings." These early laws were probably as difficult to enforce as those later.

In the Middle West the whole subject of legal regulation of the licensing of doctors was intimately involved with the organization of, and qualifications for membership in, the medical societies.

In Ohio, largely through the efforts of Dr. Samuel P. Hildreth of Marietta, a law was enacted in 1811 which divided the state into five medical districts, in each of which a board of three censors, or examiners, was to be appointed by the legislature. The boards were to satisfy themselves as to the moral character and medical knowledge of the applicant for a license. Unlicensed physicians were not forbidden to practice, but could not use legal processes to collect fees. A year later licensing privileges were put into the hands of the President and Fellows of the Medical Society of the State of Ohio and the state was divided into seven medical districts for administration. The names of one hundred twenty eligible physicians were written into the law. At the first "convention," at Chillicothe, November, 1812, only five delegates appeared, whereas the law required ten; it adjourned *sine die*. By this law those who practiced without licenses not only could not use legal means to collect fees, but for each offense were subject to fines of from $5 to $100, to be shared by the informant and the medical societies. The fines were changed by subsequent laws. The next General Assembly repealed this law and returned to the law of 1811. Between 1813 and 1821 the statute was amended, repealed, and reenacted at least three times.[13] In 1818 graduates of recognized medical institutions were made eligible to licenses without examination.

By law in 1821 each of the nine circuits of the Courts of Common Pleas was constituted into a medical district, and in each district a board of five censors was appointed to examine medical candidates annually. The board also was to elect a delegate to the Medical Convention of Ohio, a corporate body, which was to meet annually at Columbus, and be given exclusive power to license candidates and prescribe "periods and methods of study and qualifications of the candidates."

The first Medical Convention, at Columbus in 1821, adopted a rather stiff set of requirements which included good moral character, knowledge of Greek, Latin, "Mechanical Philosophy, two years practice with some reputable physician and at least one course of lectures from some 'respectable Medical Institution.' "[14]

In 1824 the law of 1821 was repealed. The new statute created twenty medical districts. As penalty for not conforming to the procedure specified for licensing, a physician could not receive the benefit of the law for debt collecting and was subject to a fine of $10 for each offense.

After five medical conventions were held the legislature gave up; in 1833, largely as the result of the Botanic lobby, it repealed all laws for the regulation of physicians and surgeons.[15]

Some carping criticism had, from the beginning, questioned the right of the legislature to regulate medical practice, but the regular faculty argued that that body had the same right to govern medical procedure, as to regulate marriage.[16] Such a right meant little, since irregular practice continued to thrive. In 1868 medical regulation by law was again attempted, but it was not until 1896 that anything like effective laws were enacted.

The law having failed to effect medical organizations, it was left to the doctors to take action. Frequently they disagreed when they tried to do so. For instance, when in the summer of 1821 proposals were made for a Cincinnati Medical Association which might determine a scale of fees and establish professional standards, a member of the faculty of the Ohio Medical College argued against it. "Justice" in a letter to the *Liberty Hall and Cincinnati Gazette* particularly attacked the proposal that members of the Association not consult with doctors who were not. Other criticisms followed. Similar arguments and differences were encountered in most of the early attempts at forming medical societies.

From 1835 to 1851 the "Medical Conventions of Ohio" were open to all regular physicians; membership was individual and voluntary. Notice of the first triennial meeting "To be holden . . . January 1, 1838" appeared in the Columbus *Daily Journal and Register*. The object was "organization, advancement and elevation of the Medical Profession as well as the promotion of objects of general benevolence." All "Scientific Practitioners of Medicine and Surgery" of Ohio were invited, also "Brethren from the sister States who can make it convenient." In 1846 the

Ohio State Medical Society was organized. In the early years a large part of its work had to do with encouraging the formation and passing upon the requirements of the local or auxiliary societies. About a dozen of these were functioning by 1850. Despite urgent requests on the part of the State Society, these societies were still largely indifferent and dilatory in furnishing reports on membership, papers read, and actions taken. Prior to 1860 the only district society in Ohio was the Medical Association of Adams, Brown, and Clermont counties, organized in 1847.

In Indiana the first General Assembly created each of the three Circuit Court districts into a medical district and provided for boards of censors to regulate the practice of physic and surgery, examine candidates, grant licenses, and fix fees.[17] The members of each board of censors were named in the statute. Persons who showed qualifications and "reasonable evidence of their moral character" were to be admitted to the "board" of their district, a body "corporate and politic." No person not a member of these "boards" (local societies) could have the benefit of the law for collecting any charges. In 1818 any person who was already practicing in the state in 1816 was excepted from this provision. The next year the State Medical Society was incorporated and granted powers to license physicians.[18] Any person who practiced without a license from the State Society (or a district society in the interim) was subject to a fine of from $10 to $20 for the first offense, and double thereafter. The money so collected was to go to the State Society for the promotion of medical science. By amendment in 1823 it was switched to the county seminaries.

Following the law of 1816 the censors of the first district met at Vincennes in June, 1817, examined five candidates, and organized the board for the district. At the May, 1819, meeting, two delegates were selected by ballot to meet with those from the two other districts to form a State Medical Society. At the same meeting it was resolved that no person be admitted to examination before the censors if he could not produce satisfactory evidence of having "studied physic and surgery for the full term of three years"; also a committee was appointed to choose a delegate to meet in convention to formulate a District Pharmacopoeia.

Other district delegates were likewise selected. Physicians of the third district met at Madison, August 1, 1817. In 1820 the Medical Society of the State of Indiana met at Corydon, the capitol. Annual meetings were held for several years. Just why the set-up under this law was unsatisfactory is not clear, but at any rate in 1825 another law provided all over again for the organization of the Medical Society of the State of Indiana; a quorum of five representatives of the county societies was empowered to do it. From the words of the law, "the society when thus formed," it would appear that no society was formed under the law of 1818. This time the society was given the additional power to establish "a uniform system of the course and time of medical study," to qualify for license.

How effective this was may be judged from the law of 1830[19] which said that "owing to defects in the law regulating the practice of physic in this state, the medical societies which now exist, have never been legally organized, and the provisions of the act are such as do not induce a large portion of qualified physicians to become members of any medical society, or sufficiently to guard against licensing unqualified men to practice medicine . . . ."

To remedy these evils the law legalized the existing societies when they should file their names and those of their officers with the proper county auditors, all powers granted by the law of 1825 were extended to them, and all licenses granted by them in the interim were recognized. It was provided that after one year no person not regularly licensed in Indiana, or in an adjoining state of which he was a resident, or not "at the passage of this act a resident practitioner of medicine in this State" could recover anything by law for medical services. But there was a big "Provided"; nothing in the act was "to affect the right of females to practice midwifery, or apothecaries, or others not professing to prescribe or practice medicine, from selling medicine and recovering payment therefor." This last section had the effect of leaving the state wide open to whosoever wished to engage in medical practice. Farmers, blacksmiths, and others frequently tried their hands at it.

Local medical societies continued to exist, but though notices of their meetings appeared in the newspapers, one surmises from the frequent "reorganizations" that attendance was small and interest languishing. The Indiana State Medical Society was revived in 1849 and its continued existence dates from that year.

Illinois, too, started off with an impressive paper effort. In 1817, since "well regulated medical societies have been found to contribute to the diffusion of true science and particularly to the knowledge of the healing art," the territory was divided into two medical districts by a meridian running north from the mouth of the Ohio. The medical society of each was empowered to examine students and grant diplomas. After organization of the societies no one was to practice physic or surgery without a diploma; the penalty was disqualification "forever after" for use of the law for collecting any debts incurred by such unauthorized practice. Practicing rights of those who came into Illinois territory with licenses from their former states were recognized. Assessments of $10 each upon members of the societies were authorized "for the purpose of procuring a medical library and apparatus, and for the encouragement of useful discoveries in chemistry, botany, and such other improvements as the majority of the society shall think proper."

In 1819 the first General Assembly divided Illinois into four medical districts, in each of which was to be "held a board of physicians." These boards or societies when organized were to examine students and present diplomas. Persons who did not have a diploma from a medical school or who had not previously practiced in the state had either to pass an examination before a society or be disqualified from collecting any fees by use of the courts. All physicians were required by this law to render to the president of the medical society of his district "a true and accurate record of all the births, deaths and diseases which may take place within the vicinity of his practice." Any physician who refused to attend the state meetings of the said societies was to be fined $5.

That this law had little effect may be concluded from the fact that, under the law of 1825, which divided the state into five districts, the "practicing physicians" of each district were authorized to elect a censor. The five censors so elected were to meet at Vandalia in November and form a board to examine candidates and grant licenses. Those with medical school diplomas or licenses from any "respectable medical society" were not required to submit to examination. Once the board of censors was organized it could certify the censor and physicians of each district, or their appointees, to conduct the examinations. Any person who practiced physic contrary to the provisions of this law was subject to a fine of $20, which was to go to the county poor fund.

Only about twenty persons attended the first meeting of the "Illinois Medical Society" (the board of censors), which was held at Vandalia in November. Most of these were applicants for licenses.[20]

The law of 1825 in its last section provided that the board of censors lay before the next General Assembly a plan for a permanent system of licensing. If they did so, nothing came of it, for on January 25, 1826, the legislature repealed the law of 1825 and no further legislation for this purpose was passed until 1877.

Kentucky, which had some advantage in years over the states of the Old Northwest, might logically be expected to have pioneered in medical regulation. But it did not. Prior to 1860 there was no definition by law of who was a doctor of medicine.[21] Practice of medicine was open to all, subject only to the power of opinion and influence of the various medical societies. An irregular or "quack" could be professionally blacklisted or read out of the profession, but there was always the law of libel to be considered, or, in the earlier period, the possibility of the matter's being made a point of honor, to be settled with swords or pistols.

The first medical society in Kentucky was probably the one organized at Louisville on February 24, 1819.[22] The Lexington Medical Society had held a number of regular meetings prior to 1828. In the early 1830's it was endeavoring to establish a medical library. A society had also been in existence in Caldwell County since about the middle 1830's. It reported harmony among its members and eminent success in running out all "steam doctors" and a medicine peddler. Late in 1839 physicians from Mason, Fleming, and Bracken counties organized the Medical Association of Northeastern Kentucky and resolved that county and district societies be formed, and that a state convention be held in Frankfort for the purpose of organizing a State Medical Society.

At the meeting in Frankfort in January, 1841, twenty-eight counties were represented by delegates and a dozen others by proxies. Resolutions were approved that more emphasis be placed on scholarship and scientific background in the training of medical students; that three years be standard in a reputable college or four years preceptorial training under the direction of "some respectable medical practitioner." A constitution and by-laws, as well as a table of approximate fees, were drawn up. The convention adjourned, and did not meet again for ten years.

Simultaneously with this effort, physicians of Jefferson County were attempting to organize the Louisville District Medical Society. The *Louisville Daily Journal*, December 30, 1840, asked what had become of the movement to organize a state society "to crush empirics, etc." Nothing had, immediately, even after the meeting.

Additional local societies were organized during the decade of the 1840's, and in October, 1851, the Kentucky State Medical Society came into permanent existence. Problems and grievances of the profession were well presented in the report on ethics submitted at the second annual meeting of the Society, held in Louisville in 1852.

At this time it was pointed out that the public owed doctors consideration and respect comparable to that given ministers and lawyers and commensurate with the importance of their functions. If a doctor warned of an epidemic, he was likely to be berated as an alarmist, threatening to business; if brought in on a private case, liable to be "interfered with, beset, given advice, actually assailed by friends of some other practitioner." The practice of contracting for medical service on a yearly basis was denounced as being as bad as that of splitting fees with the apothecary. Nostrums, and the fact that ministers sometimes recommended them, were noted, and attention was called to false systems, secret medicines, and homeopathy. Quackery, not specifically defined, was to be severely dealt with; "anatomy, physiology, pathology, chemistry, physical diagnosis, etc., are now indispensable."

In 1819 the Governor and Judges of Michigan Territory incorporated the Medical Society of Michigan. When a quorum, not less than four in number, of physicians then practicing in the territory, should meet and organize, the Society would constitute a corporate entity. The Society was given the right to elect by ballot two new members each year from physicians residing in the territory. County societies were authorized to be formed in the same manner. Physicians who became members were to be excused from jury service and militia duties in time of peace. No person, unless duly certified in another state, was to commence the practice of physic or surgery until he was examined and certified by one of the societies established by this law. No society was to examine any candidate until he furnished testimony that he had studied with a respectable practitioner for the full term of three years. If any candidate felt that he did not get just consideration from any of the county societies, he might present himself to the Society of the Territory of Michigan. Anyone in the territory who practiced contrary to the provisions of this law was to be liable to a fine of $25 for each offense and forbidden to use the courts to collect fees for services performed.

In 1825 an amendment prescribed four years of study, after the age of sixteen, "with a regular physician and surgeon," but one year of classical studies or one course of lectures at a medical college might be counted as one year of this preparation. Physicians from outside the territory were required to file a copy of their diplomas or certificates with the society of the county where they had practiced.

Another amendment in 1829 declared that any person who practiced medicine outside the provisions of the law should be deemed guilty of a misdemeanor, punishable by a fine not to exceed $100, imprisonment up to six months, or both.

In 1838 an elaborate law re-enacted many of the provisions of the law of 1819. County societies already created were recognized. The penalty for unlicensed practice was merely to be denial of court procedure for collecting fees. After due notice, and filing of evidence in writing, licenses of physicians might be annulled for "infamous crimes, habitual drunkenness, or gross ignorance or incompetency," by a two-thirds vote of the members present of a county society.

In 1843 the penalties of the law of 1838 for unlicensed practice were repealed, but if "any person who proposes to be a physician or surgeon, or shall hold himself out to the public or any person employing him to be such," should be guilty of neglect or malpractice, action might be had at common law.

Three years later (1846) a law of thirty-seven sections went through the whole business once more of erecting a State Medical Society and county societies, and fixing their powers to examine and license. Section thirty-six declared unlicensed practice a misdemeanor punishable with one year's jail sentence and a fine of $1,000, or both. This section was repealed by law in 1851. In 1849 the Supreme Court of the state in the case of *Sulton v. Facey* refused to decide who was a doctor.

Wisconsin in 1841 incorporated the Medical Society of the Territory of Wisconsin and provided for the organization of county societies along the general model of the law of Michigan, from which it had recently been separated.[23] Yet in 1883 the Secretary of the Wisconsin State Board of Health wrote: "I do not know how the impression has gone abroad, as it has, that we have a law regulating the practice of medicine, for we have none."[24]

Such a statement would have been substantially correct, as far as results were concerned, for any state in the Middle West prior to the Civil War. The laws cited above serve as samples for the region; they are evidences of intent rather than records of accomplishment in determining who was a doctor. The story was the same in Tennessee, Missouri, and Iowa. The organization of the American Medical Association in 1846 was supposed to stimulate and strengthen the movement for state societies and regulation. The 1850 meeting was held at Cincinnati and the 1859 meeting at Louisville. Although influential in encouraging organization of state societies, the national association had no important immediate effect in tightening state regulation in the West. The penalties of fines were seldom, if ever, enforced. The usual penalty on irregulars of not being able to use the courts to collect fees meant little; the regulars could not collect their fees even with the aid of the courts.

For all practical purposes, anybody was a "doctor" who called himself a doctor.

NIRVANA IN BOTTLES: DRUGS AND "PATENTS"

CHAPTER VII

"Ye would be dupes and victims, and ye are."

*   *   *

"Is it enough? or must I, while a thrill
Lives in your sapient bosoms, cheat you still?"

The rise of the drug trade paralleled the development of medicine in the West. During the period between home-made herb medicines and the rise of American pharmaceutical manufactories, the United States depended largely upon Europe for its drugs. Philadelphia, the American medical center, was the chief importer of English chemicals; New York handled largely French, Spanish, German, and Italian articles; Boston was the center of trade in East Indian products, such as indigo, nutmeg, cinnamon, cloves, general spices, and gums.

A few western druggists prior to 1830 made annual purchasing trips to one or more of these eastern cities, but the majority had to be content with a visit to Philadelphia, or even Pittsburgh, where most of the necessities could be had. Ten years later it was not necessary for any but jobbers or distributors to go even to Pittsburgh. In Indianapolis in 1835 Scudder and Hannaman required a full newspaper column to report the following items as having been "selected in Philadelphia from late importations and are fresh and of good quality": medicines, family medicines, and surgical instruments and equipment, which included "Amputating, Trepanning, Obstetrical, and Pocket Cases, various sizes; American & German Spring Lancets, Evans' Crown and Com. Thumb Lancets, Gum Lancets, Tooth Drawers assorted, Forceps do. Elastic Bougies, Catheters and Pessaries, Glass and Ivory Pessaries, Silver Male and Female Catheters, Syringes of all sizes, Breast Pipes, Nursing Bottles, Nipple Shells, Hull's Patent Truss, Com. do. Stethiscopes, Surgeons' and Spaying Needles, Scales and Weights, Tweesers, Scarificator's and Cups."[1]

Dr. G. Dauson, of Pittsburgh, in 1825 advertised fresh drugs and medicines—family, patent, and horse—surgeons' instruments, trusses, mortars, pestles, syringes, nipple glasses, oils, varnishes, paints, dyes, perfumery, and all sorts of chemicals and gums. Within a few years not only Cincinnati firms, but others in Louisville, St. Louis, Detroit, Indianapolis, Springfield, Chicago, and Columbus were engaging in both the wholesale and the retail trade. Such houses as J. J. Smith Jr. and Company and "Apothecaries Hall" (Johnsons and Lott) of St. Louis, Mitchell's in Cincinnati, and John M. Kerr of Columbus, carried in stock paints, oils, dye stuffs, patent and botanic medicines, "fancy articles," English, French, American, and other drugs. They also handled optical supplies, surgical instruments, and store furnishings. Their advertisements appeared in newspapers throughout the West.

These large stores supplied the drug stores and merchants of the smaller towns, as well as the peddlers who worked the country districts in covered wagons. But before the drugs were ready for the "saddle bag trade" they had to be processed, usually by the druggist or his apprentice, sometimes by the doctor himself.

"Doctor *Thomson, and* doctor *Swaim, and* doctor *Rafinesque have received new 'gifts,' and are ready to distribute them. . . . We have never known these pretended superior remedies, circulated among the ignorant populace, to live long in the admiration of their own eulogists. One folly after another floats down the current, and each is caught at with avidity—till death engulphs both deceiver and deceived."*

Not without reason were pestle and mortar (or bottles and balances) the sign of the drug store. Sugar of milk, gum arabic, opium, bloodroot—in fact, most powders except jalap, rhubarb, and ipecac—were produced by slow and monotonous work with pestle and mortar. "Sugar of milk came in what we called 'cobs' because it looked somewhat like an ear of corn. A stick 12 or 14 inches long was put in the saturated solution which crystallized about the stick. This was extremely hard to powder. A man might work it in a mortar all day and not get more than a pound. A day's work might not furnish more than two pounds of powdered gum arabic."[2] "A ponderous iron mortar, a tincture press and a Swift's drug mill were the ever present dread of the apprentice."[3] Tincture of iron was made from iron rust, the result of the action of nitric or muriatic acid fumes on thin plates of iron. Making ointments, mercurial ointment, for instance, was a tedious task. What could be accomplished with mechanical aids in fifteen minutes a generation later required as many days in the 1840's.

Castor oil, sweet oil, essence of lemon, peppermint, cinnamon, wintergreen, horehound, alum, salts, borax, copperas, saleratus, seidlitz powders, quinine, calomel, opium, and the like, were usually to be found in even the smaller stores. The influence of the herb and botanic practice is noticeable in the lists in the *United States Pharmacopoeia* of 1820 and 1830, for among other items listed were digitalis, bittersweet, juniper, geranium, garlic, tulip tree bark, sassafras, hops, tobacco, guiac, delphinium, parsley, iris, wild lettuce, and ergot; also gold, isinglass, prunes, musk, and yeast.

Not all the drug inventory was made up of medicines. Indigo, logwood, fustic, nicwood, madder, and cochineal were used for dyes; gums were ingredients of dyes, plasters, inks, and, with turpentine and alcohol, of varnishes and burning fluids. Other articles were used for confections, perfumes, and seasoning.

In addition to paints, varnishes, glassware, and doctors' instruments — at times hardware, notions, and even groceries — the drug store handled "patent" medicines, wines, soft drinks, and usually hard liquor as well. Brandy, port, and sherry were for "medicinal" purposes. When the prohibition movement became a factor to reckon with, drug stores sometimes compromised on "Kentucky wine," also presumably for medicinal purposes. The drug store's chief competitors in the sale of both patent medicines and liquor were the general store, so well known as a dispenser of whiskey as to be called a "groggery" rather than a grocery by those with a prohibition bias, and the book store or stationer's shop, which often had monopoly rights on certain of the proprietary medicines.

Daniel Drake's soda fountain in his Cincinnati drug store in 1816 is the first in the West to which we have certain reference. A dozen years later soda water with syrup and flavors was widely advertised. Prominent citizens as well as town loafers, when they dropped in to pass the time of day, asked for a little soda "with a stick in it." One surmises that the straw, which came later, as did the ice cream, never did entirely replace the "stick." A popular drink of the period was Sarsaparilla Mead, which was advertised not only as a thirst-quencher, but as an aid to digestion and a preventive of fevers, headaches, indigestion, and diarrhea. Some drug stores advertised botanic medicines, Thomsonian remedies, and vapor baths. In 1845 W. W. Brown of Lexington, among others, seems to have specialized in botanic medicines; he listed those of Thomson, Mattson, Beach, Curtis, Howard, House, and Professor Rafinesque.[4]

Truly the early drug store was the department store of its day. As was the general store, it was willing, especially during scarce-money days, to accept beeswax, ginseng, flaxseed and hempseed, and other articles in trade. After 1840 the drug store inclined to restrict its functions more specifically to drugs, only to become a general store again in the twentieth century.

Druggists, like many doctors, learned their trade by the apprentice system. Trained chemists were few. This may account for the fact that by the middle of the century the druggist was very often a German. In Cincinnati, and to a certain extent in Evansville, St. Louis, and elsewhere, Germans predominated in the drug business. At Cincinnati in the 1850's Edward S. Wayne, at one time professor at Ohio Medical College, received a salary of $7000 a year as chief pharmacist with the drug establishment of Suire and Eckstein. Wayne, Adolph Fennel, and others secured a charter in 1850 for the Cincinnati College of Pharmacy, the third school of its kind in the United States. In its early days its quarters were the upstairs rooms of W. J. M. Gordon's drug store.

Even fairly accurate estimates as to the importance of drug manufacturing in the West are difficult to make. The census of 1840 listed the output, including paints and dyes, as follows: Ohio, $101,000; Indiana, $47,000; Illinois, $19,000; and Michigan, $1,500. It is hard to believe that the annual sales of Thomson's western manufactory, or later, of the eclectic tincture concentrate producers alone did not equal or exceed this total.

The pioneer doctor wrote few prescriptions. When people called a doctor they wanted him to do some doctoring. Not only did he prescribe and administer his medicines, but to a certain extent he prepared and mixed them. Some of the drugs came to him unprocessed; pestle and mortar, balances, spatula, and mixing and measuring board were almost as necessary to him as to the druggist. Some drugs he mixed into liquids, some into pills, while others he skillfully rolled into dosage-size powder papers. The saddle bags were, in fact, small travelling drug stores.[5]

* * *

The ailing pioneer, uncured by home remedies and local "Hippos," was all too prone to place his trust in the certain promises of the marvelous elixirs, extracts, and balms which came in bottles and pills. Superstition and charm cures were bad enough, but at worst they were largely negative evils. With the growth of traffic in "patent" medicines came a positive menace, one which a century of education in an age of science has not been able to eradicate. Interesting it is that the rise of the patent medicine business was synchronous with, and dependent upon, the development of education and the newspaper. Schools made it possible for the majority to read; the newspaper furnished something to read. The newspaper made the patent medicine business and the medicine advertisements sustained the newspaper. The only other considerable source of income for the country paper was the public printing — laws, legal notices, and such — and because of the shifting fortunes of party politics, these were not always to be depended upon. But the medicine advertisements spread their financial blessings regardless of politics or creed. They paid the printer and the printer's devil, bought paper, paid postage, carried deadhead and delinquent subscribers, and sometimes provided something over for the grocer and the candlestick maker.

The amount of space devoted to patent medicines varied greatly with the paper. Generally it was relatively less in the elephant-folio and blanket-sheet weeklies, the triweeklies, and the dailies of the cities than in the smaller-sized county-seat or country papers, but this was not always true. Such papers as the *Western Sun*, the *Illinois Intelligencer*, and the *Kentucky Gazette* in the 1820's, small-sized, four-page sheets, usually carried from one to three columns

Great Female Medicine

In cases of nervous debility, female obstructions, Fluor Albus, &c., they have proved the most successful medicine in use. These are the most prevalent of all derangement of the female economy inducing from their debilitating effects, a train of maladies that tend to embitter personal comfort more than any other human ill. That great agent of death, Consumption, is sure to mark two-thirds of the females who thus suffer. The Sanative or Great American Pills in female complaints should be strictly administered, and if followed up with proper attention will soon effect a perfect cure.

of medicine advertisements. A trifle on the extreme side was the *Hamilton Intelligencer* (Ohio) of 1840, a four-page paper with seven columns to the page. Two columns on page one and seven on page four were filled with medicinal notices. The editor later announced that the big "Evans Fever and Ague Pills" display would be reduced to give more room for reading matter, but frankly admitted that such advertisements were necessary to maintain the paper. Otherwise county newspapers would need a paid circulation of two thousand instead of a few hundred. "The bones are sold with the beef."[6]

Occasionally an editor joined the regular doctors and thinking people in viewing with alarm the baneful effects of the pernicious advertising of dangerous nostrums. A Fort Wayne editor *pro tem* in 1847 noted that "Every village newspaper from the North to the South, and from the East to the West, is filled with their trash." When the regular editor returned, he repudiated not only the political blunders made by his understudy, but the *faux pas* in connection with advertising policy as well.[7] Ideals were all right, but —

Although newspapers carried the main load of medicine advertising, almanacs, broadsides, travelling and local agents, travelling "doctors," hawkers, pitchmen, and the general storekeeper all did their share. Travelling agents representing firms which marketed their products over a wide area called upon the drug and general stores, but no outlet was too small to be cultivated. Most of the well-known sponsors of patents published their wholesale and retail prices in the newspapers, but a few sold their goods with the understanding that the retailer could charge what the local traffic would bear. Some sold their product unlabeled and let local distributors put on their own names. Under such arrangements the profits were likely to be one hundred per cent when the product was sold for currency, more if given in trade. The medicine shelf was one of the general store's busy, as well as profitable, corners. The storekeeper himself was often consulted and could prescribe on the basis of customer testimonials or of the margin of profit allowed. Many country peddlers displayed a few choice medicines along with their pretty calicoes and household utensils. A few who specialized in medicines were hard to distinguish from the travelling "doctors" and pitchmen.

These last-named gentry were of various stripes. Some had formerly been "yarb and root" men who found it easier, as well as more profitable, to sell an already-prepared, widely-advertised product than to make and sell their own. Some had been actual doctors or had tried to be doctors; others simply adopted the title. Whatever their origin, they were aware of the fact that the customer paid for his pills and patents more promptly and frequently than for regular medical service. Many were pure venders who, if they had not been selling medicine, would have been selling something else. On muster days and court days, at political rallies, at "protracted meetings," wherever and whenever a crowd assembled, these men could be counted upon to make their appearance. They knew all the tricks long before there were courses in the psychology of salesmanship; they knew human nature. Like the Hindu fakirs or the sideshow ballyhoo artists, they caught the attention of the people by one means or another — an Indian costume, a touch of magic, or, by the 1850's, a combination of banjo, blackface artist, and bit of minstrel music. Medicine salesmen were adept at making their listeners feel and recognize all the symptoms; in fact, they could make them practically enjoy having such symptoms. Besides the inevitable bargain offered, there were innuendoes and allusions to the monopoly of the regular doctors who sought to withhold secrets and medicines necessary for the good of the people. Above all, these men were humanitarians; like "the people's doctors," they appealed largely to the "common man."

Nor was it entirely a matter of psychology and sales technique. People did have pains and aches, coughs and colics. Agues, malaria, a long, wet winter on a diet deficient in vitamins — a "round of calomel" or a "course of medicine" would be indicated as a part of the spring routine. Women really had "that tired feeling"; children did have croups and worms; people did get constipated and have hurts and sores. Attractively presented and flavored medicines were harder to resist than plain calomel, salts, castor oil, or lard and sulphur. Some persons became regular customers because of the opium or other narcotics in the "pain-relievers" or because the high alcoholic content in some of the "bitters" gave a feeling of well-being. Some liked the pleasant herb flavors, just as some people like to chew chewing gum. Besides, taking medicine was something to do; many "just plain had the medicine habit."

Incidentally the advertising methods pioneered by the patent-medicine sellers were later to be extended to many fields.

Most "patent" medicines never did have patents; rather they were proprietary medicines, possibly invented or concocted by the person whose name was attached, but more often only sold under that name. Since a patent served to convey the idea of government sanction, perhaps recommendation even, peddlers of proprietaries, either by direct statement or implication, sought to create the notion that their particular product was a patented medicine. Though by and large possessed of a fair sense of appreciation of the ludicrous—himself a lover of and creator of tall tales— the pioneer could get taken in by his own badger fight. Change the name of the game, take it out of his immediate experience—after all, the word in print was hard to get around. The bigger the lie the harder to disprove. Allowing a discount of ninety per cent, there still remained enough potency in the cure-all to warrant a try. Besides, the pitchman had put on a good show; the artist was worthy of his hire. If his product did not cure rheumatiz or sweeny it might clean a copper kettle or soften a pair of stiff boots.

Specimens of patent medicine blurbs might be listed *ad plethoratum.* To the student whose work takes him to the newspapers of a century ago they prove irresistible; however seriously bent upon scholarly pursuits, he faithfully reads, in the absence of comic strips, the "latest" jokes and the patent serials.

Long before the country had roads passable by anything on wheels the good people of the Ohio Valley were assured that most of their troubles, as far as health was concerned, were over. Dr. Yernest's Elixir had seen to that. It gave strength to and enlivened the vital spirits, heightened the animal senses, cured the trembling of the nerves, softened and lessened rheumatic pains and prevented them from progressing upwards; cleansed the stomach of bad humors which caused indigestion, sourness, headaches and vapors; killed the worms; cured the colic of the intestines in some minutes; relieved the dropsy, often in an hour's time; took away pains of the head and softened the ears of the deaf; soothed aching in the hollow tooth, cleansed the blood and served as an antidote against poison. "It is useful for females, gives color and a fair complexion; purges imperceptibly and without pain; cures all intermittent fevers at the third, and is a preservative from all contagious disorders."[8]

Four years later at Cincinnati the firm of Richard Lee and Son, of Baltimore, was advertising worm-destroying lozenges, essence of mustard, grand restorative, antibilious pills, sovereign ointment for the itch, ague and fever drops, Persian lotion, genuine eye water, toothache drops, corn plasters, lip salve, restorative powder for the teeth and gums, anodyne elixir, and Indian Vegetable Specific. "These medicines having come into general use, they are frequently purchased not only by Druggists, but by country store keepers to sell again . . . ." And Daniel Drake and Company, of all people, besides books, marble mortars, and regular drugs, was selling Dr. S. H. P. Lee's valuable antibilious pills, Dr. Rogers' celebrated vegetable pulmonic detergent for coughs and beginning consumptions, and an "Essential oil of worm seed, a new and valuable worm medicine."[9]

Widely advertised in the early years were the thirteen patent medicines of Dr. T. W. Dyott, M. D., of Philadelphia, guaranteed to cure any ills from gout to female disorders. It required three columns of the small four-page Vincennes *Western Sun* in 1815 to set forth the virtues of these medicines.[10] Advertising simultaneously was Dr. J. Shinn, whose Panacea (Swaim's) was the only thing for scrofula or King's Evil, putrid sore throat, rheumatism, diseases of the bones, syphilis, "ulcers of the laryrux," liver complaints, and "that dreadful disease occasioned by a long and excessive use of mercury &c." Testimonials were appended from two members of the faculty of the University of Pennsylvania.[11] Panaceas seldom come cheap. Shinn's cost $24 the dozen, or $2.50 each.

Already by 1830, in addition to the miscellany of individual nostrums, had developed several systems or complete lines. "Dr." Swaim, whose remedies were advertised in the West in the 1820's under Dr. Shinn's name, was originally, according to Dr. Drake, a saddler and harness-maker of New York. From contacts with ostlers and farriers he got the urge to become a doctor. Having obtained some sort of recipe proposed by a French physician, he moved to Philadelphia and began to advertise his panacea at $3 the bottle. He sent an agent to England and soon laudatory notices of the panacea appeared in Liverpool and elsewhere. One of the emphasized virtues of this medicine was its efficacy in curing diseases incurred by taking too much mercury (calomel). When it was revealed that Swaim's cure-all, besides borage, senna, and sassafras, contained corrosive sublimate, the strongest of the mercurial preparations, the popularity of his medicine waned somewhat, but it continued to be sold for many years.[12]

One of the West's noted characters was Constantine Samuel Rafinesque-Schmaltz, of Transylvania University and elsewhere. A sort of learned "Johnny Appleseed," he dressed the part and acted it. He was equally ready to write a serious two-volume *Medical Flora of the United States*[13] or to lecture on phrenology; to produce *Ichthyologia Ohiensis* (Lexington, 1820), which made him the country's most famous ichthyologist, or to batter up J. J. Audubon's beloved Cremona killing bats. (For this last offense he paid by taking on faith several imaginary fish which Audubon drew—one of them ten feet long with bullet-proof scales—and classifying them scientifically, to the confusion of scientists for fifty years.)

In 1829 "Professor Rafinesque, Ph. D. and Pulmist, Professor of Practical and Medical Botany, Natural and Civil History &c. &c.,"[14] brought forth at Philadelphia *The Pulmist; or, Introduction to the Art of Curing and Preventing the Consumption or Chronic Phthisis.* This medical essay, according to the author, included a new and better distinction of the causes, kinds, remedies, diets, and other peculiarities of the disease. It was decorated with a woodcut which bore the motto "I heal."

The remedy came by means of a new medicine, Pulmel, whose virtues were available in several forms. There was Syrup of Pulmel for internal use; Balsam of Pulmel, both liquid and solid, for inhalation; Balsamic Syrup, for either

DR. MOORE & CO'S. MAGNETIC

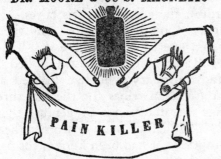

PAIN KILLER

"Essentially vain in his pretensions of an infallible method of curing diseases the nostrum vender requires no light of symptomatology, or pathology to be reflected on the case. He can prescribe by intuition and accomplish his purposes in the mystery of a dark and deceptious legerdemain. . . . 'In folly's cup still laughs the bubble quackery;' Yes! and that bubble will forever laugh as long as there is ignorance to be duped, and credulity to operate upon."

internal use or inhalation; Lotion or Milk of Pulmel, for external use as a wash, for frictions, and for a fragrant inhalant; Wine of Pulmel, "made with sweet fragrant and healthy wines" for general use in debility; Sweet Chocolate of Pulmel, in cakes, for internal use; Liquid ditto, in bottles, merely requiring to be mixed with water or milk for a cup of instant chocolate; Sugar of Pulmel to be used in tea, coffee, or chocolate; Honey of Pulmel, to be eaten with bread; Lozenges of Pulmel, for the dry cough, sore throat, and painful consumptions; Powders of Pulmel, for internal use—"may be sent by mail"; and Pulmelin, or Concentrated Salt of Pulmel, for internal use, also easily sent by mail. Rafinesque was willing to back his medicines with his personal services at $5 for the first visit and $1 each for repeats; also "The Poor taught to use Tan bark for $1. Liable individuals taught how to prevent the disease for $1." For a while Rafinesque advertised under the name "Medicus"; despite his modesty, he published in the *Saturday Evening Post* several statements from doctors regarding the efficacy of his cures.

Daniel Drake thought no more of the Professor's medicines than those of Swaim or even "Dr." Salmon.[15] Yes, this was Rafinesque, the distinguished "fishtaker," chronicler, and antiquary who had located all the wigwams of all the Indian tribes for the last three thousand years. "Strange metamorphosis of genius! that can make an apothecary's muller of such a learned head." As for curing consumptions, it had been known for centuries that human ills could be overcome by medicines made from the animal which was strong where the person was weak (the doctrine of signatures). Dr. Salmon's recipe was, no doubt, as good:

"An Extract or Electuary of *Fox Lungs* is reported to be good against Coughs, Colds, Asthma's, all manner of Obstructions of the Lungs, shortness of Breath, difficulty of Breathing, &c. And for these Purposes the Lungs of a *Hart, Buck,* or *Doe,* are yet preferable; now if the gross Body of the Lungs, will do this, what may be supposed the *Volatile Salt* will do? Truely, it will do that in *three minutes,* which the other will not so well do in *10 days;* it will do all the aforementioned things, and cure an *exquisite Pleurisie* upon the Spot, this I speak by experience."[16]

Although Rafinesque was probably looked upon in his medicine peddling as just another "quack," his biographer thinks he should not be so regarded. First, because he actually believed in his medicines; he had cured his own chronic "fatal phthisis" with his knowledge of medical botany. Second, there were extenuating circumstances: the motive was not sordid gain, but the need to finance further explorations, publish scientific brochures, and still be indebted to no man.[17] Rafinesque wrote: "I introduced also a new branch of medical knowledge and art. I became a Pulmist, who attended only to diseases of the lungs, as a Dentist attends only to the teeth. Being thus the first Pulmist, and perhaps the only one here or elsewhere. The new Profession changed my business for awhile; yet enabling me to travel again in search of plants or to spread my practice, and to put my collections in better order, publishing many pamphlets, &c." Despite his fame and Pulmel, the distinguished scientist must not have profited much. He died in abject poverty, alone, and almost unnoticed, in a Philadelphia attic in 1840. In his will he requested his executors not to divulge the secrets of Pulmel, and left any future profits to his sister and daughter.

Far more successful financially than Pulmel, judging by the volume and duration of advertisements, were the contemporary LaMott's Cough Drops, "peculiarly adapted to the present prevailing disorders of the lungs leading to consumptions." These were to be had wholesale in 1825 at Pittsburgh, Wheeling, Cincinnati, Cleveland, and Columbus.

Weak lungs were not entirely dependent on pills and pulmels for protection. An early form of the modern gas mask was available in Lyman's Patent Health Preserver, a "useful and highly valuable Inhaling and Respiring Apparatus . . . so constructed, that a direct communication is formed between the lungs and a small reservoir worn on the head, and, through which reservoir, all the atmosphere to be inhaled, is compelled to pass . . . can be worn at all times and under all circumstances, without any inconvenience whatever." The reservoir was to hold disinfecting agents, by whose action the atmosphere would, upon inhalation, become purified "from all that poisonous *miasma* combined with it, and which is generally admitted by all medical men, to be the primary or exciting cause of *Cholera,* Yellow Fever, Bilious Fever, Ship Fever, Fever and Ague, &c. . . ." Though it might be worn at all times, the proprietor for the state of Ohio in 1849, D. Whitney, believed that six to eight hours' use during the night would be sufficient for rendering "the inhalation of the common air perfectly safe during the day, without its use." This instrument was useful as a disinfectant and a curative, as well as a preventive. Said Whitney: "We are confident, that, we cannot be reasonably charged with HUMBUGGERY, in offering to the public the HEALTH PRESERVER."

Other popular remedies were Hepatica Triloba for coughs, consumption, and liver complaints; Dr. Felix's celebrated Liver Pills; Hay's Liniment for dropsy, swelling, sores, and rheumatism; Vegetable Rheumatic Drops for same; Morrison's Pills, a sure remedy for all diseases from consumption to epilepsy; and Dr. Fahnestock's Celebrated Vermifuge and Liquid Opeldoc which could safely be administered to the tenderest infant. The manufacturer of Parker's Vegetable Renovating Panacea—"equal to Swaim's or any other and $1 cheaper"—for rheumatism, liver complaint, ulcers, mercurial and syphilitic diseases, rewarded editors who copied and inserted the advertisement up to twenty times with a proportionate quantity of the medicine.

Dr. Peter of Peter's Pills, who claimed to be a graduate of Yale College and the Medical College of Berkshire, Massachusetts, combined literature with his science.

> "The King of terrors looked awhile,
> As though his soul was turned to bile
> At that unsparing scourge of ills,
> By all men known as Peter's Pills,
> These pills of Peter's stop the slaughter,
> And leave the blood as pure as water.
> Now Peter makes I've heard him say,
> Five hundred thousand Pills a day;
> So that the chance is very small,
> Of people dying there at all,

For soon the cheeks so marked for doom,
Begin like any rose to bloom."

As a result, no doubt, of this classic, sales of six million
boxes of pills were claimed for the period 1835-40.

The patent of Dr. Galleckes of Germany, "The Greatest
of Human Benefactors," possessed triple powers derived
from the vegetable, animal, and mineral kingdoms, and by
"filling the vacuum in the *Materia Medica,* proved the
conqueror of physicians." Dr. Robertson's Stomach Elixir
of Health, Dr. Godbold's Vegetable Balsam of Life, Evans'
Camomile Pills, Resurrection or Persian Pills for fever,
ague, pregnancy, and so forth, and the famous Extract
of Wa-ahoo, an Indian medicine for consumption, all had
their devotees.

The justly famous Hygeian Vegetable Remedy of the
1830's was highly renowned as a cure for consumptions,
cholera morbus, inflammation, dyspepsia, fevers, ague,
indigestion, diseases of the liver, gout, rheumatism, lumbago, dropsy, St. Vitus's Dance, epilepsy, apoplexy, paralysis, green sickness, smallpox, measles, whooping cough,
and syphilis—in fact, about all the complaints and disorders to which human flesh was heir. Still the competition
was keen, for simultaneously Dr. Gallopore was advertising in the Pittsburgh *Statesman* and elsewhere, that he
could cure "all disorders incident to the human body,
without exception, no matter what may be the age, circumstance, or place of residence of the afflicted patients."
He did not even need to see his patients, but merely to
know the precise time of their birth. By his pills he could
cure all accidents, including those persons supposedly
scalded to death by the bursting of boilers, struck by lightning, or injured by falling trees. In fact, he guaranteed
to keep anyone in such a perfect state of health that he
could drink two gallons of alcohol per day, which, as the
editor of the *Cleaveland Herald* said, was almost as bad
as so much new whiskey.[18]

Fifteen years later Morrison's Pills still were claiming to be "The Genuine Hygean Vegetable Medicine," which operated on the theory that impurities in the blood were the cause of all disease.

Sufferers from sprains, stiff joints, and general debility in the 1820's could find the old reliable Rattlesnake Oil under various brand names. A few years later they could try Whitmore's Penetrating Vegetable Liniment, excellent for horses as well as persons, or Gardner's Vegetable Liniment "for every external complaint to which Horses are liable. Also for the Human Flesh." Nerve and Bone Liniment might do the work, or French Jejube Paste, "a valuable article"; if these did not prove effective, and if the pain held over until the late 1840's, Jew David's or Hebrew Plaster had no equal in the world for removing all seated pains, whether in the joints, back, or breast, "also corns, wens and humours." In 1844 these plasters caused an "Awful Excitement in the Wabash Valley! Great Disappointment of the People." Many feared they could not go to the polls to save the country because of their lame backs. But the public was "assured that whether our next President shall be a hero, a statesman, or a traitor, the hitherto uncompromising principle of the Hebrew Plaster and Persian Pills will be fully carried out by showing quarters to no cases of disease for which they were recommended."

Those with anti-Semitic prejudices could use Coal Oil Liniment prepared from "Canal" coal, or better still, Dr. M. S. Watson's Great Invincible Birgharmi Stiff Joint Panacea, which, discovered on the Nile, "has astonished every beholder, and no discovery in Medicine since the day of the illustrious Hippocrates, is probably equal in amount of usefulness to the one under consideration." In one six-months' period the latter had cured eighty-three hundred cases of stiff joints, chronic rheumatism, white swelling, contracted spinal cords, and gout. Really bad cases might have to resort to Dr. Christie's Galvanic Belt, or at least a necklace, which, by disseminating galvanic fluid, took care, not only of neuralgia pains and lumbago, but also fits, cramps, palsey, paralysis, epilepsy, deafness, nervous tremors, palpitation, apoplexy, curvature of the spine, gout, and general debility. Sixty thousand people had been permanently cured by its use. McLean's Volcanic Oil Liniment cured everything not taken care of by the Great Invincible or the Belt.

Another contrivance calculated to bolster the body and morale of debilitated humans was Dr. Banning's Patent Lace, or Body Brace. This apparatus made no claim to "miraculous powers such as the prevention of old age nor the curing of confirmed consumption or any other humbug!!! But does profess and establish, beyond successful contradiction, the important fact, that Nature only requires help! And that Help is here afforded!!!" Advertising under the slogan "Truth Is Mighty" it was proclaimed that "The object of this Instrument is to relieve or cure the following Diseases, viz: Weakness of the Breast; Bronchitis; Shortness of Breath; Pain in the Chest; Weakness and Bleeding at the Lungs; Palpitation of the Heart; Dyspepsia; Costiveness and Piles; Pains in the Back; Spinal Curvature and Enlargement of one Hip and Shoulder; Falling of the Bowels; Prolapsus Uteri; Irregular, Painful or Profuse Menstruation; a Tendency to Abortion, and Painful Pregnancy, and the bad shape incident to childbearing; a disposition to drooping, lounging and weariness; Hysteria, melancholy, causeless crying, and thoughts of suicide; habitual Bilious Colic; Sea Sickness and Chronic Diarrhoea; Milk-leg, with old Ulcers; Varicose Veins; Pains, coldness, numbness, and swelling of the extremities; Weaknesses peculiar to males and females, as such, whether from solitary abuse, or the debility common at puberty. The deformities of weak and rickety children, are greatly under its control." This patent lace or brace was marketed from the main office in New York through local agents and drug stores in the West.

Perhaps something like this was the device which Dr. William A. Ashton, an Eclectic doctor in eastern Indiana, had in mind in the 1850's when he wrote his prescription for prevention of sea sickness: "Tie down the intestines so as to prevent their jolting by using two belts—one passing under the thorax and the other between the legs."

Two very important new medicinal discoveries of the 1830's were "Kreosot" and the tomato. The former, it was found, would resist putrefaction and preserve meat. Soon it was being recommended for both external and internal use; for sores and wounds it was the best remedy known. "People afflicted with the dreadful disease cancer, after having been despaired of by the most skilful physicians, have been completely cured by Kreosot."

The lowly tomato, sometimes called "the love apple," was either regarded as poisonous or was used only to garnish the meat platter in the 1820's. A few brave souls began to eat it in the early 1830's, and from then on its rise was rapid. Soon it was a universal favorite, and recipes for every sort of culinary use began to appear, including omelets, soup, dried tomato with ham, and "Katchup." Physicians proclaimed it not only not obnoxious, but useful and healthful. Dr. Bennet, Professor of Midwifery, Hygiene, and Acclimatement at the Medical College of Lake Erie, was no more enthusiastic than many others when he stated that the tomato was one of the most powerful deobstruents of the materia medica, and in certain liver affections probably the most effective and least harmful agent known. It would prevent bilious attacks, serve as a remedy for dyspepsia, was successful in treating diarrhoea, and would render one less liable to cholera. It should be eaten daily, raw or cooked.[19] The medicine men were right up with, if not ahead of, the doctors. Phelps' Compound Tomato Pills, Dr. Miles' Compound Extract of Tomato, and other brands were advertised as substitutes for calomel and "peculiarly adapted to the treatment of *bilious fevers* and other diseases in which a *torpidity* or congestion of the *liver* and *portal circle* prevail," at prices somewhat higher than a modern bottle of catsup. In fact, Extract of Tomato was "undoubtedly one of the most valuable articles ever offered for public trial and inspection." From poison to panacea in five years—yet this rapid inflation did not spoil the tomato, a previtamin vitamin which ultimately made good on its merits.

Antedating the tomato as a general tonic and rejuvenator, if not outliving it, was sarsaparilla, which "purifies, cleanses and strengthens the fountain springs of life and infuses new vigor throughout the whole animal frame." Sands' Sarsaparilla, besides purifying the blood, cured scrofula, rheumatism, stubborn ulcers, dyspepsia, salt rheum, fever sores, erysipelas, pimples, bile, mercurial diseases, cutaneous eruptions, liver complaints, bronchitis, consumption, female complaints, loss of appetite, and general debility. Dr. Townsend's Sarsaparilla, "The Wonder and Blessing of the Age, the most extraordinary Medicine in the World," created new blood and in a five-year period cured one hundred thousand persons, including fifteen thousand incurables. By the 1850's sarsaparilla sots were thrilled by the announcement of the "Important Medical Discovery the Greatest Remedy in the World for Purifying the Blood," Dr. Easterly's Iodine and Sarsaparilla, six times stronger than other brands and only one dollar the bottle. Easterly's was recommended by the "Medical Faculty and men of the highest erudition." From the best information available this remedy had within three years cured more than twenty-five thousand severe cases of disease: three thousand of scrofula; two thousand of dyspepsia and indigestion; one thousand of gout and chronic inflammatory rheumatism; two thousand of general debility; twenty-five hundred of liver complaint, dropsy, and gravel; fifteen hundred different forms of female complaint; and six thousand of syphilitic or venereal coughs, pimples, salt rheum, and headaches—all very conveniently in round numbers.

By this time a medicine had to be pretty good, to compete with Merchants' Celebrated Gargling Oil for Man and Beast, which was deservedly popular in the cure of "Spavins, Sweeney, Chapped Hands, Cake Breasts, Sore Nipples,

Piles, &c." (No testimonials from the horses were attached).

Attempts to supplant the old family bottle of bitters were made by Dr. Lin's Temperance Life-Bitters and Chinese Blood Pills. (The Chinese lived to "such immense ages" because they purified their blood.) Time and space forbade the listing of all the brilliant effects of this medicine, even by the proprietor. But beware! "FRADULENT COUNTERFEITS will be attempted." Brandreth's Pills, sold by special agents, were "allowed to BE ALL that can be accomplished in medicine, both for POWER and innocence." Illinois and Michigan resounded with their praises; there people rode sixty miles through the woods for a box. "Shun a Drug Store for . . . you are certain to get a Worthless Counterfeit Article." Boerhave's Holland Bitters, with the lions-rampant emblem, particularized in diseases of the liver, kidneys, and stomach, as well as fevers and agues.

Dr. John Bull's Great American King was truly a sovereign remedy, which ruled its subjects from the principal office in Louisville. In comparison "the power of the crowned heads of Europe sink into insignificance . . . European Kings employ the power vested in them to increase the riches of the rich and lordly, and to reduce to greatest misery and degredation, the poor and dependent. Our American King goes forth with equal willingness to the lordly mansion and humble cabin, ready alike to administer relief and to offer health and happiness to the lofty and lowly the rich and poor." This medicine, "The Tenth Wonder of the World," was at the people's command. "All those who still suffer, and will not accept the proffered Balm, deserve not the pity of their families."

The medicine ads seldom made a direct appeal to the babies. Their mothers were reminded, however, that Irish Moss was "valuable as a diet for infants afflicted with Debility, Derangement of the Stomach, and for those brought up by hand or after weaning." If babies were restless and their mothers aware of the dangers of too frequent use of soothing syrups which contained opium—which they probably were not—a harmless substitute was recommended: smear baby's fingers with thick molasses, then put half a dozen feathers into its hands. The youngster would pluck feathers from hand to hand until it dropped asleep. When it awakened, supply more molasses and feathers.

Hemmbold's Genuine Preparation of Highly Concentrated Compound Fluid Extract of Buchnu was a "joy to the afflicted . . . Beware of Quack Nostrums and Quack Doctors." Dr. Sappington's Vegetable Febrifuge Pills—a simple treatment for a simple disease; Farr's Ague Tonic; Beckwith's Anti-Dyspepsic; Dr. Taylor's Balsam of Liverwort; Stout's Highly Improved . . . or Great Western Fever Panacea; Dr. Chipman's Vegetable Blood Purifier; McLean's Strengthening Cordial Blood Purifier—illustrated by before-and-after-taking pictures; Dr. Guysott's Extract of Yellow Dock; Wistar's Balsam of Wild Cherry; Dr. Phillips' Diarrhoea Syrup; Moffat's Vegetable Life Pills and Phoenix Bitters; Dr. Duponco's Golden Periodical Pills for Females; Dr. R. Thompson's Pelvic Corset; Jayne's Hair Tonic and Expectorant; Carthusian Cough Drops; Bartholomew's Pink Expectorant Syrup; Circassian Lymph for pimples, scurvy, and rash; Dr. Baker's Specific—for seminal weakness and venereal diseases, "may be used by either sex with *entire secrecy*"—and dozens of other items decorated the pages of the newspapers.

Naturally no general store or drug store carried a complete "line" of patents, proprietaries, and nostrums, but some of them tried. Considering that many of the brands named were of local or short-lived fame, it is interesting to note that some stores, even in the 1840's, advertised two or three dozen different name-items.

Analysis of these medicines will not be attempted here. They differed importantly in no wise from those later exposed by the American Medical Association, *Collier's*, and other pure drug advocates. Some with herbs, flavors, and a fair amount of alcohol were relatively harmless; about the only difference between a powerful healing salve and a box of axle-grease was that the latter smelled better.

Others contained laudanum, opium, morphine, calomel or other forms of mercury, digitalis, and other drugs, useful when given in proper doses for definite ills, but certainly harmful as administered by the store keeper or the self-dosing medicine addict.

The dangers of nostrums were recognized by some people at the time. Thinking editors whose consciences outweighed their financial considerations copied articles of warning from eastern papers and added their own. In the mid-1820's even, a western editor wrote:

"However lenient we are at present with respect to the notorious, illiterate empiries, that infest this country, more care was taken formerly, of the peoples constitutions, and their health was not suffered to be infected by these poisoners of whole countries.

"Any idle mechanic, not caring longer to drudge at day labor, by chance gets a dispensatory, or some old receipt book, and poring over it, or having it read to him (for many of these present doctors cannot read), he finds that mercury is good for the itch, and old ulcers; that opium will give ease; and that a glass of antimony will vomit.

"Down goes the hammer, or saw, razor, awl, or shuttle—and away to work to make electuaries, tinctures, elixirs, pills, plasters, and poultices . . . .

". . . hundreds of little infants are yearly destroyed by the remedies the unhappy parents were prevailed on to administer in order to destroy those supposed worms, which never existed but in their brain.

"Cobblers now set up for regular-bred physicians; hackney coachmen and barbers for anatomists and natural philosophers; washerwomen for chymists; tumblers and scavengers, for bone setters and occulists, et cetera. Nothing can equal the ignorance of such empiries but the stupidity of those people who buy their unwholesome preparations."[20]

Perhaps a better form of attack was that adopted by the editor of the *Portsmouth* (Ohio) *Journal* in 1824:

"Dr. Balthasar Beckar respectfully informs the public, that he is possessed of the genuine ABRACADABRA and understands the true use of the Dandelion flowers.

"He is the inventor of a PILL that will straighten a Roman nose into Grecian; sharpen a bullet-nose to a keen edge; and bring down the most inveterate pug-nose to a reasonable degree of earthy mindedness. His DROPS are sovereign for all disorders of the teeth: they will extract the future decayed tooth from the gums of a nurse child, with intense delight, and will insert in lieu thereof a piece of polished ivory; they will give the breath any fragrance that the Patient may desire, and change the same at pleasure. *Dr. Balthasar Beckar* has a portable machine by which he frequently amuses himself with distilling rose water from his own breath. Onion-Eaters may be supplied with an apparatus for condensing their breath into Gum Assafoetida at a reasonable price. He has also a LOTION for converting the outer integuments into fur or broadcloth, at the will of the Patient.

"The Unborn Doctor (for so Dr. Balthasar Beckar is commonly termed in the place of his nativity) scorns to make any professions which he is not able to fulfil.—As soon as the crowd of Patients will afford him a little leisure, he will endeavor to sell for publication a few of the cerficates with which the gratitude of the world is continually loading the U. States' mail. His correspondence is immense, and he has the honor of having under his care at this moment several of the crowned heads of Europe.

"N. B. Cancers cured by inspection. Boots and shoes cleaned and every favor gratefully acknowledged.

"P. S. No cure, no pay.

"* * To prove the security of his professions, Dr. Balthasar Beckar will, on Monday next, precisely at 12 o'clock, standing on the pavement in front of the Athenaeum swallow one of his own Pills. Practitioners of Medicine, and men of science generally, and all others who are fond of philosophical experiments, are invited to attend and witness this heroic achievement."[21]

That these attempts to educate the public were very successful cannot be said; the booming patent-medicine business of the next hundred years indicates the contrary.

* * *

Coinciding as it did with a period in which medicine was undergoing a transition from medievalism to modernity, in which the standards of medical education on the whole were declining, the history of medicine in the Middle West in the first half of the nineteenth century illustrates in striking degree some of the best, as well as some of the worst, features of the science. Rapid expansion of the country, the passion for business, the high esteem placed upon practicality, were not conducive to prolonged education for young men in any field of learning. Medicine, like the land, was, even by those within the profession, all too frequently exploited extensively rather than intensively. What the doctor lacked in training and knowledge he was supposed to compensate for with ingenuity and the American's reputed ability to rise to any emergency. This being the prevailing view, the careers of the Drakes, the Dudleys, and the Grosses, men who devoted their lives to the serious study of medicine and the elevation of its standards and accomplishments, stand out in all the more distinct contrast. It was not yet, so far as the generality of men were concerned, a scientific age. Science had to develop gradually.

In agriculture the American accepted improvements in machinery first and easiest; these saved labor. Next came improvements in animals; they saved dollars. Last and hardest to the farmer came general science—soil chemistry, diets, plant pathology—the "book larnin' " of the "printer farmers." So it was in medicine. The first to receive popular acceptance were the manual services of the profession: setting of broken bones, amputations, and the like, especially after the advent of anaesthesia. Second came more general reliance upon the physician in cases of contagious diseases. Many persons who would not call a doctor for croup, dysentery, or rheumatism would do so for smallpox, diphtheria, or even measles. Last—and this after the pioneer period—came common acceptance of the germ theory, vaccines, hospitals, and preventive medicine. Medicine, as compared with applied science in mechanics was at a disadvantage. Advances in general education at times served but to make the people more critical of their doctors, who themselves were critical of each other. Though in retrospect, this period of confusion in medicine proved to be salutary, it did not so appear at the time. If public confidence was not lost, it at least developed slowly and intermittently. At all times the pioneer reserved the sovereign right to try to make the science of medicine conform to his concept of democracy, to criticize, complain, refuse to regulate, do his own doctoring or none at all. Yet in spite of everything—folk cures, household remedies, "hippos," calomel, lancet, Lobelia No. 6, trillionths, animalculae, nervauric influences, "patent" pills and bottles—some survived. Of that we have concrete and visible evidence.

NOTES

NOTES: CHAPTER ONE

[1] Described in the New York *Medical Repository,* X (1808), by Dr. Samuel P. Hildreth of Marietta.

[2] Dr. Hildreth in his presidential address before the Ohio Medical Convention in 1839 listed the following as major epidemics in Ohio: 1790-95—Belpre, smallpox and scarlatina; 1796—Gallipolis, malignant fever; 1800-01—Chillicothe, epidemic fever; 1807—very general, epidemic fever; 1813, measles; 1822-23, epidemic fever, "The Great Epidemic"; 1824-25, measles and scarlatini; 1826, influenza; 1832-33, epidemic cholera. Another article, on the epidemic of 1822-23, was published in the *Philadelphia Journal of the Medical and Physical Sciences,* V (1824).

[3] A. D. P. Van Buren, "The Pioneers' Foes," *Michigan Pioneer and Historical Collections,* V (1884), 300-2.

[4] *Daily's Family Physician* (Louisville, 1848), 26-7.

[5] Dr. Leon G. Zerfas presents an interesting account of this disease in some of the southern counties of the state, "Milk Sickness in the Lincoln Family," in Indiana State Medical Society *Journal,* XXIX (1936), 88-9. A more recent treatment, with particular emphasis on prognosis, is Philip D. Jordan's, "The Death of Nancy Hanks Lincoln," *Indiana Magazine of History,* XL, 2 (June, 1944).

[6] Dr. Guy S. Wright, "Observations on the Atmospheric Origin of the Endemic Sick Stomach . . . ," *Western Medical and Physical Journal,* I (1827), 369.

[7] The disease has been confined largely to the Ohio Valley. For the history, description, and cure of milk sickness see James Fitton Couch, "Trembles (or Milk Sickness)," United States Department of Agriculture *Circular* 306 (1933 and 1938).

[8] Dr. A. A. Benezet, *The Family Physician; . . . calculated particularly for the Inhabitants of the Western Country, . . .* (Cincinnati, 1826), 123 ff; Dr. John C. Gunn, *Domestic Medicine* (Springfield, Ohio, 1835), 194 ff; Dr. Daniel Drake, "Practical Observations in the Typhoid Stage of Autumnal Fever," *Western Journal of the Medical*

and Physical Sciences (hereafter referred to as *Western Journal*), I (1828), 381 ff.

⁹ First tried on his pupil, Daniel Drake, if tradition can be believed. See Reginald Fitz, " 'Something Curious in the Medical Line,' " *Bulletin of the History of Medicine*, XI, 3 (March, 1942), 239-64, for an excellent survey of the introduction of Dr. Edward Jenner's discovery and the pioneering of Dr. Benjamin Waterhouse of Cambridge, Massachusetts. Also Morris C. Leikind, "The Introduction of Vaccination into the United States," *Ciba Symposia* (Ciba Pharmaceutical Products, Inc., Summit, New Jersey, 1934—), III, 10 (January, 1942).

¹⁰ Perhaps the best treatment of the horror and destruction of this scourge available at the present time is John Sharpe Chambers, *The Conquest of Cholera* (New York, 1938). For contemporary accounts of its progress consult *Niles Register* (Baltimore, 1811-49), XLII and XLIII (1832-33), and the more important newspapers of the various areas afflicted. See also *Western Journal*, VI (1833), 78-120, 321-64; VII (1834), 161-81, 341-9, for excellent discussions of the disease, with particular emphasis upon its appearance in certain parts of Ohio.

¹¹ Dr. Daniel Drake, "Epidemic Cholera:—Its Pathology and Treatment," *Western Journal*, V (1832), 612. Again in 1849 Dr. Drake wrote two letters of advice to the people of Cincinnati. No new cures had been found in the interim.

¹² Not until 1843 was the contagious nature of puerperal fever definitely established. In that year Dr. Oliver Wendell Holmes read his essay "The Contagiousness of Puerperal Fever" before the Boston Society for Medical Improvement. At the request of the Society it was printed in the April, 1843, issue of the *New England Quarterly Journal of Medicine and Surgery*. Since his message failed to obtain wide circulation, it was reprinted with additions in 1855. Dr. Holmes's proof has been considered one of the two major contributions to medical science in the period between 1840 and 1850.

¹³ "Mothers rejoiced rather than mourned, as they are apt to nowadays. Then a mother's joys were her children, now they are in the way of these gay women, who want cards and society; in the way of these poorer ones who think they can't provide for them. Have devoted mothers, like many other things, gone out of style? Lord send a reform to the men and women of today! Bring them back to the life of the goodsized family circle of boys and girls. . . . Oh, Lord, bring my beloved land back to homelife and motherhood again." Illinois Historical Society *Journal*, XVII (1924), 620-1.

·NOTES: CHAPTER TWO

¹ Oliver W. Smith, *Early Indiana Trials and Sketches* (Cincinnati, 1858), 12-13.

[2] For background of almost four thousand years of folk medicine see bibliographical essay. An excellent brief survey is Loren MacKinney, "The Vulture in Ancient Medical Lore . . . in the Medieval World . . . and in the Modern World," a series of three articles in *Ciba Symposia*, IV, 3 (June, 1942).

[3] *The Badianus Manuscript*, translated and annotated by Emily Walcott Emmart (Baltimore, Johns Hopkins Press, 1940). For comment on the literature of herbals see bibliographical note.

[4] Francesco Hernandez (1514 ? -1587), personal physician to Philip II, at the King's request, explored the New World, 1570-77, for plants and medicines. In this work he accumulated twenty-six folio volumes of notes and drawings. An abridged edition of these was published in Rome in the seventeenth century. The originals were destroyed by fire in 1611. Much of the knowledge acquired by Hernandez was incorporated in Francisco Ximinez's *Four Books on the Nature and Medicinal Properties of the Plants and Animals Found in New Spain*, which appeared in Mexico in 1615.

[5] Contrast with the Pennsylvania German theory: the leaves of boneset stripped upward act as an emetic, downward as a purgative. Edward Miller Fogel, *Beliefs and Superstitions of the Pennsylvania Germans* (Philadelphia, 1915), 278.

[6] The Aztec recipe was white incense, earth of a decomposed corpse, well ground up in dragon's blood and white of egg, and applied to the temple. *Badianus Manuscript*, plate 13.

[7] Nicholas Culpepper, in his *The English Physician—Enlarged, A Compleat Method of Physick, whereby a Man may preserve his Body in Health or Cure himself, being sick, with things only as grow in England, they being most fit for English Bodies*, 1704, had set forth the idea that every region of the earth produced indigenously the curative plants necessary for any disease there prevalent.

Remedies of the vegetable kingdom in use in colonial times, according to Dr. Rufus W. Griswold of Rock Hill, Connecticut, in Alexander Wilder's *History of Medicine. . . .* (New Sharon, Maine, 1901), 406-7, included the following: yellow dock, sarsaparilla, wintergreen, birch bark, elecampano, comfrey, sassafras, plantain, whitewood, dandelion, snake-root, hardhack, horseradish, peppermint, spearmint, red peppers, Indian tobacco, wormwood, tansy, yarrow, star-grass, marshmallow, Indian hemp, wild ginger, mullein, pink-root, nightshade, barberry, sweet flag, catnip, wormseed, golden thread, dogwood, skunkcabbage, bittersweet, slippery elm, boneset or thoroughwort, blue gentian, crane's bill, pennyroyal, frostwort, henbane, blue flag, butternut bark, juniper berries, burdock, wild cherry bark, flaxseed, pumpkin seeds, parsley root, May apple, black alder, elderberries, white oak bark, sumach berries, rosemary, blackberry root, willow bark, sage, blood-root, skull-cap, seneca, mustard, golden rod, queen's root, stramonium seeds, uvaursi, valerian, hellebore, prickly ash, touchwood, agrimony, sweet fern, mandrake, marjoram, colt's foot, mistletoe, Peruvian bark. Many of these same remedies were indicated in Culpepper's treatise.

[8] But not original: "Celtiberia in terra, quod quisque minxit, hoc sibi solet mane dentem atque russam defricare gingiuam, ut quo iste uester expolitior dens est, hoc te amplius bibisse praedicet loti." Catullus, *Carmina*, XXXIX. Also "They [Iberians] have regard not for rational living, but rather for satisfying their physical needs and bestial instincts —unless some one thinks those men have regard for rational living who bathe with urine aged in cisterns and wash their teeth with it, both they and their wives, as the Cantabrians and the neighboring peoples are said to do." Strabo, III, 164.

[9] R. E. Banta, "The Indian Doctors," *Wabash Bulletin*, XL (January, 1942), 24.

[10] *Indiana Republican* (Madison), August 1, 1833.

[11] For note on folk cures and superstitions see bibliographical note.

[12] Debate regarding the efficacy of this cure continues in the press a hundred years later.

[13] "Took it by storm," said Dr. Morris Fishbein, *The Medical Follies* (New York, 1925), 21; this may be a slight exaggeration.

[14] *Daily Cincinnati Gazette*, January 1, 1849.

[15] *Louisville Journal* in *Columbus* (Ohio) *Daily Journal*, August 2, 1837.

[16] Dr. Otto Juettner, *Daniel Drake and His Followers* (Cincinnati, 1909), 95.

[17] *Columbus Daily Journal*, July 25, 1837; *Portsmouth Journal* in (Cincinnati) *National Republican and Ohio Political Register*, January 20, 1824.

[18] *Cincinnati Times*, in Juettner, *Daniel Drake*, 93.

[19] *Cincinnati Lancet and Observer*, I (1858), 442-3.

[20] *Ibid.*, 400-1.

[21] The Worcester and Philadelphia editions of 1804 and 1806 carried the title *Domestic Medicine: or a Valuable Treatise on the Prevention and Cure of Diseases by Regimen and Simple Medicines. With an Appendix, containing a new Dispensatory, for the Use of Private Practitioners. To which are added, observations on the diet of the common people; recommending a method of living less expensive and more conducive to health, than the present.* Buchan was graduated at Edinburgh in 1761 and began his lectures there in 1766. He became a fellow of the Royal College of Physicians in 1772. Later years were spent in London where he published several other books on medicine and health.

[22] Hugh P. Greeley, "Early Wisconsin Medical History," in *Wisconsin Medical Journal*, XX (1922), 558-69.

NOTES: CHAPTER THREE

[1] This instrument was in use in southern Ohio in the early 1830's but not in other parts of the state until after 1835. Dr. Howard Dittrick, "The Equipment, Instruments and Drugs of Pioneer Physicians of Ohio," *Ohio State Archaeological and Historical Quarterly*, XLVIII, 3 (July, 1939), 201-3.

Dr. Drake in Cincinnati in 1830 was urging "such of our readers, by far the greater number, as have not yet given it a trial, the *duty* of doing so." He was not convinced of its superiority in all cases, however, and reported an instance of "one patient in whom the respiratory murmer was more audible and distinct, when heard by the application of the ear to the chest, than when listened to through the cylinder." Laennec described the stethoscope as being composed of wood of medium density, a foot long and an inch and a quarter in diameter, preferably cylindrical, with a canal one-fifth the diameter. The instrument was equipped with a stopper which was used in certain cases. Ordinarily the shaft was made in two parts, although this was for convenience in transporting rather than an essential to the functioning of the instrument. "A Treatise on the Diseases of the Chest in which they are described according to their anatomical characters; and their Diagnosis as established on a new principle by means of Acoustick instruments, with plates," translated from the French of Rene T. H. Laennec, M. D., Paris edition of 1819, First American edition, Philadelphia, 1823, in *Western Journal*, III (1830), 68-99.

[2] Dr. Robert Boal of Cincinnati, quoted by Juettner, *Daniel Drake*, 87-8.

[3] Dr. John C. Reeve, "A Physician in Pioneer Wisconsin," in *Wisconsin Magazine of History*, III (1919-20), 308.

[4] Dr. Morris Fishbein, "Some Physician's Fees," in *Bulletin of the Society of Medical History of Chicago*, II, 2 (1919), 181.

[5] Etolie T. Davis, "Memoir Ebenezer Grosvenor," in *Michigan Pioneer and Historical Collections*, XXXVIII (1912), 703; Fishbein, "Some Physician's Fees," 181.

[6] *Atlas and History of Franklin County* (S. H. Beers and Company, Chicago, 1882), 95.

[7] *Sangamo Journal*, April 10, 1840.

[8] *Ohio State Archaeological and Historical Quarterly*, LII, 4 (October-December, 1943), 318-9.

[9] Juettner, *Daniel Drake*, 96-7.

[10] Dr. William H. Wishard, in Indiana State Medical Society *Transactions*, 1889, 12.

[11] Ruth Hoppin, "Personal Recollection," *Michigan Pioneer and Historical Collections*, XXXVIII (1912), 414.

[12] The best brief treatment of the emergence of modern medicine is in

Chapter IX of Richard Harrison Shryock's *The Development of Modern Medicine* (Philadelphia, 1936).

[13] Dr. John Hunter in I. G. Rosenstein, *Theory and Practice of Homeopathy* (Louisville, 1840), 8-9.

[14] Dr. Robert and Johanna Peter, *The History of the Medical Department of Transylvania University*, Filson Club *Publications*, XX (Louisville, 1905), 66. Jalap seems at times to have been even more feared than calomel. At a Mackinac party in 1769 the guests, including some who crashed the party, inbibed freely of a wine and brandy punch. When Dr. Daniel Morison, one of the hosts, told them that he had put in four ounces of jalap (a few grains was a good dose) some of the guests later broke into his house and gave him a bad beating. Dr. Morison's "Narrative" (Burton Historical Collection, Detroit Public Library) as quoted in Milo M. Quaife, *Lake Michigan* (Indianapolis, 1944), 92-3.

[15] Dr. William H. Wishard, Indiana State Medical Society *Transactions*, 1889, 14.

[16] Dr. Joel Pennington, *ibid.*, 1873.

[17] For illustration of the lancet most popularly used and an explanation of its use see Donald D. Shira, "Phlebotomy Lancet," in *Ohio State Medical Journal*, XXXV (1939), 66-7.

[18] Dr. T. B. Harvey, Indiana State Medical Society *Transactions*, 1881, 2.

[19] Kansas City *Star*, September 22, 1929, in *Missouri Historical Review*, XXIV (1929-30), 329-30.

[20] *Western Lancet*, V (1843-44), in *Ohio State Medical Journal*, XXXV (1939), 1329.

[21] Margaret Lafever, "Story of Early Day Life in Michigan," *Michigan Pioneer and Historical Collections*, XXXVIII (1912), 675.

[22] Baynard Rush Hall, *The New Purchase* (New York, 1855), 254; J. Sellman to Captain Samuel Vance of eastern Indiana, undated letter (some time prior to 1827), Vance Papers, Miscellaneous, Vol. I, William Henry Smith Memorial Library, Indianapolis, Indiana.

[23] Juettner, *Daniel Drake*, 95.

[24] Dr. Wilson Hobbs, Indiana State Medical Society *Transactions*, 1889, 24.

[25] Dr. Joel Pennington, *ibid.*, 1873.

[26] Address at Centennial Celebration of the College of Physicians and Surgeons, Columbia University, June 11, 1907, in *Papers and Addresses*, III (3 volumes, Baltimore, 1920), 292-3.

[27] Dr. Howard Dittrick, "Introduction of Anesthesia into Ohio," *Ohio State Archaeological and Historical Quarterly*, L (1941), 338 ff.

[28] August Schachner, *Ephraim McDowell, "Father of Ovariotomy" and Founder of Abdominal Surgery* (Philadelphia, 1921), 67. Mrs. Jane Todd Crawford, the patient, is buried at Graysville, Sullivan County, Indiana.

[29] Dr. John Richmond, "History of a Successful Case of Caesarian Operation," *Western Journal,* III (1830), 485-9.

[30] Dr. Bobbs's operation is reported in the Indiana State Medical Society *Transactions,* 1868; apparently no account of the Wolcott nephrectomy was written by the surgeon himself, but Dr. Charles L. Stoddard reported it in the Philadelphia *Medical and Surgical Reporter,* VII (1861-62), 126 ff. See also Martin B. Tinker, "The First Nephrectomy and the First Cholecystotomy, with a sketch of The Lives of Doctors Erastus B. Wolcott and John S. Bobbs," *Johns Hopkins Hospital Bulletin,* XII, 125 (August, 1901), 247 ff.

[31] Dr. Francis Randolph Packard, *History of Medicine in the United States* (2 volumes, New York, 1931), I, 480. The subject of surgery in Kentucky has been well treated in A. H. Barkley, *Kentucky's Pioneer Lithotomists* (Cincinnati, 1913). See also Dr. Joseph Nathaniel McCormack, *Some of the Medical Pioneers of Kentucky* (Bowling Green, 1917).

[32] "Medical and Surgical History of Elkhart County," Indiana State Medical Society *Transactions,* 1875, 85 ff; Alfred Theodore Andreas, *History of Chicago* (3 volumes, 1884-86), I, 465; B. F. Uran, "The Names and a Brief History of Early Physicians of Kankakee County," *Bulletin of the Society of Medical History of Chicago,* II, 2 (1919), 183-90; Packard, *History of Medicine,* I, 482; Dr. W. T. S. Cornett, Indiana State Medical Society *Transactions,* 1874, 30.

[33] Dr. Jesse S. Myer, *Life and Letters of Dr. William Beaumont* (St. Louis, 1912), 569. Two Beaumont notebooks, ably edited by Genevieve Miller of The Johns Hopkins Institute of the History of Medicine, have been published as *Wm. Beaumont's Formative Years; Two Early Notebooks 1811-1821* (New York, 1946). The influence of Dr. Beaumont's work on his medical contemporaries and successors has been ably treated by Dr. George Rosen, *The Reception of William Beaumont's Discovery in Europe* (New York, 1942).

[34] *Western Journal,* III (1830), 317-40.

[35] Dr. W. H. Wishard thought that in 1825 in Indiana not over ten per cent of the physicians were graduates of medical colleges and not over twenty-five per cent had ever attended any lectures. Indiana State Medical Society *Transactions,* 1889. In Ohio it is estimated that the percentage of graduates rose from around ten to approximately twenty by 1835. *Ohio State Archaeological and Historical Quarterly,* XLVIII (1939), 190.

[36] Dr. Robert Peter, *Transylvania University, Its Origin, Rise, Decline, and Fall,* Filson Club *Publications,* XI (Louisville, 1896), 18-20, 64. The later publication by Dr. Peter (edited posthumously by his daughter Johanna) *The History of the Medical Department of Transylvania University,* 405, gives 1796 as the date for the establishment of the Kentucky Academy.

[37] J. Christian Bay, "Dr. Daniel Drake, 1785-1852," *Filson Club History Quarterly*, VII (1933), 6-7. His differences of opinion with Dr. Dudley may not have been wholly responsible for Drake's resignation; it is possible that he may have recognized Lexington's lack of future as a medical center. Though it is often told, the story of the Drake-Dudley duel is given no credence by Juettner. According to the story, Drake was challenged by Dudley and at the critical moment refused to fight; his place was said to have been taken by Richardson. Juettner maintains that this story was invented and circulated by Dr. Alban Gold Smith, Drake's bitter enemy. It is true, however, that a duel occurred between Dudley and Richardson, and that in the conflict Richardson was shot in the thigh (groin?) and would have bled to death had Dudley not ligated his femoral (inguinal?) artery. Richardson and Dudley afterwards became good friends. Dudley, "a fighting Southerner of the revolutionary type," is known to have had a fiery temper which was not at all conducive to amicable relations; Drake's temperament did not help matters much. *Daniel Drake*, 44.

[38] *Filson Club History Quarterly*, VII (1933), 151. The Transylvania war of 1837-44 may be followed in the *Kentucky Gazette, Lexington Observer and Reporter*, Cincinnati and Louisville papers or in James C. Cross's *Appeal to the Medical Profession* (Louisville, 1846).

[39] Dr. John Shaw Billings, speaking in later years of Dr. Drake. Billings began his medical education in Drake's Medical College of Ohio. He later "achieved excellence and gained distinction in no less than six different fields, in military and public hygiene, in hospital construction and sanitary engineering, in vital and medical statistics, in medical bibliography and history, in the advancement of medical education and the condition of medicine in the United States and as civil administrator of unique ability." Of these accomplishments, the work for which he is probably best known is the creation of the Surgeon General's Library and the institution of the *Index Catalogue*, accompanied by the monthly bibliography of medical literature, "Index Medicus."

A more effusive estimate of Drake has been written by his biographer, Dr. Juettner: "In the medical history of the West one colossal figure looms up in the very foreground. It is of such gigantic proportions that all else appears accidental and merely like a part of the stage-setting. Even when viewed through the aisles of time at a distance of many decades it appears as large and distinct as it did when it first emerged in the center of the stage of events. It is the figure of him who was the Father of Western Medicine, one of the greatest physicians America has produced, a patriot of the truest blue, a nobleman by nature, a scholar by ceaseless toil, the peer of any of the Eastern pioneers in medicine, the bearer of one of the most distinguished names in the intellectual history of our country—Daniel Drake." *Daniel Drake*, 8.

[40] In later years Drake recaptured these early days in a delightful

series of letters to his children; these were gathered up and in 1870 published by his son Charles as *Pioneer Life in Kentucky. A Series of Reminiscential Letters from Daniel Drake, M.D., of Cincinnati, to his Children* (Cincinnati). These letters are being republished by Henry Schuman, with a biographical foreword by J. Christian Bay.

[41] It has been said that Daniel Drake was "predestined for the medical profession" by his father. Isaac Drake had met Dr. Goforth, one of the original party of emigrants from New Jersey, on the journey down the Ohio River. Half jokingly, half in earnest, he told Dr. Goforth that Daniel, then not quite three years old, should some day become a doctor, and that Dr. Goforth should be his teacher.

[42] Juettner, *Daniel Drake*, 20.

[43] *Ibid.*, 22.

[44] *Ibid.*, 24, for a facsimile of this diploma.

[45] That Drake had no intention of staying when he accepted the Jefferson appointment might be inferred from his continuing to edit his *Western Journal*, published in Cincinnati, in which he stated more than once that his "associations are all in the West" and that he expected "to live on this side of the mountains."

[46] Juettner, "Rise of Medical Colleges in the Ohio Valley," Ohio Archaeological and Historical Society *Publications*, XXII (1913), 488.

The crisis in the Medical College of Ohio and the organization of the rival school is reviewed by Drake in the *Western Journal*, IX (1836), 169-203. No doubt one of the weaknesses of the Medical College of Ohio was that it was not connected with any college or university; it was, as Drake said, "perhaps the only separate and independent medical school in the United States."

[47] Dr. Emmet F. Horine, "A History of the Louisville Medical Institute and of the establishment of the University of Louisville and its School of Medicine 1833-1846," *Filson Club History Quarterly*, VII (1933), 133-47; William Cassell Mallalieu, "Origins of the University of Louisville," *ibid.*, XII (1938), 34-5.

[48] For full title and description see later in this chapter.

[49] Mrs. Alice Guffey Ruggles, "Unpublished Letters of Dr. Daniel Drake," *Ohio State Archaeological and Historical Quarterly*, XLIX (1940), 203.

[50] *Ibid.*, 210-11.

[51] Howard A. Kelly and Walter L. Burrage, *Dictionary of American Medical Biography* (New York, 1928), 784-5.

[52] *Ibid.*; Packard, *History of Medicine*, II, 833-4; Lucius P. Henry Zeuch, *History of Medical Practice in Illinois* (Chicago, 1927), I, 106-11; James Thomas Flexner, *Doctors on Horseback* (New York, 1937), 154.

[53] J. H. Walsh, "Early Medical Practice in the Illinois Country," *Illinois Medical Journal*, XLVI (1924), 199; Zeuch, *Medical Practice in Illinois*, 543-53.

[54] Zeuch, *Medical Practice in Illinois*, 396-406; Carl E. Black, "Illinois College Medical School," *Bulletin of the Society of Medical History of Chicago*, I, 2 (August, 1912), 171-95.

[55] Rush Medical College became affiliated with the University of Chicago in 1898 and in 1924 was incorporated as its Medical Department. After June 1, 1942, its undergraduate courses were discontinued and it became Rush Graduate School of Medicine.

[56] Packard, *History of Medicine*, II, 870-1.

[57] Henry B. Favill, "Early Medical Days in Wisconsin," *Bulletin of the Society of Medical History of Chicago*, I (1911), 101-4; Packard, *History of Medicine*, II, 903-4.

[58] Isaac Reed, *The Christian Traveler* (New York, 1828), 224.

[59] Juettner, "Rise of Medical Colleges," 489-90.

[60] Cincinnati *National Republican and Ohio Political Register*, January 20, 1824.

[61] A factor which helped to account for the small number of trained eastern physicians found in the Midwest was, of course, their relative scarcity even in the East, and the consequent esteem with which they were regarded. Few indeed were the trained physicians who would wish to give up a settled practice for a life in the "wilderness."

[62] Frank Luther Mott, *A History of American Magazines* (3 volumes, New York and Cambridge, 1930, 1938), I, 199.

[63] For these see bibliographical note.

[64] Drake's temporary acceptance of the weird fact of spontaneous combustion of the human body probably resulted from an article by M. Marc, published in the *Dictionnaire des Sciences Medicales*. He translated and summarized the article in the *Western Journal*, II (1829), 130-41. The *Dictionnaire* reported a number of "well authenticated" cases. Marc and others arrived at certain general conclusions: women were more subject to this accident than men; the aged more susceptible than the young; inactive and fleshy ("polysarcous") persons were good subjects; heavy drinkers particularly good; most accidents of this sort transpired in winter when the atmosphere was cold. Sparks caused by the "idio-electricity" in animals set off the naturally-produced hydrogen and its compounds. Drake commented that he was unable to say why more cases had been recorded on the Continent than in the United States. The fact that he recorded no cases in his *Diseases of the Interior Valley* might indicate that there were none.

NOTES: CHAPTER FOUR

[1] In Rosenstein, *Theory and Practice of Homeopathy*, 26.

[2] Dr. William H. Loppe, "Quacks and Quackery in Indiana," Indiana State Medical Society *Transactions*, 1883, 118.

[3] Dr. George Rowland, "Medical Legislation," *ibid.*, 172.

⁴ For analysis of the six patented Thomsonian medicines see "The Secret Six," *Ohio State Archaeological and Historical Quarterly*, LII, 4 (October-December, 1943), 350 ff.

The idea of heat potencies of herbs was not new. William Turner in his *Herbal* of 1568 wrote: "There are certain herbs, that are temperate, that is, of a mean quality or property between hot and cold, and are neither notably hot nor cold. And if any herb depart from the temperate herbs toward heat, and is sensible felt a little hot, it is called hot in the first degree; and if it be a little hotter, it is called hot in the second degree, as though it had been made two steps or departings from temperate. If an herb be very hot, it may be called hot in the third degree. If it be hot as it can be, then it is called hot in the fourth degree. And so ye may understand the degrees of cold, moist, and dry herbs." Dr. Sanford V. Larkey and Thomas Pyles, *An Herbal* [1525] (New York, 1941), Introduction xx.

⁵ For accounts presenting this trial from both sides see Thomson, *Narrative*, 93-104, and Barton, *Materia Medica*, II, 188-95, quoting Tyng's *Reports*, VI, 134. In Boston in 1824 (?) Thomson published a pamphlet, *Learned Quackery Exposed; or, Theory according to Art. As exemplified in the practice of the Fashionable Doctors of the present day*, which contained a poem which he claimed to have written in Newburyport jail in 1809. This poem had been circulated as a handbill, "as a looking-glass in which the doctors might see their own conduct and the effects of their medicine on patients in cases of pleurisy and fevers, when treated according to art."

⁶ This was the first of the Thomsonian periodicals of any importance. Under the original title, it appeared with irregularity—sometimes weekly, sometimes trimonthly, but for the most part semimonthly —until 1837, when it became the *Botanico-Medical Recorder*. In 1835 Hersey withdrew to establish, also at Columbus, the *Independent Botanico Register*, which lasted only one year (to May, 1836). For a list of leading Botanic periodicals see bibliographical note.

⁷ On first glance it appears that Horton Howard was printing his books after his death. Howard, the Thomsonian sales manager, died of cholera in 1833, but Horton J. Howard, the printer, was still operating. The third edition, with Columbus imprint, 1836, printed by Horton J. Howard carried, besides Horton Howard's preface to the first edition, a preface of W. Hance of Cincinnati. Hance spoke "in the name of present proprietors, the heirs of the late Dr. Howard."

⁸ *Thomsonian Recorder*, II, 11 (March 1, 1834), 174. Thomson prescribed for himself a somewhat similar treatment during the last days of his final illness. Report of Nathaniel S. Magoon, his attendant, *Botanico-Medical Recorder*, November, 1843, reprinted in *Bulletin* of the Lloyd Library, No. 11 (Reproduction Series No. 7), 86-9.

⁹ *Ibid.*, II, 13 (March 29, 1834), 200.

[10] J. E. Carter, *The Botanic Physician,* . . . (Madisonville, Tennessee, 1837), 8.

[11] *Columbus* (Ohio) *Daily Journal,* July 13, 1837.

[12] *Medical Investigator,* I (1847), 8.

[13] *Ibid.,* 90.

[14] *Ibid.,* 54.

[15] *Ibid.,* 38.

[16] Dr. A. Biggs, *The Botanico Medical Reference Book, comprising the Fundamental Principles of Life—the True Theory of Fever and Inflammation—The Union of Mind and Matter—the Instinct in Animals and the Mind in Man—Sanity and Insanity—Causes of Insanity, how Treated, &c. Also the Theory and Practice of Medicine, upon Botanico-Medical Principles, A Materia Medica, containing a Description of the Various Articles Used. Pharmacy—Teaching the Mode of Preparing, Compounding, and Preserving Medicines, with a Number of Recipes* (Memphis, 1847), 99.

[17] *Medical Investigator,* I, 384.

[18] One concludes, from perusal of some of the students' lecture notes, that this was one of the more important purposes of many of the lectures. In fact, the "Suggestions to Students" printed inside the front cover of Buchanan and Newton's *Eclectic Medical Journal,* 1853, carried the following: "The Materia Medica, as taught in the Institute . . . affords a large number of new and concentrated remedies, not known in the common practice." One is impressed by the wide discrepancy in the nature of the knowledge obtained by the student in anatomy and in materia medica: in the former field detailed and elaborate drawings of the human body and its parts; in the latter medicine lists and prescriptions for scores of medicines such as Anti-Bilious Pills, Alternative Powders, Vegetable Emetic, Pulmonary Powder, Rheumatic Pills, Anti Dyspeptic Pills, Female Pills, Cough Pills, Nervous Pills, Dieuretic Drops, Sudorific Tincture, etc., etc.—which revealed little. Manuscripts of Dr. William A. Ashton, Franklin County, Indiana, in possession of the authors.

NOTES: CHAPTER FIVE

[1] A file in the Hering Laboratory, 1930-35, has been said to show twelve hundred references substantiating homeopathic doctrines in general practice from old school sources. Lucy Stone Hertzog, "Rise of Homeopathy," *Ohio State Archaeological and Historical Quarterly,* XLIX (1940), 336.

[2] This volume ran to five editions. The second, 1819, was much different from the first, but the next edition, 1824, was very similar to the second. Hahnemann says in his preface to the third edition that the translation of the preceding edition into French had been "a great help

to the spread of the good cause in foreign lands." The fourth, of 1829, had some important variations from the text of its immediate predecessor, and the last, in 1833, contained several novelties, such as the theories of the "vital force," the belief that the action of drugs was due to their power of stimulating cells of the body to curative reactions, and of "the dynamisation of medicines."

3 Dr. Frederick C. Waite, "Thomsonianism in Ohio," *Ohio State Archaeological and Historical Quarterly,* XLIX (1940), 330.

4 Hertzog, "Rise of Homeopathy," *ibid.,* 332.

5 See his review in *Western Monthly Review,* I (1827), 357. Also review of the pamphlet "New Views of Penitentiary Discipline and Moral Education and Reform," *ibid.,* III (1829), 50-6.

6 *Daily Cincinnati Gazette,* January 3, 1849.

7 Grace Adams and Edward Hutter, *The Mad Forties* (New York, 1942), Chapter XI, give a clever account of these developments.

8 *Therapeutic Sarcognomy, A Scientific Exposition of the Mysterious Union of Soul, Brain and Body, and a New System of Therapeutic Practice without Medicine, by the Vital Nervaura, Electricity and External Applications, Giving the only Scientific Basis for Therapeutic Magnetism and Electro-Therapeutics. Designed for the use of Nervauric and Electric Practitioners, and also for intelligent families, for the prevention and cure of diseases, and moral and physical development of youth.*

9 *Ibid.,* 258-9.

10 In California in the 1930's Dr. Albert Abrams, licensed physician, hooked up a couple of cheap resistance boxes and an old Ford spark coil and announced to the world that he had a magic detector of such delicacy that he could tune in on the electronic vibrations which emanate from a drop of blood. Given a drop of blood from a human being and this apparatus, one could determine exactly what the patient was suffering from, if anything. Also whether he was Chinese or Jewish, Catholic or Presbyterian. *Annual Report of the Smithsonian Institution,* 1937, 414.

Somewhat less awe-inspiring, but more valid, is the work of Dr. Edgar Douglas Adrian, fellow of Trinity College, Cambridge, who received a Nobel prize in physiology in 1932 for his experiments in measuring electrical impulses from, and locating images in, different portions of the brain, when stimulated by sight, sound, etc. The scientist modestly states, "The present technique of recording brain events, by oscillographs connected with electrodes on the head, is not likely to lead very far." *Time,* XLIII (May 8, 1944), 74. Perhaps it was just as well that Dr. Buchanan was not handicapped by modern apparatus.

NOTES: CHAPTER SIX

1 See Shryock, *Development of Modern Medicine,* Chapter IX.
2 *Ibid.,* 160.

304

³ *Western Journal,* III (1830), 394-5.

⁴ *Ibid.,* 395-6.

⁵ Well presented, for example, in an article on the honor of the profession, danger of quacks, weakness of the law, etc., in the Springfield, Illinois, *Sangamo Journal,* May 10, 1834.

⁶ July 17.

⁷ *Ravenna* (Ohio) *Courier,* August 20, 1825.

⁸ "An Essay on Bilious Fever and Calomel etc.," reviewed in *Western Monthly Review,* II (1829), 465. Hunn was editor 1829-30, of the *Medical Friend of the People* (Danville and Lexington).

⁹ Juettner, *Daniel Drake,* 392.

¹⁰ *Liberty Hall and Cincinnati Gazette,* January 11, 1832.

¹¹ Michigan by law in 1844 and 1846 gave the keepers of county prisons the right to deliver bodies of executed criminals with no relatives or friends, to local medical societies; also, the bodies of criminals who died in state prisons might be turned over to medical societies. Exclusive privileges to these bodies were to go to the Medical Department of the University, when organized. How well these provisions took care of needs is not known.

¹² "An Introductory Address, intended as a defense of the Medical Profession against the charge of Irreligion and Infidelity, with thoughts on the truth and importance of Natural Religion; delivered November 2d, 1824." Reviewed in *Western Monthly Review,* I (1827), 155 ff. Caldwell's *Introductory Address on Independence of Intellect* was published at Lexington in 1825. He also defended the teaching of Natural Religion at Transylvania in a written debate with Dr. James Fishback, pastor of the First Baptist Church of Lexington. *The Correspondence Between Dr. Charles Caldwell—and Dr. James Fishback,* etc., was printed at Lexington in 1826, as was Caldwell's *Medical and Physical Memoirs.* His *Autobiography* was published in Philadelphia in 1855, the second year after his death.

¹³ Dr. Robert G. Patterson, "The Role of the 'District' as a Unit in Organized Medicine in Ohio." *Ohio State Archaeological and Historical Quarterly,* XLIX (1940), 370.

¹⁴ *Franklin Chronicle* (Worthington, Ohio), July 2, 1821.

¹⁵ *Ohio Laws, 1832-33,* 27.

¹⁶ Letter in reply to criticism in *Ohio State Journal,* December 28, 1826.

¹⁷ *Laws of the State of Indiana* (1816-17), Ch. XXXI, 161-5.

¹⁸ There is some uncertainty regarding what was the first actively functioning medical society in the Middle West. Dr. Hubbard Madison Smith maintains that the society organized at Vincennes "some time prior to 1818" was the first in the Northwest. "Medicine in the Northwest Territory: A Contribution to the Early Medical History of Indiana," Indiana State Medical Society *Transactions,* 1906, 338 ff.

[19] *Laws of the State of Indiana* (1830), Ch. XLIX, 91-3.

[20] *Illinois Intelligencer,* November 18, 1825.

[21] *Medicine and Its Development in Kentucky* (Works Progress Administration Project, Louisville, 1940), 79.

[22] Dr. Irvin Abell, "The Heritage of Kentucky Medicine," *Kentucky Medical Journal,* XXIV (1926), 477.

[23] Henry B. Favill, "Early Medical Days in Wisconsin," *Bulletin of the Society of Medical History of Chicago,* I (1911), 100; *Journal of the American Medical Association,* XLIV (1905), 1217.

[24] Dr. J. T. Reeve, in State Board of Health of Illinois *Fifth Annual Report* (Springfield, 1883), 154.

NOTES: CHAPTER SEVEN

[1] *Indiana Journal,* August 7, 1835.

[2] George W. Sloan, writing of the 1840's in "Fifty Years of Pharmacy," Indiana Historical Society *Publications,* III (1903), 335.

[3] Albert E. Ebert, "Early History of the Drug Trade of Chicago," Illinois Historical Society *Transactions,* 1903, 245.

[4] *Kentucky Yeoman* (Frankfort), March, 1845.

[5] Samples of contents of Ohio doctors' saddle bags in the period prior to 1840 are listed by Dr. Howard Dittrick, "The Equipment, Instruments and Drugs of Pioneer Physicians of Ohio," *Ohio State Archaeological and Historical Quarterly,* XLVIII (1939), 208-9. J. J. Tyler, in "Dr. Luther Spellman, Early Physician of the Western Reserve," *Ohio State Medical Journal,* XXXIV (April, 1938), lists the following drugs as having been purchased by a doctor in Canfield, Youngstown, and Pittsburgh between 1811 and 1816: opium, senna, sulphur, castor oil, Glauber's salts, ipecac, lead acetate, orange peel, magnesia, potassium bitartrate, rhubarb, ginger, calamine, ginseng, citrine ointment, oil sweet almonds, ferrous sulphate, guiac, Peruvian bark, calomel, saltpeter, wormwood, rosin, cantharides, Bergundy pitch, balsam copaiba, mercurial ointment, gum ammoniac, aloes, camphor, myrrh, sweet spirit of nitre, serpentaria, zinc sulphate, alum, liquorice, steel filings, gum arabic, calumba, tartar emetic, white arsenic, silver nitrate, sponge, jalap, asafoetida, anise, gentian, cloves, squills, kino, creta preparata, juniper, red precipitate of mercury, turpentine, dyanthos, peppermint, spigelia, lavender, nitric acid, muriatic acid, cassia, castile soap, and olive oil.

[6] June 18, November 6, 1840.

[7] *Fort Wayne Times and Peoples Press,* August 21, September 11, 1847.

[8] *Liberty Hall,* January 13, 1806.

[9] *Ibid.,* July 18, 1810; May 1, 1811.

[10] Also *Illinois Intelligencer,* September, 1825, etc.

[11] *Western Sun*, 1824, June-December; *Hamilton Intelligencer and Advertiser*, May, 1824, etc., etc.

[12] Daniel Drake, "The People's Doctors," *Western Journal*, III (1830), 416; Gunn, *Domestic Medicine* (Springfield, 1836 edition), 635-6.

[13] See Chapter II.

[14] Also, according to the title page, "Member of the Medical Societies of Cincinnati and Lexington; the Philadelphia Society and Lyceum of New York; the Academy of Natural Sciences of Philadelphia; the American Antiquity Society of Worcester and Nashville; the Kentucky Institute, &c; and of several learned Societies of Europe, in Paris, Bruxelles, Vienna, Bonn, Florence, Naples, &c."

[15] William Salmon, Professor of Physic, *The Compleat English Physician, or, the Druggists Shop Opened* (London, 1693). Salmon prescribed for eye trouble: Ashes of a Cat's Head, white vitriol and Saccharum Saturni mixed with honey. His "Elixir Universale, Not particular for any Distemper" was made of Rex Metallorum, Pouder of Lyons Heart, Filings of a Unicorn Horn, Ashes of a whole Chameleon, Bark of Witch-Hazel, Earth Worms ("a score"), Dried Man's Brains, and Egyptian Onions, mixed in Spirits Universalis.

[16] Quoted in *Western Journal*, III (1830), 459.

[17] Richard Ellsworth Call, *The Life and Writings of Rafinesque*, Filson Club *Publications*, No. X (Louisville, 1895), 51-2.

[18] June 11, 1829.

[19] *Ohio Farmer* (Batavia), August 1, October 1, 1835.

[20] *Western Sun*, July 6, 1826.

[21] *Portsmouth Journal* in (Cincinnati) *National Republican and Ohio Political Register*, January 20, 1824.

BIBLIOGRAPHICAL NOTE

Since most of the important medical books used in this study are identified in the text and notes, this bibliographical sketch is largely supplementary, and intended in part to round out a brief guide to the study of early middle western medicine.

BIBLIOGRAPHICAL AIDS: Two articles which provide an excellent introduction to the study of source materials in the medical history of the United States are Richard H. Shryock, "Medical Sources and the Social Historian," *American Historical Review*, LXI (April, 1936), 458-73; and Philip D. Jordan, "Some Bibliographical and Research Aids to American Medical History," *Ohio State Archaeological and Historical Quarterly*, L (December, 1941), 305-25. The best brief guide to bibliographical collections is *A Handbook of Medical Library Practice*, edited by Janet Doe for the Medical Library Association (Chicago, 1943). A list of about a thousand medical titles is also included in this work. The most complete general bibliography in any of the histories of medicine is that in Garrison.

The *Quarterly Cumulative Index Medicus* of the American Medical Association (1927—) [with its predecessors, the *Index Medicus* and *Quarterly Cumulative Index to Current Medical Literature*], and the comprehensive *Index-catalog of the Library of the Surgeon General's Office*, United States Army, are indispensable bibliographical tools for the study of medical history.

GENERAL: Histories of medicine which have been found

useful for background, as well as for occasional specific facts, are J. H. Bass, *Outlines of the History of Medicine* (English translation by H. E. Handerson, New York, 1889); Arturo Castiglioni, *A History of Medicine* (English translation and edition by E. B. Krumbhaar, New York, 1941); Fielding H. Garrison, *An Introduction to the History of Medicine* (fourth edition, Philadelphia, 1929); Samuel D. Gross, *History of American Medical Literature from 1776 to the Present Time* (Philadelphia, 1875); Francis R. Packard, *A History of Medicine* (two volumes, New York, 1931); Richard H. Shryock, *The Development of Modern Medicine* (Philadelphia, 1936); Henry E. Sigerist, *American Medicine* (English translation by Hildegard Nagel, New York, 1934); W. M. and M. S. C. Smallwood, *Natural History and the American Mind* (New York, 1941). Henry Burnell Shafer, *The American Medical Profession, 1783 to 1850* (Columbia University Studies in History, Economics, and Public Law, No. 417, New York, 1936), is especially good on early medical education in the United States. Published too late for use in this study is William Frederick Norwood, *Medical Education in the United States before the Civil War* (Philadelphia, 1944), a scholarly and valuable work.

Howard A. Kelly and Edward L. Burrage, *Dictionary of American Medical Biography* (New York, 1928), is convenient for ready reference to biographical data, but must be checked for details. Additional material is contained in earlier compilations by these authors: Kelly, *A Cyclopedia of American Medical Biography, comprising the lives of eminent deceased physicians and surgeons from 1610-1910* (two volumes, Philadelphia, 1912), and Kelly and Burrage, *American Medical Biographies* (Baltimore, 1920). Older biographical works are Richard F. Stone, *Biography of Eminent American Physicians and Surgeons* (Indianapolis, 1894); William Biddle Atkinson, *The Physicians and Surgeons of the United States* (Philadelphia, 1878); Samuel D. Gross, *Lives of Eminent American Physicians and Surgeons of the Nineteenth Century* (Philadelphia, 1861), and *Autobiography with Sketches of His Contemporaries* (Philadelphia, 1887); James Thacher, *American Medical Biography* (two volumes, Boston, 1828); and Stephen West Williams, *American Medical Biography* (Greenfield, Massachusetts, 1845). A fairly recent popular, yet useful series of sketches is presented by James T. Flexner, *Doctors on Horseback, Pioneers of American Medicine* (New York, 1937). Frank J. Jirka, *American Doctors of Destiny* (Chicago, 1940), contains chapters on Drake, McDowell, and other western doctors.

Among the state medical histories of varying value are: C. B. Burr, *Medical History of Michigan* (two volumes, Minneapolis, 1930); G. W. H. Kemper, *Medical History of Indiana* (Indianapolis, 1913); Lucius P. Henry Zeuch, *A History of Medical Practice in Illinois* (one volume published, Chicago, 1927); *Medicine and Its Development in Kentucky* (W.P.A. Medical Historical Research Project, Louisville, 1940); J. N. McCormack, *Some of the Medical Pioneers of Kentucky* (Bowling Green, 1917); E. J. Goodwin, *A History of Medicine in Missouri* (St. Louis, 1905); M. A. Goldstein, *One Hundred Years of Medicine and Surgery in Missouri* (St. Louis, 1900); *A Collection of Source Material Covering A Century of Medical Progress, 1834-1934* (Ohio State University Medical School, Blanchester, Ohio, 1934); D. S. Fairchild, *History of Medicine in Iowa* (one volume published, Des Moines, 1927); and Theodore Diller, *Pioneer Medicine in Western Pennsylvania* (New York, 1927).

These may be supplemented by J. N. Hyde, *Early Medical Chicago* (Chicago, 1879); *History of Medicine and Surgery and Physicians and Surgeons of Chicago* (Chicago Medical Society, Chicago, 1922); L. F. Frank, *The Medical History of Milwaukee, 1834-1914* (Milwaukee, 1915); Otto Juettner, *Daniel Drake and His Followers* (Cincinnati, 1909), which is in effect a medical history of early Cincinnati; and Howard Dittrick, *Pioneer Medicine in the Western Reserve* (Cleveland, 1932).

The standard histories of the states of the region contain

relatively little on the history of medicine. A notable exception is *The History of the State of Ohio*, edited by Carl F. Wittke (Columbus, 1941—), particularly Volume II, *The Frontier State, 1803-1825*, by William T. Utter, and Volume III, *The Passing of the Frontier, 1825-1850*, by Francis P. Weisenburger. More useful, on the whole, are the numerous local and county histories, some of which give space to accounts of early medical history as well as biographies of doctors.

STATE PUBLICATIONS AND HISTORICAL PERIODICALS: The state historical society publications contain much material on pioneer life. Particularly valuable are the *Michigan Pioneer and Historical Collections* (Lansing, 1874-1915); Illinois State Historical Society *Transactions* (Springfield, 1900—); Wisconsin Historical Society *Collections* (Madison, 1855—); and Indiana Historical Society *Publications* (Indianapolis, 1897—).

Likewise the history magazines: Illinois State Historical Society *Journal* (Springfield, 1908—); *Missouri Historical Review* (Columbia, 1906—); *Indiana Magazine of History* (Indianapolis and Bloomington, 1905—); *Register of the Kentucky State Historical Society* (Frankfort, 1903—); *Filson Club History Quarterly* (Louisville, 1926—); *Michigan History Magazine* (Lansing, 1917—); *Wisconsin Magazine of History* (Menasha and Madison, 1917—); *Iowa Journal of History and Politics* (Iowa City, 1903—). The *Ohio State Archaeological and Historical Quarterly* (Columbus, 1887—), 1939 to 1943, devoted one number each year to papers read before the annual meetings of the Committee on Archives and Medical History of the Ohio State Archaeological and Historical Society. In these articles have been assembled valuable material on various phases of the medical history of the state.

MEDICAL PERIODICALS AND PUBLICATIONS: Current periodicals which deal primarily with medical history are: *Bulletin of the (Institute of the) History of Medicine* (Baltimore, Johns Hopkins Institute of the History of Medicine, edited by Henry E. Sigerist, 1933—); *Annals of Medical History* (edited by Francis R.

Packard, New York, 1917-42); *Bulletin of the Society of Medical History of Chicago* (Chicago, 1911—). *Medical Life* was published by the American Society of Medical History (New York) from 1894 to 1938. The most recent periodical in the medical history field is Henry Schuman's *Journal of the History of Medicine and Allied Sciences,* a quarterly whose first number appeared in January, 1946.

Journals of the state medical societies, such as: *Illinois Medical Journal* (Springfield, 1899—); *Missouri State Medical Society Journal* (St. Louis, 1904—); *Indiana State Medical Association Journal* (Ft. Wayne, Indianapolis, 1908—); *Kentucky Medical Journal* (Bowling Green, 1903—); *Michigan State Medical Society Journal* (Lansing, 1902—); *Wisconsin Medical Journal* (Milwaukee, 1903—); *Journal of the Iowa State Medical Society* (Des Moines, 1911—); and *Ohio State Medical Journal* (Columbus, 1905—), contain articles on the early medical history of the respective states.

Transactions of state medical societies, particularly in the earlier years, are sources of valuable historical data. Those of the Ohio society date from 1846 to 1904; Indiana, 1850 to 1907; Illinois, 1850 to 1898; Iowa, 1850 to 1858, followed by those of a later society, 1867 to 1905; Kentucky, 1851 to 1902; Missouri, 1851 to 1852, followed by a new series, 1867 to 1903; Wisconsin, 1855 to 1902; and Michigan, 1867 to 1901. The early volumes of the American Medical Association *Transactions* from 1848 to 1852 contained a number of essays in the form of reports on American medical literature. Other committee reports of the American Medical Association make it possible to study the status of the profession at any given time.

The early eastern medical journals published some articles by western doctors, and others on subjects pertaining to western medicine. Besides the *Medical Repository* (See Chapter III), important eastern publications were: the *Philadelphia Medical and Physical Journal* (1804-08), which was edited by Professor Benjamin Smith Barton. This periodical concerned itself with zoology and botany as well as medicine. In 1804 John Redman Coxe, professor of chemistry at the University of Pennsylvania, started the *Philadelphia Medical Museum,* which continued through 1809, and then began a new series, 1810-11. The *Eclectic Repertory and Analytical Review* was conducted by an association of physicians for ten years, from 1810 to 1820, then merged into the *American Medical Recorder* which lasted until 1824. The *Eclectic Repertory* in October, 1816, and October, 1818, published the important accounts of Dr. Ephraim McDowell's ovariotomies.

In 1820 Dr. Nathaniel Chapman founded the quarterly *Philadelphia Journal of the Medical and Physical Sciences.* In 1827 Dr. Isaac Hays became virtual editor of the journal; late in the year its name was changed to the *American Journal of the Medical Sciences.* Dr. Hays continued as the editor for more than fifty years; when he died in 1879 his son took over. The *American Journal* is still in existence. Philadelphia's later medical periodicals included: the *North American Medical and Surgical Journal,* a quarterly which published twelve volumes from 1826 to 1831; the *American Medical Intelligencer,* a monthly which was in existence from 1837 to 1842; the *American Journal of Pharmacy,* oldest pharmaceutical journal in the English language, which ran from 1825 to 1835 as the *Journal of the Philadelphia College of Pharmacy,* then in 1835 adopted the name which it now bears.

The *New York Medical and Physical Journal* was issued from 1822 to 1830, and the *New York Journal of Medicine* from 1843 to 1860. Baltimore's Dr. Tobias Watkins in 1808-09 published one volume of the *Baltimore Medical and Physical Recorder,* and from January to December, 1811, Dr. Nathaniel Potter was editing the *Baltimore Medical and Philosophical Lyceum.* The *Baltimore Monthly Journal of Medicine and Surgery,* 1830-31, was followed by the *Baltimore Medical and Surgical Journal and Review,* which ran from October, 1833, to September, 1834, under that title, then became the *North American Archives of Medical and Surgical Science,* and continued for another year. The *New England Journal of Medicine and Surgery, and Collateral Branches of Science* (1812-26) became in 1827 the *New England Medical Review and Journal.* This united in October, 1827, with the *Boston Medical Intelligencer* (1823-28) to form the *Boston Medical and Surgical Journal* which still exists as the *New England Journal of Medicine.*

Of the western professional periodicals most valuable is the *Western Journal of the Medical and Physical Sciences* (Cincinnati, 1828-38). Others which contain useful materials are: *Western Journal of Medicine and Surgery* (Louisville, 1838-55); *Transylvania Journal of Medicine and the Associate Sciences* (Lexington, 1828-39); *Western Lancet,* etc. (Cincinnati, 1842-1916); *Illinois Medical and Surgical Journal,* etc. (Chicago, 1844-89); *Peninsular and Independent Medical Journal,* etc. (Ann Arbor and Detroit, 1853-60); and *St. Louis Medical and Surgical Journal* (St. Louis, 1843-61; 1864-1907).

NEWSPAPERS: Scattered through the contemporary newspapers is a considerable amount of medical history: accounts of epidemics, articles on health, household "receipts," folk cures, discussions on medical education, anecdotes, advertisements of medical schools, patent medicines, etc. From their exchanges the papers copied widely from eastern papers, American, and even European periodicals. In the preparation of this study the authors have drawn heavily upon most of the important extant newspaper files of the states north of the Ohio River prior to 1840, upon scattered files of adjacent states for the same period, and upon representative papers for the whole region from 1840 to 1860. Among the more important papers used, which were published over a considerable period of time, were: *Liberty Hall and Cincinnati Gazette; Cincinnati Gazette; National Republican and Ohio Political Register* (Cincinnati); *Western Intelligencer and Columbus Gazette; Ohio State Journal* (Columbus); *Ohio Statesman* (Columbus); *Delaware Patron and Franklin Chronicle* (Delaware); *Piqua Gazette,* etc.; *The Supporter* (Chillicothe); *Scioto*

Gazette (Chillicothe); *St. Clairsville Gazette; The Miami Intelligencer* (Hamilton); *Portsmouth Gazette*, etc.; *Western Herald and Steubenville Gazette; Western Courier* (Ravenna); *Cleveland Herald; Cleveland Gazette; Cleveland Advertiser; Detroit Gazette; Detroit Journal and Michigan Advertiser; Northwestern Journal* (Detroit); *The Free Press* (Detroit); *Western Sun* (Vincennes); *Indiana Republican* (Madison); *Republican and Banner* (Madison); *Madison Courier; Indiana State Journal* (Indianapolis); *Indiana State Sentinel* (Indianapolis); *Richmond Palladium; Democratic Pharos* (Logansport); *Logansport Telegraph; St. Joseph Valley Register* (South Bend); *Fort Wayne Times; Wabash Courier* (Terre Haute); *Illinois Intelligencer* (Kaskaskia and Vandalia); *Edwardsville Spectator; Illinois Advocate* (Edwardsville and Vandalia); *Illinois State Register* (Springfield); *Sangamo Journal*, etc. (Springfield); *Quincy Whig; The Galenian; Chicago American; Chicago Democrat; Chicago Daily Journal; Wisconsin Free Press* (Green Bay); *Wisconsin Territorial Gazette and Burlington Advertiser; Green Bay Intelligencer* (Navarino and Green Bay); *Belmont Gazette; Milwaukee Sentinel; Milwaukee Advertiser; Wisconsin Enquirer* (Madison); *Wisconsin Democrat* (Green Bay); *Miners' Free Press* (Mineral Point); *Kentucky Yeoman* (Frankfort); *Louisville Herald; Louisville Journal; Lexington Intelligencer; St. Louis Republican.*

HOME REMEDIES AND DOMESTIC MEDICINE: The herb and root recipes have been collected from various domestic-medicine books, the more important of which are discussed in the text, and from newspapers, pioneer reminiscences, manuscripts, and articles on folklore. These check with compilations from interviews and written communications, such as Elzia G. Rogers, *Early Folk Medical Practice in Tennessee* (Carthage, Tennessee, 1941), and Pauline M. Black, *Nebraska Folk Cures* (Lincoln, Nebraska, 1935).

Herbal practice dates from primitive man. In Egypt the

Edwin Smith and the Ebers papyri reveal herbal practices of the second millennium B.C. Both probably drew upon earlier sources. For a summary of early Egyptian papyri see Dr. Logan Clendening, *Source Book of Medical History* (New York, 1942). Indo-Aryan herbal medicine was well systematized before the Christian era. Charaka about 100 A.D. classified five hundred herbs; Susrata (fifth century) listed seven hundred sixty.

A brief introduction to herbal medicine may be had in three articles by Arturo Castiglioni, "Magic Plants in Primitive Medicine," "Herbs in the Medicine of Eastern Peoples and of the American Indians," and "Herbals from Antiquity to the Renaissance," in *Ciba Symposia* (Ciba Pharmaceutical Products Inc., Summit, New Jersey, 1939—), V, Nos. 5 and 6 (August-September, 1943). Eleanor Sinclair Rhode, *Old English Herbals* (London, 1922); A. C. Klebs, *A Catalogue of Early Herbals* (Lugano, 1925); and Agnes Arber, *Herbals, Their Origins and Evolution* (Cambridge, 1938), are standard works on herbals. The history of early English herbals is developed in H. M. Barlow, "Old English Herbals, 1525-1640," *Proceedings* of the Royal Society of Medicine, Section on History of Medicine, VI (1913), and in the introduction to *An Herbal* [*Banckes's Herbal 1525*], edited by Dr. Sanford V. Larkey and Thomas Pyles (New York, 1941). *Banckes's Herbal*, probably compiled from earlier works, was the first book printed in England which was devoted exclusively to herbs. It became the most popular of British herbals and went through at least twenty editions. Henry S. Wellcome, *Ancient Cymric Medicine* (London, 1903), sketches the plant and folk cures of the Druids and the one-hundred-seventy-five-plant materia medica of the Welsh Myddfai physicians of the late fifteenth century. Margaret B. Freeman, in *Herbs for the Mediaeval Household* (Metropolitan Museum of Art, New York, 1943), has assembled a selected number of recipes and cures, largely from the *Hortus Sanitatis* or *Gart der Gesundheit* (published by Peter Schoeffer, Mainz, 1485).

The first American herbal, *The Badianus Manuscript,* was written and probably illustrated by an Aztec Indian, Martin de la Cruz, in 1552, and translated into Latin by a mission colleague, Badianus. In 1929 the manuscript was found in the Vatican Library. Translated and annotated by Emily Walcott Emmart, it was published with one hundred eighteen color plates by the Johns Hopkins Press, 1940. Through this work comparisons may be made with herbal practice of Europe and of other American Indians. See also H. W. Youngken, "Drugs of the North American Indians," *American Journal of Pharmacy,* Volumes XCVI and XCVII (1924-25).

CHARM CURES: The literature of folk medicine is extensive. Between the Ebers papyrus of about 1550 B.C., with its recipe for restoring hair on a bald head by means of an ointment of lion-hippopotamus-crocodile-serpent-ibex fat, to the latest pamphlet on the same subject, hundreds of books have been written on magic, necromancy, "Egyptian Secrets," witchcraft, hexadukt'r, powwowing, and the like.

Vulture medicine of the period of Pliny, Dioscorides, and Sextus came down by way of such documents as the *Epistula Vulturis,* an eighth-century Paris manuscript, medieval handbooks, and early modern compilations, such as Pictorius's *Medicinae . . . Seu Leporarium Quorundam Animalium Quadrupedum* etc. (Basel, 1560), Conrad Gesner's *Historia Animalium* (Zurich, 1551-58), and Lovell's *Compleat History of Animals and Minerals* (Oxford, 1660). It was kept alive in books on medicines and drugs—Becher's *Parnassus Medicinalis Illustratus* (Ulm, 1663), Pomet's *Histoire Generale des Drogues* (Paris, 1694). and Chatenier's *Histoire . . . des Medicaments* (Paris, 1871).

Similar vulture and animal cures developed among the Indians of Peru, Mexico, and the Cherokees of North America. Besides the article by Loren MacKinney cited in the footnotes, see Wilton Marion Krogman, "Medical

Practices and Diseases of the Aboriginal American Indians," *Ciba Symposia,* I (April, 1939); E. Stone, *Medicine among the American Indians* (New York, 1932); J. Mooney and F. M. Olbrechts, *The Swimmer Manuscript: Cherokee Sacred Formulas and Medicinal Prescriptions* (Bulletin 99, Bureau American Ethnology, Washington, 1932); and William T. Corlett, *The Medicine Man of the American Indian* (Springfield, Illinois, 1935).

William George Black, *Folk Medicine, A Chapter in the History of Culture* (London, 1883), covers the subject in general, as does Howard Wilcox Haggard, *Devils, Drugs and Doctors* (New York, 1929).

The folk beliefs of the Pennsylvania Germans have been rather thoroughly studied, and fortunately so, for no group was more important in supplying folk medicine to the Middle West. The most complete studies are Edwin Miller Fogel, *Beliefs and Superstitions of the Pennsylvania Germans* (Philadelphia, 1915), and Thomas R. Brendle and Claude W. Unger, *Folk Medicine of the Pennsylvania Germans,* monograph of the Pennsylvania German Society, XLV (Norristown, Pennsylvania, 1935). Shorter studies are William J. Hoffman, "Folk Medicine of the Pennsylvania Germans," American Philosophical Society *Proceedings,* XXVI (1889); "Folk Lore of the Pennsylvania Germans," *Journal of American Folklore,* I (1888), and II (1889); John Baer Stout, *The Folk-Lore of the Pennsylvania German,* Pennsylvania German Society *Proceedings,* XXIII Supplement (1915); David E. Lick and Thomas R. Brendle, "Plant Names and Plant Lore among the Pennsylvania Germans," *ibid.,* XXXIII (1922); J. G. Owens, "Folk-Lore from Buffalo Valley, Central Pennsylvania," *Journal of American Folklore,* IV (1891); Emma Gertrude White, "Folk-Lore among Pennsylvania Germans," *ibid.,* X (1897).

In 1930 Ammon Monroe Aurand edited and reprinted (Harrisburg) John George Hohman's *Long Lost Friend or Book of Pow-Wows,* "A Collection of Mysterious and Invaluable Arts and Remedies; for Man as Well as Animals;

with many Proofs of their Virtues and efficacy in healing diseases; etc., the greater part of which was never published until they appeared in print for the first time in the United States in the year 1820." Of this book it has been said that it was "Next to the Holy Bible a source of more satisfaction and comfort to the Pennsylvania 'Dutch' and many others throughout the entire United States, than possibly any other known book." Aurand also published *Popular Home Remedies and Superstitions of the Pennsylvania Germans* (Harrisburg, 1941), and *Little Known Facts about the Witches in our Hair* (Harrisburg, 1938).

Interesting for purposes of comparison are D. L. and L. B. Thomas, *Kentucky Superstitions* (Princeton, New Jersey, 1920); Charles B. Wilson, "Notes on Folk Medicine," *Journal of American Folklore*, XXI (1908); Gertrude C. Davenport, "Folk Cures from Kansas," *ibid.*, XI (1898); Letitia Humphreys Wrenshall, "Incantations and Popular Healing in Maryland and Pennsylvania," *ibid.*, XVI (1903); W. R. Smith, "Animals and Plants in Oklahoma Folk-Cures," *Folk-Say*, I (Oklahoma Folk Lore Society, Norman, Oklahoma, 1929); Charles B. Wilson, "Folk Beliefs in the Ozark Hills," and L. S. M. Curtin, "Pioneer Medicine in New Mexico," *ibid.*, II (1930).

REGULAR DOCTORS AND MEDICAL EDUCATION: Additional sources of early Cincinnati-Lexington-Transylvania medical history are: Edward Deering Mansfield, *Memoirs of the Life and Services of Daniel Drake, M. D.* (Cincinnati, 1855), and the following writings of Daniel Drake: "An Anniversary Discourse on the State and Prospects of the Western Museum Society . . . ." (Cincinnati, 1820); "An Inaugural Discourse on Medical Education . . . ." (Cincinnati, 1820); "An Introductory Lecture on the Necessity and Value of Professional Industry . . . ." (Lexington, 1823); "Anniversary Address, Delivered to the School of Literature and the Arts at Cincinnati" (Cincinnati, 1814[?]); "A Narrative of the Rise and Fall of the Medical College of Ohio" (Cincinnati,

1822); "Discourse on the History, Character, and Prospects of the West . . . ." (Cincinnati, 1834); "Remarks on the Importance of promoting Literary and Social Concert in the Valley of the Mississippi . . . ." (Cincinnati, 1820); "Strictures on some of the Defects and Infirmities of . . . Students of Medicine" (Louisville, 1847); "War of Extermination" (Cincinnati, 1839).

The history of medical education in the Chicago area is covered in Alfred Theodore Andreas, *History of Chicago* (three volumes, Chicago, 1884-86); Zeuch, *Medical Practice in Illinois*; Bessie Louise Pierce, *A History of Chicago* (two volumes, New York, 1937); and Packard, *A History of Medicine*, II. For Indiana medical schools, see Indiana State Medical Society *Transactions*, 1874, and Burton D. Myers, "The History of Medical Education in Indiana," *Indiana History Bulletin*, XIX, 3 (March, 1942). Dr. Myers's "Medical Education in Indiana," still in manuscript is the only adequate work on the subject. A contemporary study of medical education is presented in the work of N. S. Davis, *History of Medical Education and Institutions in the United States* (Chicago, 1851). The best treatment of dentistry is C. R. E. Koch, *History of Dental Surgery* (three volumes, Ft. Wayne, 1910).

Two medical reference works very useful for study of the period prior to 1850 are Robley Dunglinson, *A New Dictionary of Medical Science and Literature, containing a Concise Account of the Various Subjects and Terms; with the Synonymes in Different Languages and Formulae for Various Officinal and Empirical Preparations* (two volumes, Boston, 1833), and the same author's revised American edition of the *Cyclopoedia of Practical Medicine*, edited by James Forbes, Alexander Tweedie, et. al. (four volumes, Philadelphia, 1845).

The history of medical periodicals is summarized briefly in J. S. Billings, "Medical Journals of the United States," *Boston Medical and Surgical Journal*, C (January, 1879); the literature commitee reports in the American Medical Association *Transactions*, 1848-52; Daniel Drake, "Discourse before the Medical Library Association" (Cincinnati, 1852); and Victor Robinson, "The Early Medical Journals of America," *Medical Life*, XXXVI (1929), 553-606. Many of the western medical journals are listed in Frank Luther Mott, *A History of American Magazines* (three volumes, New York and Cambridge, 1930, 1938); and Ralph Leslie Rusk, *The Literature of the Middle Western Frontier* (two volumes, New York, 1925).

IRREGULARS: No attempt is made here to list the numerous Botanic medical books published or circulated in the Middle West. There is no adequate check-list to date. Many previously unknown works constantly appear; on the other hand a number mentioned in the Botanic periodicals either did not materialize or else have long since disappeared. Important Botanic works not identified in the text are Eleazer G. House, *The Botanic Family Friend: being a complete guide to the new system of Thomsonian medical practice* (Boston, 1844); Abel Tennant, *The Vegetable Materia Medica and Practice of Medicine. Containing in detail his practical knowledge of American remedies, in curing diseases* (Batavia, New York, 1837); Alfred N. Worthy, *A Treatise on the Botanic Theory and Practice of Medicine, compiled from various sources, with revisions and additions* (Forsyth, Georgia, 1842); Meeker Day, *The Improved American Family Physician or Sick Man's Guide to Health* (New York, 1833); and Morris Mattson, *The American Vegetable Practice, or a New and Improved Guide to Health Designed for the Use of Families* (two volumes, Boston, 1841). A general view of the Botanics, as well as other irregulars, is given by Alexander Wilder, *History of Medicine . . . with An Extended Account of the New Schools of the Healing Art in the Nineteenth Century, and especially a History of the American Eclectic Practice of Medicine, never before Published* (New Sharon, Maine, 1901).

Students of Botanic medicine are greatly indebted to the collections and publications of the Lloyd Library of

Botany, Pharmacy and Materia Medica of Cincinnati, Ohio. J. U. and C. G. Lloyd published at Cincinnati, 1884-87, a quarterly, *Drugs and Medicines of North America*. This publication, with its comprehensive treatment of the more important medicinal plants of North America, was republished in the *Bulletin of the Lloyd Library*, 29, Reproduction Series, 9 (1930). Of special interest are the articles on "Hydrastis Canadensis" (Yellow Root) and "Lobelia," also reproduced separately in the same series as Bulletins 10 and part two of 11 (1908 and 1909), respectively. Other publications of the Lloyd Library Reproduction Series include: Benjamin Smith Barton, *Collections for an Essay Towards a Materia Medica of the United States* (Philadelphia, 1798 and 1804), Bulletin No. 1, Reproduction Series No. 1 (1900); Peter Smith, *The Indian Doctor's Dispensatory Being Father Smith's Advice Respecting Diseases and Their Cure* (Cincinnati, 1813), Bulletin No. 2, Reproduction Series No. 2 (1901); Johann David Schoepf, *Materia Medica Americana Potissimum Regni Vegetabilis* (Erlangen, 1787), Bulletin No. 6, Reproduction Series No. 3 (1903); Rev. Manasseh Cutler, *An Account of Some of the Vegetable Productions, Naturally Growing in This Part of America* (Memoirs of the American Academy of Arts and Sciences, 1785), Bulletin No. 7, Reproduction Series, No. 4 (1903); William Downey, *An Investigation of the Properties of the Sanguinaria Canadensis; or Puccoon* (Eaken and Mecum, 1803), and Jonathan Carver, *Travels Through the Interior Parts of North America in the Years 1766, 1767 and 1768* (London, 1768), Bulletin No. 9, Reproduction Series No. 5 (1907); Samuel Thomson, *Life and Medical Discoveries of Samuel Thomson* (Boston, 1822) and a history of the Thomsonian Materia Medica, as shown in *The New Guide to Health* (1835), and the literature of that day, Bulletin No. 11, Reproduction Series No. 7 (1909); *The Genesis of The American Materia Medica* including a biographical sketch of "John Josselyn, Gent" and the medical and materia medica references in Josselyn's "New-Englands

Rarities Discovered" (London, 1672), etc., and in his "Two Voyages to New-England" (London, 1672), with critical notes and comments by Harvey Wickes Felter, Bulletin No. 26, Reproduction Series No. 8 (1927).

The most complete account of the Botanics is to be found in their own periodicals, many of them short-lived, which came into being during the period of popular acceptance of the movement. In addition to middle western publications, periodicals from eastern and southern Botanic centers circulated in the region. By articles copied from their exchanges or through original articles, editors in the older Botanic localities could keep followers informed of the progress of the cause in newer areas.

Some of the non-western periodicals were: *Thomsonian Spy* (Manchester and Bennington, Vermont, April to December, 1838); *Botanic Advocate and Journal of Health* (Montpelier, 1836-39); *Boston True Thomsonian* (August, 1840-43); *Thompsonian Advertiser* (Boston, 1844-45); *Boston Thomsonian Medical and Physiological Journal* (1845-46); *Boston Thomsonian Manual and Lady's Companion* (1835-45); *Botanic Journal* (Boston, February, 1836, to January, 1837); *Botanic Advocate and Thomsonian Family Physician* (New Haven, July, 1843, to May, 1844); *Thomsonian Advocate or New Haven Botanic Advertiser* (1836-37); *Thomsonian Messenger* (Norwich, Connecticut, 1841-45); *Thomsonian Botanic Watchman* (Albany, New York, January, 1834, to August, 1835); *Philadelphia Thomsonian Sentinel and Family Journal of Useful Knowledge* (August, 1835, to June, 1844); *Philadelphia Thomsonian Medical Journal* (April, 1853-54); *Botanic Medical Reformer and Home Physician* (Philadelphia, May, 1840, to January, 1842); *Thomsonian and Botanic Medical Advertiser* (Baltimore, 1831); *Botanic Investigator* (Vicksburg, Mississippi, March to October, 1835).

In addition to middle western Botanic periodicals named in the text were the *Botanic Luminary*, 1836 to 1838, published at Saline and Adrian, Michigan; and the *Thom-*

sonian Defender, July, 1835, to August, 1836, at Maryville, Tennessee. Largely Botanic, but defying absolute classification, was Anthony Hunn's monthly and semimonthly *Medical Friend of the People*, Harrodsburg, Kentucky, 1829-30.

Not so numerous, but none the less interesting, are publications of irregulars other than the Botanics, such as: *Water-Cure Monthly* (Glen Forest and Yellow Springs, Ohio, 1859-60); *Phreno-Magnetic Society of Cincinnati Journal* (1842); Buchanan's *Journal of Man* (Cincinnati and Boston, 1849-56); Dr. Alvah Curtis's *Journal of Medical Reform* (Cincinnati, 1854-55); *Physio-Medical and Surgical Journal* (Cincinnati, 1849-52); the *Michigan Journal of Homeopathy* etc. (November, 1848, to June, 1854); *Cincinnati Journal of Homeopathy*, edited by Dr. Benjamin Ehrmann and others (1851-52); *American Magazine of Homeopathy and Hydropathy*, by Drs. Pulte and Gatchell (Cincinnati, 1852); and the *Western Journal of Homeopathy* (St. Louis, October, 1850, to February, 1860).

Files of the *Homeopathic Times' Annual Retrospect of Homeopathic Literature* (New York) are available for the years 1875 to 1897 in the New York Public Library. Homeopathy's growth is well covered in William Harvey King's *History of Homeopathy and Its Institutions in America* (four volumes, New York and Chicago, 1905). Wilder's *History of Medicine* also devotes considerable space to the subject.

DRUGS: Development of drugs may be traced in the *United States Pharmacopoeia*, begun in 1820 by Lyman Spalding and continued down to the present day. An interesting work is Jacob Bigelow, *A Treatise on the Materia Medica, Intended as A Sequel to the Pharmacopoeia of the United States* (Boston, 1822). Additional information may be obtained from the *American Journal of Pharmacy* (1825—), the *Proceedings* of the American Pharmaceutical Association (1852-1911), and *Drugs and Medicines of North America.*

Excellent biographical material is to be found in H. A. Kelly, *Some American Medical Botanists* (Troy, New York, 1914). More recent popular accounts are C. H. Lawall, *The Curious Lore of Drugs and Medicine* (New York, 1937), and M. M. Silverman, *Magic in a Bottle* (New York, 1941). Later history of patent medicines may be followed in *Nostrums and Quackery* (two volumes, edited by Arthur J. Cramp, Chicago, 1912, 1921), the American Medical Association's reprints of a series of articles which appeared in *Collier's* in 1905.

INDEX

328

Holmes aey 69 $\frac{3}{4}$